COMAP'S

Mathematics: Modeling Our World

DEVELOPED BY

COMAP, Inc.

57 Bedford Street, Suite 210

Lexington, Massachusetts 02420

PROJECT LEADERSHIP

Solomon Garfunkel

COMAP, INC., LEXINGTON, MA

Landy Godbold

THE WESTMINSTER SCHOOLS, ATLANTA, GA

Henry Pollak

TEACHERS COLLEGE, COLUMBIA UNIVERSITY, NY, NY

W. H. FREEMAN AND COMPANY

41 Madison Avenue

New York, NY 10010

www.whfreeman.com

The Consortium for Mathematics and Its Applications (COMAP)

57 Bedford Street, Suite 210
Lexington, MA 02420

Published and distributed by

South-Western Educational Publishing
Cincinnati, OH 45227

This book was prepared with the support of NSF Grant ESI-9255252. However, any opinions,
findings, conclusions, and/or recommendations herein are those of the authors
and do not necessarily reflect the views of the NSF.

ISBN 0-538-68224-8

Printed in the United States of America.

1 2 3 4 5 6 7 8 VH 06 05 04 03 02 01 00 99

I(T)P'

International Thomson Publishing

South-Western Educational Publishing is an ITP Company.
The ITP logo is a registered trademark used herein under License by
South-Western Educational Publishing.

EDITOR: Landy Godbold
AUTHORS: Allan Bellman, WATKINS MILL HIGH SCHOOL, GAITHERSBURG, MD; John Burnette, KINKAID SCHOOL, HOUSTON, TX; Horace Butler, GREENVILLE HIGH SCHOOL, GREENVILLE, SC; Claudia Carter, MISSISSIPPI SCHOOL FOR MATH AND SCIENCE, COLUMBUS, MS; Nancy Crisler, PATTONVILLE SCHOOL DISTRICT, ST. ANN, MO; Marsha Davis, EASTERN CONNECTICUT STATE UNIVERSITY, WILLIMANTIC, CT; Gary Froelich, COMAP, INC., LEXINGTON, MA; Landy Godbold, THE WESTMINSTER SCHOOLS, ATLANTA, GA; Bruce Grip, ETIWANDA HIGH SCHOOL, ETIWANDA, CA; Rick Jennings, EISENHOWER HIGH SCHOOL, YAKIMA, WA; Paul Kehle, INDIANA UNIVERSITY, BLOOMINGTON, IN; Darien Lauten, OYSTER RIVER HIGH SCHOOL, DURHAM, NH; Sheila McGrail, CHARLOTTE COUNTRY DAY SCHOOL, CHARLOTTE, NC; Geraldine Oliveto, THOMAS JEFFERSON HIGH SCHOOL FOR SCIENCE AND TECHNOLOGY, ALEXANDRIA, VA; Henry Pollak, TEACHERS COLLEGE, COLUMBIA UNIVERSITY, NY, NY, J.J. Price, PURDUE UNIVERSITY, WEST LAFAYETTE, IN; Joan Reinthaler, SIDWELL FRIENDS SCHOOL, WASHINGTON, D.C.; James Swift, ALBERNI SCHOOL DISTRICT, BRITISH COLUMBIA, CANADA; Brandon Thacker, BOUNTIFUL HIGH SCHOOL, BOUNTIFUL, UT; Paul Thomas, MindQ, FORMERLY OF THOMAS JEFFERSON HIGH SCHOOL FOR SCIENCE AND TECHNOLOGY, ALEXANDRIA, VA

Dear Student,

Mathematics: Modeling Our World is a different kind of math book than you may have used, for a different kind of math course than you may have taken. In addition to presenting mathematics for you to learn, we have tried to present mathematics for you to use. We have attempted in this text to demonstrate mathematical concepts in the context of how they are actually used day to day. The word "modeling" is the key. Real problems do not come at the end of chapters in a math book. Real problems don't look like math problems. Real problems ask questions such as: How do we create computer animations? Where should we locate a fire station? How do we effectively control an animal population? Real problems are messy.

Mathematical modeling is the process of looking at a problem, finding a mathematical core, working within that core, and coming back to see what mathematics tells you about the problem with which you started. You will not know in advance what mathematics to apply. The mathematics you settle on may be a mix of several ideas in geometry, algebra, and data analysis. You may need to use computers or graphing calculators. Because we bring to bear many different mathematical ideas as well as technologies, we call our approach "integrated."

Another very important and very real feature of this course is that frequently you will be working in groups. Many problems will be solved more efficiently by people working in teams. In today's world, this is very much what work looks like. You will also see that the units in this book are arranged by context and application rather than by math topic. We have done this to reemphasize our primary goal: presenting you with mathematical ideas the way you will see them as you go on in school and out into the work force. There is hardly a career that you can think of in which mathematics will not play an important part and understanding mathematics will not matter to you.

Most of all, we hope you have fun. Mathematics is important. Mathematics may be the most useful subject you will learn. Using mathematics to solve truly interesting problems about how our world works can and should be an enjoyable and rewarding experience.

Solomon Garfunkel
CO-PRINCIPAL INVESTIGATOR

Landy Godbold
CO-PRINCIPAL INVESTIGATOR

Henry Pollak
CO-PRINCIPAL INVESTIGATOR

2

UNIT

The Geometry of Art

In this unit, you will use mathematics to create visual models. The geometry of perspective allows you to draw accurately three-dimensional objects in a two-dimensional plane. Size and similarity, parallel lines, corresponding angles, projections, proportions, and trigonometric ratios are the key mathematical topics in the unit.

You will revisit the properties of similar figures and apply the principle of diminution to determine the correct size of objects in drawings. You will work with angles, parallel lines, perpendicular lines, and diagonals to represent the principle of convergence. You will learn right triangle trigonometry to represent with precision the principle of foreshortening. As you combine mathematics and art, you add precision to the elegance of drawing pictures to represent your world.

DRAWING FROM MATH

Look closely at a beautiful landscape. An artist does the same, then uses a pencil or brush to create a picture so others may enjoy the beauty he or she sees.

What does mathematics have to do with creating art? Pose this question to the architect who uses the geometry of one-point and two-point perspective to help a client visualize what a building will look like when it is constructed. Ask the theater set designer who uses the geometric principles of convergence to create the illusion of depth and distance on a small stage. Ask the animator who guides you into and around three-dimensional objects using a two-dimensional screen. Ask the artist who blends the geometric precision of perspective with the subtle effects of shading and color to add depth to drawings.

In this unit, you answer the question: How does an artist accurately represent three-dimensional objects on a two-dimensional page? Before you begin, take a look around you and notice the lines and shapes that make up your world. Whether you are an accomplished artist or beginner, you can use the geometry of perspective drawing to create realistic drawings of the world you see.

LESSON ONE
Keep It In Perspective

KEY CONCEPTS

Perspective

Overlapping

Point of view

Projection

Figure 1.1.
Relativity by M.C. Escher.

PREPARATION READING

Picture Perfect

S mall children view the world differently than you. Their sense of depth is not developed. Just look at pictures drawn by young children. Notice in **Figure 1.2** that the sun is too large and the building appears flat.

Suppose you work as an artist who prepares drawings for an architect. The drawings help the architect and her client visualize what a completed project might look like. The drawings must be accurate.

Artists, architects, designers, illustrators, and animators usually draw objects and scenes accurately. Many use principles of perspective drawing as a guide. However, sometimes an artist may violate a geometric principle of art in order to get your attention. An example of this is an optical illusion. Look at **Figure 1.1**. What did the artist do in this figure to fool you?

In this unit, you will combine the techniques of the artist with an understanding of geometric relationships so you can prevent such mistakes in your own drawings or make them intentionally for effect. Throughout the unit, you will investigate how to draw figures and scenes accurately.

One way to understand the importance of perspective is to study examples of paintings that break the rules. This lesson introduces the context of perspective by inviting you to detect errors, or real-world inaccuracies, in a famous painting. In later lessons, you will develop several principles of perspective drawing so you can create accurate visual models of the real world.

Jackson Barber
Age 8

Figure 1.2.

ACTIVITY

1

LET THE VIEWER BEWARE

Sometimes an artist will make a painting or drawing that does not represent an object or scene accurately. The painting shown in **Figure 1.3** contains several intentional mistakes.

Figure 1.3.
Perspectival Absurdities by William Hogarth.

1. Work together with your group to identify all the real-world inaccuracies in the painting by William Hogarth. Describe each in detail.

2. Explain what the artist needs to do to correct each of the inaccuracies you identified in Item 1.

3. Study all the corrections you suggested in Item 2 and look for common underlying ideas. Identify general principles or guidelines an artist might follow in order to create accurate pictures. Save your answers for use in later lessons.

CONSIDER:

1. Learning to draw two-dimensional representations of three-dimensional objects is not easy. How can you simplify the task of finding underlying principles behind such drawing?

2. How might mathematical calculations relate to drawings of three-dimensional objects and scenes?

INDIVIDUAL WORK 1

Move to the Front

Perspective is the technique of representing objects from three-dimensional space in a two-dimensional plane. Through the use of perspective, an artist's two-dimensional painting imitates the appearance of a three-dimensional object. Perspective has been called the geometry of vision and was invented, it is generally agreed, in Florence, Italy early in the 15th century. Artists before that time experimented with elements of perspective, and artists after that time perfected the details, but it is the artist Filippo Brunelleschi (1377–1446) who is credited with developing a systematic approach to the problem of depicting space on a flat plane.

In this individual work, you will begin to identify elements or principles that you can use to draw accurate representations of three-dimensional objects.

©The Bridgeman Art Library International, LTD.

Figure 1.4.
The Bathers by Georges Seurat.

1. Look at **Figures 1.4** and **1.5**. In both cases, the artist has tried to represent a three-dimensional subject on a two-dimensional plane (the plane of the picture). Three-dimensional objects are projected onto a two-dimensional plane in much the same way that your shadow or silhouette is projected onto a wall by a strong light source.

INDIVIDUAL WORK 1

The Folger Shakespeare Library

Figure 1.5.
Cotswold Games.

a) Suppose you are in a balloon floating over the subjects in these pictures. Draw a bird's-eye view of what you would see.

b) Explain how you determined the specific locations of particular objects in your drawing.

c) Discuss how each artist tried to convey depth.

2. **Figure 1.6** shows the top view of a table on which three cubes are sitting. Draw four views of what you would see if you were sitting at *A*, *B*, *C*, and *D*, respectively.

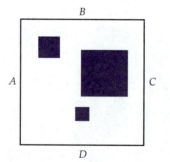

Figure 1.6.
Top view of three cubes on a table.

There are several basic elements for representing depth in perspective drawing. One basic element, perhaps the simplest, is the principle of overlapping. You use **overlapping** to show depth and distance when you place one object in front of another object in a picture. Objects that are closer to the viewer and appear to be in front of another object will hide part of the more distant object.

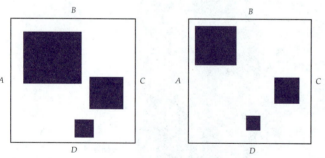

Figure 1.7.
Top view of three cubes for Item 3(a).

Figure 1.8.
Top view of three cubes for Item 3(b).

3. a) Draw four views of what you would see if you were sitting at *A*, *B*, *C*, and *D* , respectively (see **Figure 1.7**).

   b) Draw what you would see if you were sitting at each of *A*, *B*, *C*, and *D* (see **Figure 1.8**).

c) Suppose you are given a side view and asked to draw the view from the top. Sketch a top view for Arrangement #1 and Arrangement #2 (see **Figure 1.9**). Which top view do you think is more likely to be accurate? Explain your answer.

4. Refer to Figure 1.3 in Activity 1 and describe where Hogarth violates the principle of overlapping.

5. Overlapping is one way to show distance from the viewer. However, as you saw in Item 3, you need more than overlapping to show depth in a drawing. Overlapping does not show the relative distance between objects. Sometimes objects are not in front of one another. Therefore you need more principles. Revise the list you began in Item 3 of Activity 1. You may wish to include examples to illustrate your ideas.

6. a) Observe **Figure 1.10**. Does one of the people appear to be taller? Explain your answer.

   b) Observe **Figure 1.11**. Does one of the people appear to be taller? Explain your answer.

7. Your goal as you complete this unit is to develop methods for representing three-dimensional figures accurately in two dimensions. This involves representing multiple objects of many shapes from various points of view. In the spirit of using what you know about modeling to guide your investigations, list some ways that you could start simply in studying perspective.

8. Sometimes it helps to see how you have improved your model as you progress through the unit. Find a scene or group of objects to sketch, such as a house or apartment building in your neighborhood. You might draw a series of buildings in your town or city. Make sure the subject you choose allows you to create the illusion of depth, and that the scene will remain essentially the same for several weeks. You will revisit your drawing throughout this unit as you learn different aspects of perspective drawing.

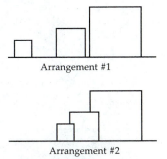

Arrangement #1

Arrangement #2

Figure 1.9.
Side view of two different cube arrangements.

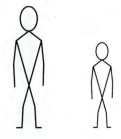

Figure 1.10.
Stick figures for Item 6(a).

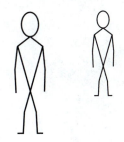

Figure 1.11.
Stick figures for Item 6(b).

LESSON TWO
Drawn to Scale

KEY CONCEPTS

Dimimution

Similarity

Lines of sight

Picture plane

Scale

The Image Bank

PREPARATION READING

Diminution

Representing three-dimensional objects accurately on a two-dimensional plane is complicated. The tricky part is how you represent the third dimension, depth. If you fail to represent depth accurately, your drawings may appear childish.

In the previous lesson, you applied the principle of overlapping to show depth in a painting or drawing. Although overlapping is a useful principle, it is not adequate for showing the relative distances between the viewer and various objects in all situations. You need more principles of perspective to produce accurate drawings.

Apply your experience with modeling and simplify the task of representing depth. Think about what goes into an image. What kinds of shapes are included? How many objects are present? From what direction is an object seen? Start simply by examining only one object, using the simplest view of a very simple three-dimensional object. A cube is a simple three-dimensional object with all faces the same size. Its edges are all straight line segments, and the edges represent only three directions, all at right angles to one another. The cube is the perfect object with which to begin the modeling process.

In Individual Work 1, you observed cubes from different points of view. The *way* you view the cube is another variable you can simplify in the modeling process.

Hold a cube directly in front of you so all you see is a square. Move the cube toward you. The square appears to become larger. Move the cube directly away from you and the square appears to become smaller. In general, due to the principle called **diminution**, objects appear smaller as they move farther away. Diminution is one of the tools of perspective for representing depth and distance in drawings.

To help you see how diminution works, pretend you have **lines of sight**—imaginary lines running from your eye to the top and bottom of some object at which you are looking. When you look at these lines of sight you see why objects must appear smaller as you move farther from the object. The science of perspective is grounded in the geometry of lines of sight. For example, in **Figure 1.12** the person is looking at a flagpole. The dotted lines represent the lines of sight from the person to the top and bottom of the flagpole.

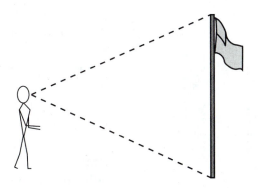

Figure 1.12.
Lines of sight to top and bottom of a flagpole.

Note, that in keeping with the principle of starting simply, this unit assumes the viewer uses only one eye, so lines of sight are completely determined by the object to which they are drawn.

Imagine a person is looking at a set of railroad ties going off into the distance. You can set up a model of this situation on a table-top using six or seven pencils of equal length to represent the railroad ties. For **Figure 1.13**, imagine you are above this person and, as you look down, you see not only the top of the person's head and the railroad ties, but also some lines of sight to the endpoints of the railroad ties (see Figure 1.13).

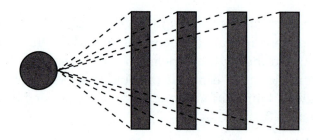

Figure 1.13.
Top view of lines of sight for person observing a series of railroad ties.

This picture is confusing, but if you look at it one tie at a time (another modeling decision), it is easier to figure out.

Figure 1.14 is a picture of a person looking at a single railroad tie through a windowpane. The lines of sight outline a projection of the tie on the pane, and this projection is shown as the dark line on the windowpane. The windowpane is called the **plane of vision,** or picture plane. The term plane of vision means an imaginary windowpane through which a person views a scene (and, perhaps, upon which an artist paints a scene).

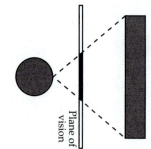

Plane of vision

Figure 1.14.
Top view showing lines of sight and plane of vision.

According to the principle of diminution, more distant objects look smaller. But how much smaller? Answering that question is the focus of this lesson. Along the way, you will investigate the role of diminution, lines of sight, and plane of vision in representing depth and distance. In the process, you will apply the mathematics of similarity and proportions first studied when you explored satellite images in Course 1, Unit 3, *Landsat*.

The cartoon in **Figure 1.15** reminds you that determining the proper sizes of objects in a two-dimensional view of the three-dimensional world requires some thought.

Figure 1.15.
B.C. Cartoon about determining sizes of objects.
By permission of Johnny Hart and Creators Syndicate, Inc.

CONSIDER:

1. What factors determine how large you will draw an object in a picture?

2. If you move an object twice as far from a viewer, will you draw it at half the size? What is the general relationship between the distance from the viewer to an object and the object's size in a drawing?

M A T H   A T   W O R K

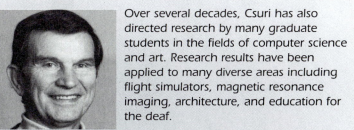

When internationally renowned artist Charles Csuri draws, paints, and sculpts in three dimensions, he does so on a computer. Since 1964 when he began to create art on a huge, unwieldly mainframe, Csuri—professor emeritus at Ohio State University—has become recognized as a pioneer, leading researcher, and master in computer-generated graphics and art. Using sophisticated computers and cutting-edge programming techniques, Csuri produces his beautiful works of art on the screen; these are then transferred into large photographic prints.

Over several decades, Csuri has also directed research by many graduate students in the fields of computer science and art. Research results have been applied to many diverse areas including flight simulators, magnetic resonance imaging, architecture, and education for the deaf.

Visit *http://www.vol.it/mirror/csuri* on the Internet to read more about Charles Csuri and to view some of his art.

BEYOND IMAGINATION

You know that diminution is the apparent decrease in size as an object gets farther from the viewer. When you look at a cube from directly in front of one of its faces, it appears to be a square. So, one simplification you can make in your early investigations of diminution is to look only at squares. That is, rather than studying diminution in the context of three-dimensional objects, simplify a bit. Focus first on its effect on two-dimensional objects as they occur at varying distances from the viewer.

Suppose you are an animator working with a team of artists. Your team is working on a project to create a video game that simulates driving a car. You are given the task of determining the proper size and location for signs that appear at regular intervals along the side of your simulated highway.

In this activity, apply the principle of diminution as you vary the size of the signs in relation to their distance from the video game's driver.

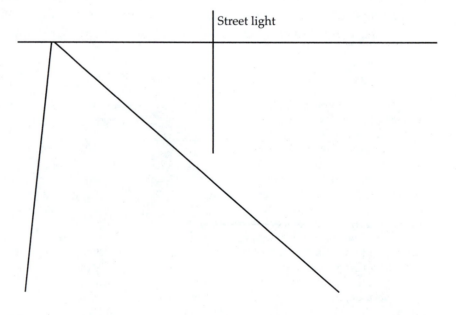

Street light

Figure 1.16.
Video game highway.

BEYOND IMAGINATION

1. **Figure 1.16** is a sketch of the highway in your video game. Copy the sketch onto your own paper (or use Handout H1.2 provided by your teacher). Apply the principle of diminution and draw three signs along the side of the highway. Assume that in real life the signs are 4-meter by 4-meter squares and are placed 50 meters apart. The streetlight seen in the picture is actually 10 meters tall. List any additional assumptions you make.

2. How do you know the signs you drew are the right sizes? How did you apply the principle of diminution?

3. How do you know the signs are spaced properly along the highway?

4. Describe any difficulties you encountered.

5. It is not easy to draw three two-dimensional signs so they appear to be equally spaced and the right sizes. In the modeling process, how can you simplify the dual tasks of investigating the sizes and spacings of equally-spaced objects represented in perspective?

INDIVIDUAL WORK 2

From a Distance

1. Which objects in the Hogarth painting (Figure 1.3 in Activity 1) appear to be the wrong sizes for their locations—or in the wrong locations for their sizes?

2. The boat in **Figure 1.17** is approximately 200 feet from the photographer.

Figure 1.17.
Scene on a river bank.

Vin Catania

a) Estimate the distance to the person standing on the near bank.

b) Estimate the distance to the building on the opposite shore.

c) What clues did you use to estimate each distance?

3. Describe examples of diminution in **Figure 1.18**.

Figure 1.18.
Painting illustrating diminution.

The Bridgeman Art Library International, Ltd.

SHRINK TO FIT

In Activity 2, you needed to answer at least two questions in order to draw a series of equally-spaced signs along a highway:

• How do you know the right size for each sign?

• How do you know the right location for each sign?

This activity helps you answer the first question. The second question will be investigated in Lesson 3, "Vanishing Point," and in Lesson 4, "The Right Space."

Since the signs are two-dimensional, having height and width, you can simplify your model by stepping back to one dimension, height. This activity introduces you to a technique called scaling that enables you to draw images of signs the correct height based on their distance from the viewer. **Scaling** is a mathematical technique for representing depth and distance by enlarging or reducing images in a drawing. Distant objects look smaller according to the principle of diminution and scaling enables you to know how much smaller. It quantifies diminution. You were introduced to scaling using similar triangles and proportions in Course 1, Unit 3, *Landsat*.

Follow this guided activity and review how to use similar triangles and proportions to determine, indirectly, the size of an object at a known distance from the viewer (Items 1 and 2) and to determine, indirectly, the distance to an object of known size (Item 3).

Then, move to the context of perspective drawing and determine the correct picture size for an object of known size at a known distance from the viewer. This will allow you to check (or find) the sizes of the signs you investigated in Activity 2.

ACTIVITY

3

SHRINK TO FIT

1. Hold a ruler or meter stick in your hand, and extend your arm in front of you at eye-level so that the ruler is vertical and your arm is extended fully (see **Figure 1.19**).

Vin Catania

Figure 1.19.
Photograph showing how
to hold the ruler.

a) Carefully measure the distance from your eye to the ruler.

b) Instruct your partner or a member of your group to stand several meters away from you. Using a tape measure or meter stick, measure the distance between your eye and the other person.

c) Use the ruler in your extended hand to measure the apparent height of the other person (the height you would draw the person if the plane of vision coincides with the ruler). See **Figure 1.20**.

Vin Catania

Figure 1.20.
Measuring the apparent
height of an object.

ACTIVITY

SHRINK TO FIT

3

d) Complete a sketch of a side view showing lines of sight (see **Figure 1.21**) and use your measurements to replace the question marks. Use your side-view drawing and properties of similar triangles to calculate the height of the other person.

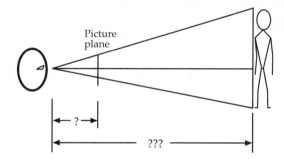

Picture plane

?

???

Figure 1.21.
Side view to reveal similar triangles.

e) Is your answer reasonable? How do you decide if your answer is reasonable?

2. a) Determine, indirectly, the height of three other objects on your school campus. Choose objects likely to be measured by other groups so you can compare your answers. For each object, draw a side view (like Figure 1.21) showing lines of sight and similar triangles. Then show the proportions and calculations you use to find the correct height.

b) Discuss the reasonableness of your answers. How accurate are your answers? What affects the accuracy of your answers?

c) Suppose you make an error of 1 cm in measuring the distance from your eye to the ruler. Determine the corresponding error in your height calculation.

3. You can use similar triangles to determine the distance to an object if you know the height of the object. Measure the height of your partner. Instruct your partner to stand an unknown distance away from you. Hold your ruler at arm's length and measure the apparent height of the person. Use your measurements and similar triangles to determine the distance between you and your partner.

SHRINK TO FIT

Imagine a picture as a window through which you view a scene. The **scale** of an object in the picture is the ratio of the image size (height or width) in the picture to the actual size of the object. You can use similar triangles and proportions to determine the scale of each object in a picture or to draw objects so they are the correct size in the picture.

4. Suppose a 10-meter tree stands 80 meters from the place you are viewing a scene.

   a) What is the apparent size of the tree on a drawing that is 60 cm from your eye?

   b) Determine the scale of the 10-meter tree in the drawing described.

   c) Determine the ratio of distances (from the viewer) to the image plane and to the tree. Comment on your result.

Note that scale is completely determined by two corresponding sizes. You can calculate it from the image size and original object size. You can also calculate it from the distances from eye to viewing plane and from eye to object. But only one set of measurements is needed; you do not need all four numbers.

5. Now you are ready to revisit the scene described in Activity 2. Trace Figure 1.16 onto your own paper, or use Handout H1.2 provided by your teacher. Assume the picture plane is 60 cm from the eye of the viewer.

   a) What is the scale of the streetlight? How far is it from the viewer?

   b) What is the image height of each 4 meters x 4 meters sign if the first sign is 80 meters from the driver and the signs are 50 meters apart?

   c) Place the three signs in the picture. Remember, each sign measures 4 meters wide and 4 meters high in the real world.

   d) Comment on the accuracy of your completed drawing.

INDIVIDUAL WORK 3

Similar Triangles

1. Review Activity 3 on your own, then complete parts (a-c) below. Draw a side view for each part (use Figure 1.21 as an example) and display your measurements. Show each proportion you solve to determine a size or distance.

   a) Indirectly measure the unknown height of an object at a known distance, such as a tree or wall.

   b) Indirectly measure the unknown distance from the viewer to an object of known height.

2. **Figure 1.22** is a sketch of your hand held up 2 feet in front of your eye.

   a) Copy the drawing on your own paper. Draw in lines of sight from your eye past the top and bottom of your hand. Extend these lines to the right edge of your page.

   b) Suppose your hand is 7 inches long and just blocks out a friend who is 5 1/2 feet tall. What is the scale of your friend in the plane of your hand? Draw your friend into your picture.

   c) How far from your eye is your friend standing? Remember, the distance from your eye to your hand is 24 inches.

   d) How much does your answer change if you made a 1/4-inch error in your hand-size measurement?

   e) How much does your answer change if you made a 1/2-inch error in the distance from your eye to your hand?

   f) Explore the effect of rounding the length of your hand and the distance to your hand from your eye. How much does going from whole numbers to one decimal place change your final answer?

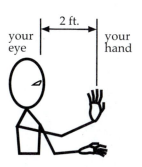

Figure 1.22.
Sketch for Item 2.

3. a) The Washington Monument is 169 meters high. How far would you have to stand from it to block it out with your hand? Assume your hand is 18 cm in length and the picture plane is 50 cm from your eye. Sketch the situation first. Watch the units.

   b) Suppose you are drawing a tree on a piece of paper taped to an easel. The paper is 2 feet from your eye. The tree is 10 feet high and 40 feet from your eye. How tall should you make the image of the tree on the paper?

4. a) Measure the height of an object and your distance from the object, and determine how large you would make the object in a painting that is 2 feet from your eye. Verify your answer directly by using a ruler as in Item 1 of Activity 3.

   b) What is the scale of the image in part (a)?

   c) How large would the object appear if it were twice as far away from your eye and the viewing plane remained at 2 feet away? What is the corresponding scale?

   d) How large would the object appear if it were at its original distance (as in part (a)), but the viewing plane were 1 foot from your eye instead of 2 feet away? What is the corresponding scale?

5. **Figure 1.23** shows the top view of a person looking at five railroad ties.

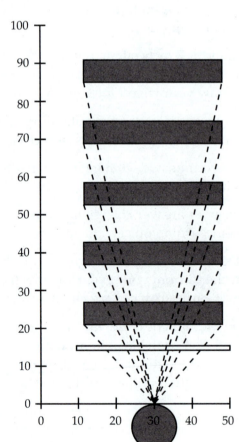

Figure 1.23.
Top view of person looking at railroad ties.

a) Measure the length of each projection in the picture plane. Then measure the distance between each tie and the viewer's eye. Record your measurements in a table similar to **Figure 1.24**.

Tie number	1	2	3	4	5
Distance to viewer's eye					
Projection length					

Figure 1.24.
Table for recording railroad tie lengths and distances.

b) Based on your measurements, describe the relationship between the length of the projection of each tie and its distance from the viewer's eye.

c) Graph your data. Label the horizontal axis "Distance To Eye" and label the vertical axis "Projection Length."

d) Predict the image length for the 10th tie, 20th tie, 100th tie, and the one-millionth tie.

e) What equation describes this graph—that is, gives apparent size in terms of actual distance from the viewer?

6. a) Simulate the experiment outlined in Item 5 for yourself. Use a piece of transparent plastic or glass as the plane of vision and some pencils as railroad ties. Place a clean transparency on your glass and mark what you see on the transparency using a marking pen. Add the ties one by one. You will probably need to sit at a table and position the transparency so that one edge of the transparency sits on the table at the edge as shown in the sketch in **Figure 1.25**. Be sure to keep your eyes in the same location as you work. (Check earlier-marked points as you work.)

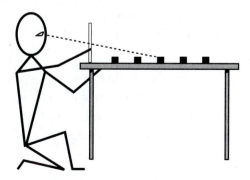

Figure 1.25.
Side view of simulation of viewing railroad ties.

INDIVIDUAL WORK 3

b) Stand some 8- or 10-penny nails on the right side of each pencil and draw what you see.

c) Suppose, instead of lying on the table top, the pencils were stacked up one by one on top of each other, parallel to your plane of vision, like a fence (see **Figure 1.26**). Draw what you would see through your window.

Figure 1.26.
Side view of stacked railroad ties.

d) Write a description of the differences in the pictures you drew in parts (a) and (c). Be as specific as you can about the appearance of the pencils in each case.

e) What is a general rule governing the apparent sizes of identical objects?

7. Return to the Preparation Reading for this lesson, and revise your answers to its Consider questions.

Scale is defined in terms of the apparent and real sizes of an object. The main control numbers affecting scale, though, are distances. The closer the viewing plane, the smaller an object looks. Also, the further away an object is from the viewer, the smaller it looks. This is the principle of diminution. Diminution only occurs when objects are observed at different distances; it is not present when everything is equally distant from the viewer.

In completing Items 1–7, you probably made use of the properties of similar triangles. You know that the corresponding sides of similar triangles are proportional and, in problems that can be modeled with drawings like **Figure 1.27**, where DE is parallel to BC, triangles ABC and ADE are similar.

Note that the custom in describing similar figures is to list the corresponding labels in the same order. Thus, saying that *ABC* is similar to *ADE* also implies that *A* corresponds to *A*, *B* to *D*, and *C* to *E*.

8. Suppose that the lengths of some of the segments in Figure 1.27 were measured and recorded in **Figure 1.28**. Assume that *BC* is parallel to *DE*.

   Find the lengths of *AE*, *EC*, and *BC*. Write the proportions you use in your calculations.

9. a) How many triangles are there in **Figure 1.29**? Compare your answer with those of others in your group and, if there are any disagreements, resolve them.

   b) In Figure 1.29, if *ABCD* is a rectangle and *GE* and *HF* are both perpendicular to *EF*, how many different shapes of triangles are there? How do you know this?

   c) List all the triangles that you think are similar to triangle *GEC*.

It is useful to refer to parts of any triangle in a manner that acknowledges the relationships between the sides and the angles. By convention, when there are no extra lines to confuse the issue:

- Vertices of triangles are labeled with capital letters.

- A side of a triangle is labeled with the same letter (but in lower case) as its opposite angle. For example, side *h* and angle *H* are opposite each other. In **Figure 1.30**, we say that side *a* is opposite angle *A*.

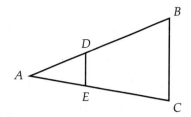

Figure 1.27.
Triangle *ABC* is similar to triangle *ADE*.

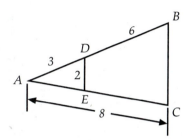

Figure 1.28.
Triangle for Item 8 with lengths identified.

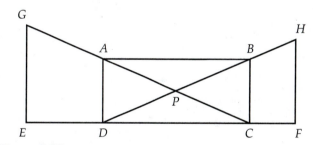

Figure 1.29.
Figure with several triangles.

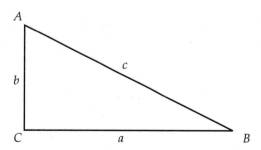

Figure 1.30.
Triangle to illustrate how to label angles and sides.

INDIVIDUAL WORK 3

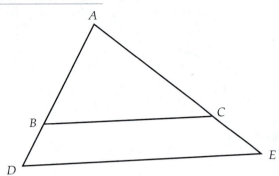

Figure 1.31.
Triangle for Item 10(a).

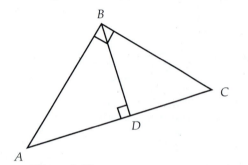

Figure 1.32.
Triangle for Item 10(b).

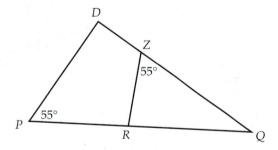

Figure 1.33.
Triangles for Item 11(a).

10. a) Use **Figure 1.31** to show that triangles *ABC* and *ADE* are similar by tracing *ABC* onto a piece of paper (or using the handout provided by your teacher), cutting it out, and fitting angle *B* onto angle *D*, and angle *C* onto angle *E*.

   b) List the similar triangles in **Figure 1.32** and list all the pairs of equal angles. Test your list by tracing the triangles (or using the handout provided by your teacher), cutting them out, and checking that the angles on your list match.

11. a) For **Figure 1.33** explain, without tracing and cutting, why triangles *QDP* and *QRZ* are similar, and list the pairs of corresponding sides.

   b) Verify your results from Item 11(a) by tracing (or using the handout provided by your teacher) and cutting out triangle *QRZ*. List pairs of **corresponding angles**—angles that are equal in measure and in analogous, or corresponding, positions.

12. Two triangles are similar if the three angles of one are equal to the three angles of the other.

   This fact about similar triangles leads to the following corollaries (immediate consequences). Explain why each is true.

   a) Corollary 1: If one triangle has two angles that are the same size as two angles of another triangle, the triangles are similar (use the symbol ≈ to mean, is similar to).

   b) Corollary 2: If an acute angle of one right triangle equals an acute angle of another, the right triangles are similar.

13. a) List all the triangles in **Figure 1.34** that are similar to each other.

   b) For Figure 1.34, sketch each right triangle you see, lettering each vertex and labelling the length of each side. Draw each right triangle so that it is standing on its shortest leg.

   c) Find the length, x, of AD and the length, y, of DC. Show the proportions you use.

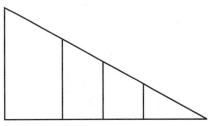

Figure 1.34.
Triangles for Item 13(a).

14. Look back at Figure 1.29 from Item 9. Trace several copies of the figure (or use several copies of Handout H1.5, provided by your teacher) and cut out all the triangles that are similar to triangle *DFH*. Arrange them so they are in the same relative position.

   a) Stack your triangles with the largest on the bottom so the stack looks like **Figure 1.35**. Use this configuration to make a conjecture about the relative sizes of the smallest angles of each triangle.

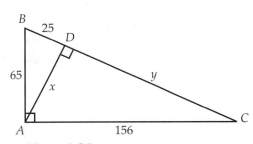

Figure 1.35.
Figure for Item 10(a).

   b) Rearrange the triangles to determine the relationships among the sizes of the larger acute angles of the triangles.

   c) Each of the triangles you have cut out is a right triangle. Using the largest triangle, measure the lengths of the hypotenuse and of the shortest leg. What is the ratio of the lengths of these sides?

   d) Measure the lengths of the corresponding two sides of the smallest triangles and find the ratio of these lengths.

   e) Do the same calculations for the other triangles you have cut out. What do you conclude?

   f) Pick another pair of sides on one of the triangles, measure them and find the ratio of their lengths. Then measure corresponding sides of the other triangles. What do you conclude?

INDIVIDUAL WORK 3

15. At many amusement parks and beaches, you can find stores that take a picture, enlarge it, and give you a larger-than-life portrait suitable for framing (if you can find a wall large enough on which to hang it). They also give you a small pocket-size copy. **Figure 1.36** shows examples using stick pictures (not to the same scales).

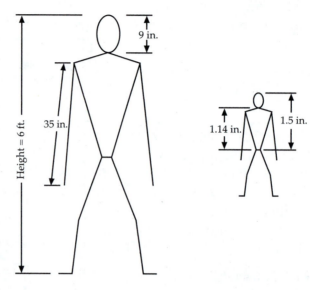

Figure 1.36.
Figure for Item 15.

a) Is enough information given to find the height of the smaller figure? If not, decide what information would be useful and make up a reasonable value for it.

b) Assume the leg length of the large portrait is 35 inches (so the torso length is 28 inches). Find the leg length and head height for the smaller figure.

c) How much of the large figure's height is its legs? How much of the small figure's height is its legs?

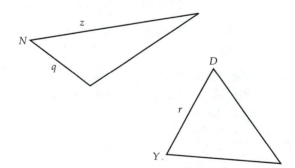

Figure 1.37.
Figure for Item 16(a).

16.a) Copy **Figure 1.37** on your own paper and label the sides and vertices of the triangles according to the conventions described in Item 10.

b) For each of the triangles in **Figure 1.38**, how long is the side opposite angle *V*?

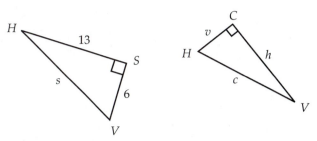

Figure 1.38.
Two triangles for Item 16(b).

For the right triangle (see **Figure 1.39**), we say that *b* is the side *adjacent* to angle *A*. Angle *A* actually has two adjacent sides, *b* and *c*. However, since triangle *ABC* is a right triangle, we can avoid confusion by referring to *c* as the hypotenuse, not as an adjacent side. The sides of the triangle other than the hypotenuse are referred to as legs, not sides.

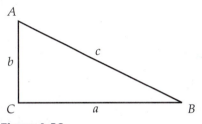

Figure 1.39.
Figure to identify adjacent sides and hypotenuse.

c) Find the lengths of the legs adjacent to angle *V* in the triangles in **Figure 1.40**.

17. Triangles *ABC* and *MNQ* (not shown) appear to be similar. Measurement shows that side *a* = 2(side *m*) and side *b* = 2(side *n*). What additional information will assure you that triangle *ABC* is similar to triangle *MNQ*? Give all possibilities.

18. When you hold a cube at eye level so one face is parallel to your plane of vision, the cube looks like a square. If the cube is transparent then you see the otherwise invisible sides and edges of the cube (see **Figure 1.41**). The dotted lines represent the edges of the hidden faces. The edges labelled *a*, *b*, *c*, *d* are perpendicular to the plane of vision.

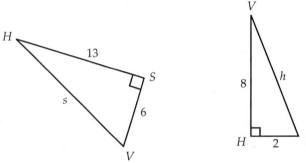

Figure 1.40.
Triangles for Item 16(c).

a) What do you notice about the vertical edges?

b) How do the front and back faces compare?

c) Why does the back face appear smaller than the front face of the cube?

d) What do you notice about the top, bottom, and side faces?

e) What do you notice about the edges labelled *a*, *b*, *c*, *d*, which are perpendicular to the plane of vision?

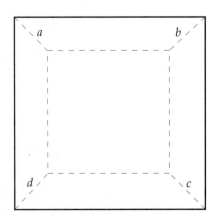

Figure 1.41.
Transparent cube.

19. Three equal-height poles are to be placed 100 feet apart, increasing in distance from the viewer. Which drawing (see **Figure 1.42**) seems to be the best representation? Explain your answer.

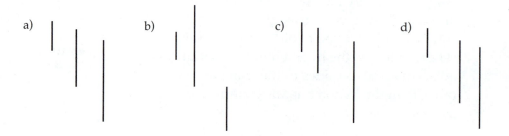

Figure 1.42.
Four different drawings of three poles.

20. **Figure 1.43** is a proper perspective rendering of a series of equally-spaced, identical light poles.

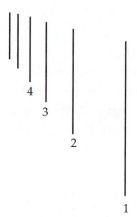

Figure 1.43.
Equally-spaced, identical light poles drawn in proper perspective.

a) What do you notice about the relative sizes of the poles?

b) What do you notice about the locations of the poles in relation to one another?

c) What would you notice if the images of poles 2 and 4 were switched?

LESSON THREE
Vanishing Point

KEY CONCEPTS

Diminution

Convergence

Vanishing point

Horizon

Similarity

Scale

The Image Bank

Figure 1.44.
The inside of a hallway.

PREPARATION READING

Tunnel Vision

*I*n Lesson 2, you were asked to sketch a picture containing several signs of the same height equally spaced along a street. According to the principle of diminution, successively distant signs will appear smaller. Proportions, based on lines of sight, tell you how much smaller, if you know the distance to the object and where the viewing plane is. That is, scale depends on the depth of the object in the scene. So you probably sized correctly the signs you drew.

Thus your work with diminution and proportions solves one problem. But it leaves one old question still unanswered and it raises a new one. The old question deals with finding the proper locations for the properly-sized signs. The new question is whether you can determine scales in pictures when you do *not* know the distances to objects or to the viewing plane. In a picture, there are a number of approaches to locating equally-spaced objects. This lesson introduces a new principle, called convergence, that can help. Along the way, you will also solve the problem of determining scale using only information within a picture—without knowing viewing distances.

Cubes are three-dimensional objects. They have length, width, and depth. The depth of the cube is not apparent when you hold the cube at eye level and look directly at one face. The third dimension, depth, is not visible. However, if it were, the faces perpendicular to the plane of vision (that is, the sides, top, and bottom) could be thought of as made of separate objects lined up further and further from the viewer, like a series of poles or cross-ties.

In the previous lesson, you made a modeling decision when you viewed the cube in such a way that you saw just one square face of the cube. Square signs represent this view. You studied the simplest view of the simplest three-dimensional object. Not only locations, but also scales depend on the depth of objects within the picture. Therefore, in this lesson you continue the modeling process by changing the way you view three-dimensional objects. For example, when you make the cube transparent or look inside the cube, you are able to see other faces and edges of the cube; you see depth. This new point of view leads to insights into representing three-dimensional objects on a two-dimensional plane.

How does diminution affect what you see when you view a transparent cube and how you draw that transparent cube? When you view the front face of the cube and the back face at the same time, you see two objects (squares) of equal size but at different distances from the viewer. The face most distant from the viewer appears smaller because of diminution. Notice what that means for the edges *a*, *b*, *c*, and *d* that connect the front face to the back face (see **Figure 1.45**).

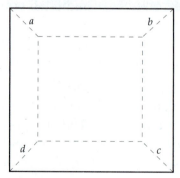

Figure 1.45.
Transparent cube.

A similar effect results when you look inside a long, narrow room or down a long hallway. Notice the sides and edges of the hallway shown in **Figure 1.44** at the start of this lesson.

The edges of the hallway, although parallel in real life, appear to be closer together at the far end. Consequently, the sides, ceiling, and floor appear to be narrower at the far end of the hall. The walls and the edges seem to converge in the distance.

The artistic principle of **convergence** is illustrated when the apparent distance narrows between parallel lines. The walls of the hallway in Figure 1.44 and the edges of the road and the edges of the shoulder in **Figure 1.46** really are parallel, yet they appear to converge as distance from the viewer increases.

Figure 1.46.
Road, with shoulder extensions, illustrating convergence.

The Image Bank

In this lesson, you will study the principle of convergence and develop techniques for applying that principle accurately to sets of parallel lines.

ACTIVITY

MORE THAN MEETS THE EYE

4

In a transparent cube, with one face parallel to the plane of vision, the edges perpendicular to the plane of vision appear to converge. For example, look back at edges *a, b, c,* and *d* in Figure 1.45.

A similar effect is visible when you look down the parallel rails of a railroad track. They, too, appear to converge in the distance (see **Figure 1.47**).

Vin Catania

Figure 1.47.
Railroad tracks illustrate convergence.

Although the rails of the railroad track, the sides of a hallway, and the edges of a cube are parallel in the real world, they appear to converge in a perspective view. In this activity, you will answer the question, Why do parallel lines appear to converge? In Individual Work 4, "Adjusting Your Sights," you will apply the principle of convergence to represent depth in perspective drawings.

To understand the principle of convergence better, it can be useful to think of the bottom face of a cube as being made of a series of separate, equally-spaced, identical lines. Railroad cross-ties make a good model. Each tie represents the distance between the parallel rails. Similarly, the side faces of a cube can be thought of as being made up of a series of poles. Each pole represents the distance between the parallel top and bottom edges of the cube.

MORE THAN MEETS THE EYE

1. **Figure 1.48** is a top view of a person observing a railroad track and a series of equally-spaced railroad ties. The lines of sight are drawn from the viewer to the ends of the first five ties.

    a) Describe the relationship between the two rails in real life.

    b) The projection of the first tie in the picture plane is almost as wide as the picture (see Figure 1.48). Compare the length of the projection of the fourth tie to the length of the projection of the first tie. How do they differ?

    c) Describe the projection of the railroad tie that is as far as the eye can see from the viewer. (What does it look like? Where is it?) Why must this be true?

    d) Each tie connects the parallel rails. What does your answer to (c) tell you about the images of the rails in the picture?

    e) What does your investigation of railroad ties tell you about the appearance of the bottom edges, *c* and *d*, of the cube in Figure 1.45?

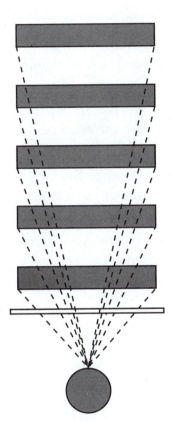

Figure 1.48.
Top view of person viewing a series of equally-spaced railroad ties.

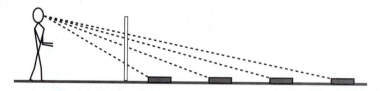

MORE THAN MEETS THE EYE

4

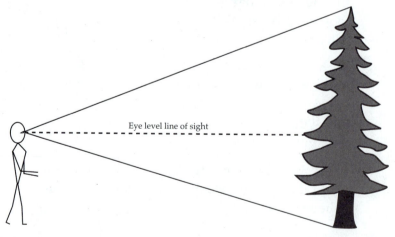

Figure 1.49.
Side view of person observing a series of equally-spaced railroad ties.

2. **Figure 1.49** is a side view of the same person viewing the same first four railroad ties.

a) The projection of the first tie appears near the bottom of the picture plane (see Figure 1.49). How is the location of the projection of the fourth tie different from the location of the projection of the first tie?

b) Describe the location in the picture plane of the tie (not shown) that is farthest from the viewer. Assume the ground is level.

Lines of sight may be drawn from a viewer to one or more objects in a scene. A line of sight parallel to the ground (assuming the ground is level) is said to be at the eye level of the viewer (see **Figure 1.50**).

Eye level line of sight

Figure 1.50.
Sketch illustrating line of sight at the eye level of the viewer.

3. In Item 2, you observed objects (railroad ties) below the eye level of the artist. In this item, you examine lines of sight to objects above the eye level of the artist.

MORE THAN MEETS THE EYE

Suppose you are looking at light poles instead of railroad ties. The side view in **Figure 1.51** shows the poles are of equal height. The top of each pole is above the eye level of the viewer. The bottom of each pole is at ground level, below the eye level of the viewer. These poles can be thought of as defining the side face of a giant cube (connecting edges *b* and *c* in Figure 1.45).

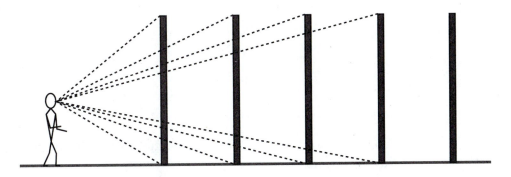

Figure 1.51.
Side view of a series of light poles, including lines of sight.

a) Suppose you draw a line connecting the tops of the poles. Then, draw a second line connecting the bottoms of the poles (where the poles meet the ground). Describe the relationship between these two lines in reality.

b) Now consider the lines of sight from the viewer to the tops and bottoms of the first four poles. Describe the difference between the projection in the picture plane of the first pole and the projection of the fourth pole.

c) Describe successive lines of sight to tops and bottoms of more and more distant poles.

d) Based on your answers to (a) through (c), where in the picture plane do you expect to find the projection of the pole that is as far as the eye can see? How large will it appear?

e) The poles connect edges *b* and *c* of the cube in Figure 1.45. What do your answers to (a)–(d) tell you about these edges?

4. In **Figure 1.52** you see a perspective view of the road as it appeared in your video-game-sign problem in Lesson 2.

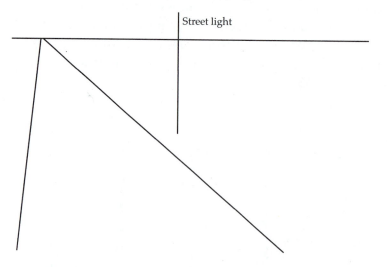

Street light

Figure 1.52.
Perspective view of a road in a video game.

a) What do you notice about the lines that form the sides of the road in the picture?

b) Sketch a top view of the road. What should be true of the lines that form the sides of the road in the top view?

Even though a series of light poles may be the same height in real life, the principle of diminution ensures that more distant poles must appear shorter than closer poles. Therefore, the line that connects the tops of the poles and the line that connects the bottoms of the poles, although parallel to one another in real life, must appear closer together at greater distances from the viewer. The same is true for the lines (tracks) connecting the ends of railroad ties. Because they go away from the viewer, these parallel lines appear to converge to a point called the **vanishing point** for these parallel lines. But, where is that point?

5. In examining convergence, you have looked at horizontal lines connecting the ends of railroad ties and horizontal lines connecting the tops and bottoms of poles. In each case, the lines were parallel and receding into the distance. They can be thought of as front-to-back edges of a cube, where you are looking directly into the (transparent) front face.

MORE THAN MEETS THE EYE

a) Think of *all* possible lines parallel to the horizontal front-to-back edges of a cube. In reality, each of these lines *is* a line, and each has the same direction. How do you think they would look in a perspective drawing? Would they still look like lines? Would they have the same directions?

b) Of all those lines, only one goes exactly through the eye of the viewer; so the viewer looks along that line. What would that line look like to the viewer?

c) The principle of diminution tells you that the apparent distance between two parallel lines that go away from the viewer must decrease. What does your observation in (b) tell you about the location of the vanishing point for front-to-back lines in a cube?

When you view railroad ties (see Item 2), the closest ties appear well below the eye level of the viewer. But the tie as far as the eye can see appears to be at eye level. When you view light poles (see Item 3), both the tops and bottoms of distant poles appear to converge to eye level.

So diminution is the answer to the question, *Why* do parallel lines appear to converge? and also it explains *where* they appear to converge. Now explore the question, *When* do parallel lines appear to converge? Continue with Items 6 through 8, and investigate which sets of parallel lines appear to converge in a perspective view and which sets do not.

6. Examine the side view of the horizontal slats of a fence shown in **Figure 1.53**.

a) Explain why the horizontal slats do not appear to converge. How does diminution play a role here?

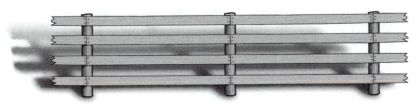

Figure 1.53.
Side view of fence with horizontal slats.

ACTIVITY

MORE THAN MEETS THE EYE

4

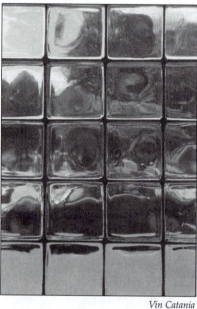

Figure 1.54.
Front view of window.

Vin Catania

Figure 1.55.
Perspective view of a
tiled floor.

Vin Catania

b) In the front view of the window in **Figure 1.54**, which lines appear parallel? Which lines appear to converge?

c) In the perspective view of the tiled floor (see **Figure 1.55**), which lines appear parallel? Which lines appear to converge?

d) Based on your observations thus far, when do parallel lines appear to converge? Explain how the principle of diminution supports your answer.

The principle of diminution guarantees that all horizontal parallel lines that increase in distance from the viewer (not parallel to the picture plane) must appear to converge to a vanishing point for that family of parallel lines. Any line in the family must appear to converge to the vanishing point. Among all lines in the family, only one actually goes through the eye of the viewer. It looks like a point, so it defines the vanishing point. Therefore, for families of horizontal parallel lines, the vanishing points are always at the viewer's eye level.

MORE THAN MEETS THE EYE

ACTIVITY

4

In **Figure 1.56**, lines *a, b,* and *c* are parallel. Both *a* and *c* look like lines to the viewer, but line *b* appears to be a point. Since all three lines must appear to approach each other, *b* must define the vanishing point.

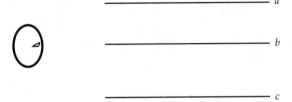

a

b

c

Figure 1.56.
Why the vanishing point is at eye level.

When only one family of horizontal parallel lines, not parallel to the plane of vision, converges to a single vanishing point, **one-point perspective** occurs. When two families of horizontal parallel lines, not parallel to the plane of vision, all converge to one of two vanishing points, **two-point perspective** occurs. (You will read more about two-point perspective in later lessons.)

7. Using Handout H1.6 provided by your teacher, draw the lines of convergence and identify the vanishing points for each of **Figures 1.57–1.59**. How do you know each point you identified is the vanishing point?

Figure 1.57.
The Bridge at Argentiuel by Monet.

ACTIVITY

4

MORE THAN MEETS THE EYE

Figure 1.58.
The Church of Saint-Severin by Utrillo.

©*The Bridgeman Art Library, International, Ltd.*

In Lesson 2, you studied the principle of diminution and concluded that objects appear smaller as their distance from the viewer increases.

In this lesson, you have begun examining the principle of convergence. The principle of convergence is a consequence of the principle of diminution. Convergence is the principle governing why parallel lines appear closer together as distance from the viewer increases and why they appear to meet at a vanishing point. But are you closer to determining scales in pictures when distances are not known, or to locating the signs you sized for the video game in Lesson 2?

Figure 1.59.
Le Pont de l'Europe 1876 by Gustave Caillebotte.

©*The Bridgeman Art Library, International, Ltd.*

INDIVIDUAL WORK 4

Adjusting Your Sights

The purpose of this individual work is to enhance your understanding of the principle of convergence and its use in representing parallel lines.

1. a) **Figure 1.60** shows a line of trees next to a roadway. Use the rulers surrounding the picture to identify the location of the vanishing point for the lines joining the tops of the trees and the bottoms. Then draw a horizontal line through that vanishing point. What does it represent?

The Image Bank

b) The shoulders of the road extend beyond the white lines on both edges of the road. Pretend a ladder is placed from the edge of the shoulder to the top of each tree, forming a triangle. Describe the corresponding triangles.

Figure 1.60.
Trees lining a roadway.

INDIVIDUAL WORK 4

Figure 1.61.
The Chemin de Sevres,
Louveciennes by Alfred Sisley.

©The Bridgeman Art Library, International, Ltd.

2. a) On Handout H1.7, which is the same as **Figure 1.61**, draw in the lines along the road, treetops, and the roofs of buildings.

   b) What is true of these lines? Explain.

   c) On Handout H1.8 draw lines along all edges that represent lines parallel to the center aisle. Extend the lines to identify the locations of any corresponding vanishing points.

   d) What is true of the vanishing points for sets of parallel lines from various objects in **Figure 1.62**? Explain.

   e) Summarize your conclusions from Items (a)–(d).

Figure 1.62.
Print Shop Interior
by Jan van der Straet.

The Folger Shakespeare Library

3. a) Obtain from your teacher a copy of Handout H1.9, showing
   Figure 1.63, or find a similar picture in a newspaper or magazine. Find the vanishing point for this picture.

   b) Look back at Figure 1.58 from Item 7, Activity 4. There you are
   not looking directly down the center of the road; the road seems
   to go off to the side. The same is true for the sides of the buildings. Explain how to find the vanishing point for this picture.

   c) What conditions determine whether the vanishing point appears
   in the center of your picture, to the right of the center, to the left
   of the center, or beyond the edge of the picture plane? Before you
   answer this question, you may want to investigate different scenarios. Recall, for example, that a vanishing point is associated
   with a family of parallel lines. How can families of lines differ?

In summary, the phenomenon that equal-sized objects appear smaller at
greater distances illustrates *diminution*. The notion that parallel lines
drawn into the distance will appear to meet at a single point illustrates
convergence. The point at which they meet is called their *vanishing point*.

The vanishing point for horizontal lines is at the eye level of the
observer (see **Figure 1.64**). This eye level is called the **horizon line**—the
line on which the earth and the sky appear to meet. The vanishing
point for the railroad ties in Figure 1.64 is a point on the horizon.

Figure 1.63.
The Flatiron Building

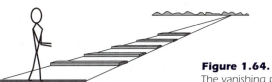

Figure 1.64.
The vanishing point is on the horizon, at the eye level of the viewer.

4. a) Revisit Figure 1.55 from Item 6, Activity 4 and identify the location of the horizon.

   b) Revisit Figure 1.61 and Figure 1.62 from Item 2 in this individual
   work and identify the locations of the horizons.

   c) Revisit Figure 1.63 from Item 3 in this individual work and identify the location of the horizon.

5. Sketch a scene that illustrates one vanishing point: Draw the view
   looking down a long, narrow hallway at your school, or draw a row
   of trees or telephone poles next to a long, straight road, or stand

INDIVIDUAL WORK 4

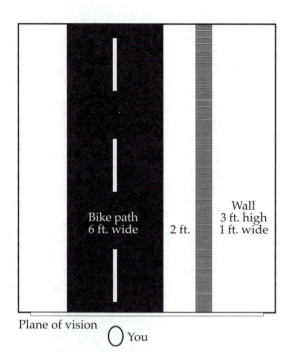

Figure 1.65.
Aerial view of a road and a wall.

close to a long building and sketch the view as the parallel edges of the building converge toward the vanishing point.

Suggestion: Begin by drawing the horizon line and the vanishing point. Then draw the converging lines for the tops and bottoms of the trees, or the sides of the road, or the roof lines of the buildings.

6. **Figure 1.65** provides an aerial view of a scene. Draw a perspective view of the same scene with one vanishing point.

7. Revisit the painting by William Hogarth (see Figure 1.3) in Activity 1. Determine where Hogarth violated the principle of convergence. Explain your answer.

Items 8 through 14 examine relationships between parallel lines so you can identify and use parallel-line relationships in your perspective drawings.

8. **Figure 1.66** shows a pair of parallel lines drawn by an architect and intersected by line *SE*.

a) Which angles must be the same size?

A mathematical term for the line *SE* is transversal. A **transversal** is a line that intersects two or more parallel lines.

In Figure 1.66, ∠2 is to the left of the transversal and above one of the two parallel lines, and ∠6 is also to the left of the transversal and above the other of the two parallel lines. These two angles are corresponding angles.

b) What angle is in the same corresponding position as ∠5?

c) Name all the other pairs of corresponding angles in the picture.

d) What can be said about the relationship of corresponding angles to each other?

e) If ∠1 measures 40 degrees, find the measures of all the other angles.

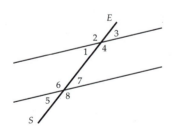

Figure 1.66.
Figure for Item 8.

9. a) In **Figure 1.67**, *ABCD* is a parallelogram. List all the pairs of similar triangles.

   b) What is the ratio of the lengths of corresponding sides in the pairs of similar triangles in the parallelogram in Figure 1.67?

10. In **Figure 1.68**, *RS* is parallel to *HK*.

    a) Which angles are equal?

    b) What is the relationship between triangles *ARS* and *AHK*? Why?

11. In **Figure 1.69**, *HK* is parallel to *RS*, and line segment *AN* bisects segment *HK*.

    a) Explain why it also must bisect segment *RS*.

    b) Create Figure 1.69 on a geometric drawing utility. Investigate angle and length relationships for different locations of *HK* (still parallel to *RS*) and for different triangles *ARS*. Make a conjecture following your investigation.

12. Use a geometric drawing utility to construct a parallelogram on the screen. Construct the parallelogram in such a way that you can vary the measures of the angles and the lengths of the sides. You should be able to move key points to create squares, rhombuses, rectangles, and a variety of other parallelograms. Identify the measures of each of the four angles, the lengths of each of the four sides, and the lengths of the two diagonals. Investigate to answer the following questions.

    a) Under what conditions are the diagonals of your parallelogram of equal length?

    b) Under what conditions do the diagonals of your parallelogram bisect the angles of the parallelogram?

    c) Under what conditions do the diagonals of your parallelogram bisect each other?

    d) Under what conditions are the diagonals perpendicular to each other?

    e) Compare the distance from the point where the diagonals intersect to each of the sides and make a conjecture. (Measure the lengths of the four segments that are perpendicular to each of the sides and that pass through the intersection point of the diagonals.)

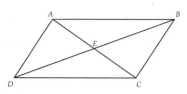

Figure 1.67.
Parallelogram for Item 9.

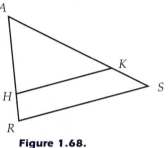

Figure 1.68.
Figure for Item 10.

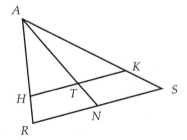

Figure 1.69.
Figure for Item 11.

INDIVIDUAL WORK 4

13. Explain when and why some rectangles appear as trapezoids in a perspective view.

14. Repeat your investigation from Item 12, this time for trapezoids. Compare the relationship between the diagonals of trapezoids with the relationship between diagonals for squares, rhombuses, rectangles, and parallelograms. Explain any similarities and differences.

15. In Activity 2, you were challenged to draw a perspective view of three signs equally spaced in the real world. Activity 3 showed that getting the signs' sizes correct is a matter of solving proportions; that was relatively easy. Putting them in the right places is a bit more difficult. However, consider the following procedure.

   a) Return to your copy of Handout H1.2 from Lesson 2 and your work in Item 8 of Activity 3. Use the scale you computed for the streetlight to draw a 4-meter-square sign beside the streetlight. (This sign is *not* one of the three you are looking for.) How large is this sign in your drawing?

   b) The line connecting the top-right corners of the four signs (the one from (a) and the three others you are looking to draw) is horizontal and parallel to the edge of the road. What does that tell you about that line's vanishing point? What about the line joining the lower-right corners?

   c) Use your answer to (b) to draw the lines connecting the top-right and lower-right corners of all the 4-by-4 signs. (Of course, the other signs aren't in the picture yet.)

   d) Now use the sizes you determined in Activity 3 to place the other three signs in their proper places.

Figure 1.70.
Photograph for Item 16(b).

The Image Bank

16. a) Item 15 demonstrates that, given the size of an object, its distance from the viewer, and the distance from the viewer to the view plane, you can use scaling to determine the proper image size and convergence to determine a correct placement for the image. Will this process work in reverse? That is, given the image size and placement of an object in a picture, can you determine its scale in order to compute its actual size? Explain your answer.

   b) Use the method you described in (a) to find the real height of the nearest right-hand tree in **Figure 1.70**. If you are unable to determine its height, explain what additional information is required.

DETECTIVE ART

In this unit, you have investigated the artistic principles of overlapping, diminution, and convergence. These principles are used by artists to draw accurate representations of the real world. Given information about the size of an object and its distance from the viewer, you can determine the proper image size, and, perhaps, its location in your picture by applying these principles of perspective.

Do the same principles work in reverse? That is, can you use a photograph or picture to determine the real-life size of the object and the real-life distance from the viewer? Can the mathematics of perspective be used by investigators to examine photographs and then draw conclusions about measurements and distances for the objects depicted?

This activity uses the definitions of scale and horizon to develop investigative tools. The accuracy of these tools depends on the geometry of perspective and the accuracy of related measurements.

Imagine a picture as a window through which you view a scene. Recall that the *scale* of an object in the picture is the ratio of its size (height or width) in the picture to its actual size. You have used similar triangles and proportions to determine the scales of objects in pictures or to draw objects so they were the correct sizes in pictures.

CONSIDER:

1. Study **Figure 1.71**. Identify lengths that are known or easily measured, and lengths that are unknown.

2. Can you determine the scale of the tree in the picture without knowing the actual height of the object or its distance from the viewer? Explain your answer.

DETECTIVE ART

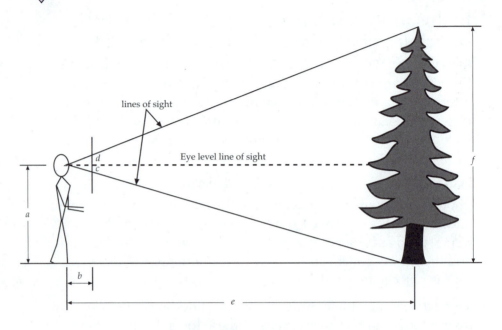

Figure 1.71.
Picture illustrating known and unknown measurements.

3. How are lengths *a* and *c* related to lengths *b* and *e*? Does your answer to this question affect your answer to question 2 above?

Assume the ground shown in the figure is level. Then the horizon in the picture corresponds to the eye level of the viewer (camera). Since a horizontal line through the eye to the horizon looks like a point, the horizon is at eye level for the viewer at all depths in the picture. Thus, if the ground in the image is level, the distance from the ground to the horizon line represents the eye height of the viewer at that depth in the picture. That means you can determine the scale of an object in the picture if you can see where it touches the ground and you know the eye height of the artist (distance between the ground and the artist's eye).

For example, in Figure 1.71, the eye level line is always at a height of *a*. That means that $\frac{c}{a}$ is the scale of the picture at the tree.

DETECTIVE ART

Complete this activity to determine scales for two of the trees in **Figure 1.72**.

Assume you are the same height as the person who took the photograph.

1. Measure your actual eye height (the distance from your eye to the ground).

The Image Bank

Figure 1.72.
Photograph showing convergence.

2. a) Select a particular tree in Figure 1.72. Carefully measure the distance from the bottom of the image of that tree up to the horizon line.

ACTIVITY

5

DETECTIVE ART

b) Since the horizon is at the viewer's eye level, the distance you measured in part (a) is the height from the ground to your eye if you were standing in the picture right beside the tree you selected. Use that fact to determine the scale of the selected tree in the photograph.

c) What is the actual height of the tree?

3. a) Generalize the steps from Items 1 and 2 to describe how to determine the scale of any object in the image.

   b) Use your method to determine the height of another tree in the picture.

4. a) Using the scale from Item 2(b), determine the width of the shoulder of the road in the picture.

   b) Repeat using your work in Item 3(b). Compare your answers for the shoulder width. Explain any discrepancies you find.

5. Assume the picture plane is 10 inches from the viewer. Use scale factors to estimate the distance from the photographer to each of the trees you examined in Items 2 and 3.

6. You assumed the eye level of the photographer was the same as your eye level. You also assumed the picture plane was 10 inches from the viewer's eye, but those assumptions could be off a bit.

   a) Recalculate the scale and height of the first tree if you missed your estimate of the photographer's eye level by 2 inches.

   b) Recalculate the scale and height of the first tree if you missed your estimate of the distance from the viewer's eye to the picture plane by 1 inch.

INDIVIDUAL WORK 5

Scale Factors

O ne application of similar figures is in enlarging (or shrinking) drawings. In mathematics, this scaling transformation is usually called dilation. The ratio of the new lengths to the old lengths (new:old) is called the **scale factor**. (With k the scale factor for the dilation, the **dilation** is a stretching away from the center by a factor of k.) Thus, if the scale factor is less than 1, then the picture or object is reduced. If the scale factor is greater than 1, then the picture is an enlargement. You may recall studying dilations in Course 1, Unit 3, *Landsat*.

Suppose you want to double the size of triangle ABC in **Figure 1.73**. That is, for this example the scale factor will be 2:1, or just 2. Select point E (arbitrarily) as the center of dilation. Extend EA through A, and mark point A' on it so that $EA' = 2EA$. Thus $EA = AA'$. Similarly draw and extend EC so that $EC' = 2EC$. Then $EC = CC'$. Repeat the same construction through point B.

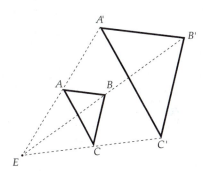

Figure 1.73.
Illustration of a dilation that doubles lengths.

1. a) Measure the sides and angles of triangles ABC and $A'B'C'$ in Figure 1.73. Confirm for yourself that these triangles satisfy all the conditions for being similar and that each side of $A'B'C'$ is twice the length of the corresponding side of ABC.

   b) From your measurements you have found that ABC and $A'B'C'$ are similar. Explain why this construction guarantees similarity.

   c) Describe a way to triple the size of triangle ABC.

   d) Describe a way to halve the size of triangle ABC.

   e) If the sides of a triangle are twice as long, respectively, as the sides of another triangle, what can you say about the relationship between the areas of the two triangles? Verify your answer mathematically.

2. Suppose you want to double the size of the same triangle ABC as above. Now E is in a new location, as shown in **Figure 1.74**.

   a) Do the construction.

   b) Does the construction produce a double-size similar triangle if you place E inside the original triangle? Does it matter where you place the point E? Explain.

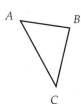

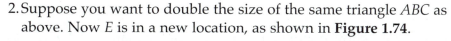

Figure 1.74.
Figure for Item 2(a).

3. In **Figure 1.75**, angles P and Q are right angles and angles G and K are equal. Write three proportion equations that apply to these triangles.

Figure 1.75.
Figure for Item 3.

4. One way to show the relationships between sides of one figure to those of another is with an arrow diagram like that in **Figure 1.76**. Another way is to use cross marks or notched arcs on the sides of the triangles or in the angles.

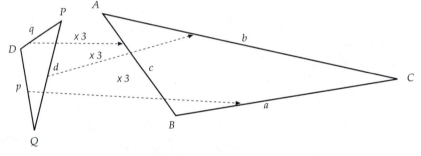

Figure 1.76.
Triangle with arrows to identify corresponding sides with dilation.

a) Suppose that in triangle PDQ the side lengths are $p = 7$, $d = 9$, and $q = 3$. Find the lengths of the sides of triangle ABC.

b) Using the lengths from (a), sketch **Figure 1.77**, draw arrow diagrams and show the relationships between the lengths of the sides within triangle ABC. For example, side c is $\frac{1}{3}$ of side b.

Figure 1.77.
Figure for Item 4(b).

c) Make the corresponding arrow diagram for triangle PDQ.

d) How are your answers to (b) and (c) alike?

e) Explain how you could use the arrow diagrams to find the length of side c if you knew only the length of side d.

5. Develop a method for creating a drawing of the front wall of your classroom at a 1/10 scale.

6. In a magazine, find a sketch or photograph for which the horizon can be determined, the ground appears level, and the point of contact of an object with the ground is clearly visible.

   Assume the eye height of the viewer/photographer is 60 inches and the distance from the viewer's eye to the picture plane is 6 inches.

   a) Determine the scale in the picture for the object you selected.

   b) Determine the height of the object. Show your method.

   c) What is the distance between the photographer and the object? Show your method.

7. Does the scale of the image of an object depend on the view height of the observer? Discuss whether or not the scale for any object is the same regardless of whether the viewer is standing or sitting.

8. Refer to the painting by William Hogarth in Figure 1.3, Activity 1. Describe at least two instances in which an object does not appear to be drawn according to the proper scale.

9. a) Suppose you are drawing the image of a pole that is 10 meters tall and a distance of 30 meters away from you. Calculate the height of the image when the picture plane is 60 cm from the viewer.

   b) Calculate the scale of the image.

   c) For the image of the pole in the drawing, calculate the vertical distance from the place where you draw the bottom of the pole to the place you draw the horizon. Assume the artist's view height is 150 cm.

   d) Suppose the distance from the viewer to the pole is doubled to 60 meters. Calculate the length of the image, the scale of the image, and the distance from the bottom of the image to the horizon.

   e) Sketch a picture of the two poles. The sketch should represent accurately your calculations in (b), (c), and (d).

10. Given a perspective view of two poles (see **Figure 1.78**), how can you determine the correct location, in the drawing, for a pole that is exactly halfway between the two poles in the real world?

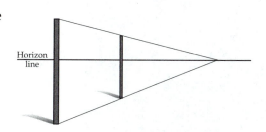

Figure 1.78.
Determining the midway location.

LESSON FOUR
The Right Space

KEY CONCEPTS

Similarity

Scale

Depth

Figure 1.79.
Error in perspective drawing of telephone poles.

PREPARATION READING

Visual Sequences

You have seen pictures of telephone poles lining a street or highway. In Activity 2, and again in Individual Work 4, you designed pictures of signs along the side of a street. Each pole or sign appears smaller than the previous one as they converge to the vanishing point. Convergence and diminution guarantee that equal-sized poles appear smaller and smaller in relation to their increasing distance from the viewer.

But something is wrong with the picture in **Figure 1.79**. Although the artist has taken great care to apply perspective with a single vanishing point, the picture does not look right. The artist failed to account for diminishing space between the poles as distance from the viewer increased.

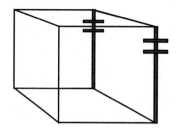

Figure 1.80.
Using cubes to locate
telephone poles.

Compare the perspective view of the telephone poles to the view of the transparent cube. Imagine that the vertical edges on one side of the cube represent two telephone poles (see **Figure 1.80**). The depth of the cube is the distance between the two poles.

How would you use the cube to represent a *series* of telephone poles all the same distance apart?

Suppose the transparent cube you viewed in Lesson 3 is the first in a series of cubes. The back face of the first cube becomes the front face of the second cube. The series of cubes is repeated until you identify the proper location for several telephone poles (see **Figure 1.81**).

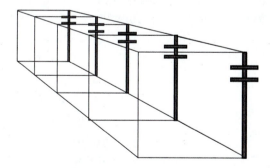

Figure 1.81.
Series of cubes to align
several telephone poles.

But how do you draw a series of cubes to identify the proper spacing of objects in a perspective drawing?

In this lesson, you will investigate how to draw equally-spaced objects accurately as they converge to a vanishing point. You will combine what you have learned about diminution and convergence and you will translate, into the world of perspective drawing, properties of rectangles and parallel lines.

ACTIVITY

6

POLES APART

Return to the challenge first posed in Activity 2 and revisited in Individual Work 4. Devise your own mathematical method for determining the proper spacing of signs or telephone poles in a drawing.

Assume the poles are of equal height and are equally spaced in the real world. You know how to use the vanishing point and horizon to make each pole the correct height. In this lesson, you will focus on determining spacing between objects in a two-dimensional view.

1. Devise a mathematical method for assuring accurate spacing between poles. Describe your method.

2. Use your method to draw a series of five poles in a copy of **Figure 1.82**. You may do this on a clean copy of Handout H1.2 supplied by your teacher or you may draw your own figure of a road and add five poles. Note that the line of the poles must be to the side of the straight-ahead line of sight to the vanishing point. Otherwise the first pole would hide all the others.

3. How would you apply your method in a new situation? What would you have to know about the situation before you could use your method?

4. Explain how you know your method is accurate.

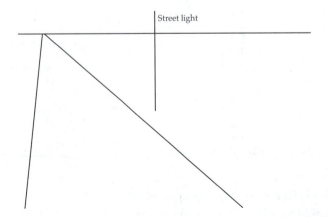

Street light

Figure 1.82.
Road converging to a vanishing point.

INDIVIDUAL WORK 6

Equal Space

This individual work utilizes ratios, proportions, similar triangles, and scale to determine the proper spacing for a series of five telephone poles.

1. Suppose you want to draw accurately a series of poles that support a cover above a walkway. **Figure 1.83** shows a top view of the poles in relation to the artist and the plane of vision. The artist chooses a viewing position 8 feet to the left of the line of poles and 22 feet from the first pole that is to be drawn in the picture. The poles are 15 feet apart. The distance between the artist's eye and the picture plane is 2 feet.

   a) Use similar triangles and proportions to determine distance *a*, the distance between the image of Pole 1 and an imaginary center line from the eye to the vanishing point (see Figure 1.83). Note: This distance is measured in the image horizontally, parallel to the horizon line.

   b) Calculate distance *b*, the distance between the image of Pole 2 and the imaginary center line.

   c) Calculate distance *c*, the distance between the image of Pole 3 and the imaginary center line.

   d) Calculate distance *d*, the distance between the image of Pole 4 and the imaginary center line.

2. Suppose telephone poles are 212 feet apart in the real world. The plane of vision is 2 feet from the eye of the viewer. The first pole in the picture is 300 feet from the plane of vision. The artist is viewing from a point 100 feet to the left of the line connecting the poles (see **Figure 1.84**).

   a) Calculate *a*, the horizontal distance between the image of Pole 1 and the imaginary center line.

   b) Calculate *b*, the horizontal distance between the image of Pole 2 and the center line.

   c) Find the horizontal distance between the center line and the image of Pole 3.

   d) Find the horizontal distance between the center line and the image of Pole 4.

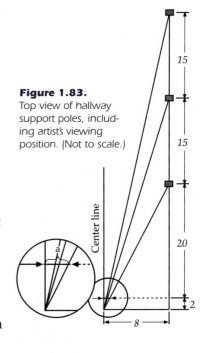

Figure 1.83.
Top view of hallway support poles, including artist's viewing position. (Not to scale.)

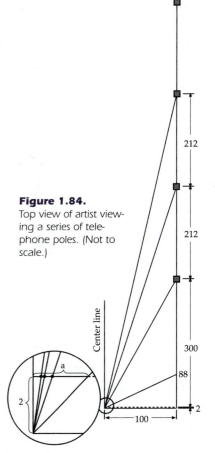

Figure 1.84.
Top view of artist viewing a series of telephone poles. (Not to scale.)

INDIVIDUAL WORK 6

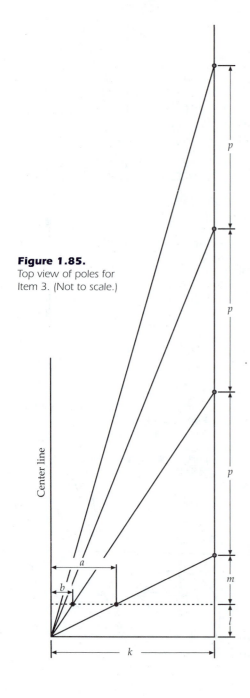

Figure 1.85.
Top view of poles for
Item 3. (Not to scale.)

e) Based on your results for (a)-(d), estimate the horizontal picture distance between the center line and Pole 5.

f) Calculate the horizontal distance in the picture between the center line and Pole 5.

g) The poles are 212 feet apart in the real world. The first pole in the drawing is 302 feet from the viewer. Explain why the pole that is 90 feet from the viewer is not drawn in the picture.

3. Generalize your results from Items 1 and 2.

Suppose the distance between poles is p units and the distance between the picture plane and the first pole is m units. The distance from the viewer to the plane of view is l units. The eye of the artist is k units to the left of the imaginary line connecting the poles. The letter a represents the horizontal distance between the image of Pole 1 and the imaginary center line connecting the eye to the vanishing point (see **Figure 1.85**).

a) Use proportions and create a formula to find a in terms of m, k, and l.

b) Use proportions and create a formula to find b in terms of m, k, l, and p.

c) Create an algebraic expression to represent the distance between the center line and the image of Pole 3.

d) Create an algebraic expression to represent the distance between the center line and the image of Pole 4.

e) Write a formula for the distance between the center line and Pole N.

4. a) Revisit Item 1 and determine each distance using your formulas from Item 3. Substitute: $k = 8$; $l = 2$; $m = 20$; $p = 15$. Compare your answers using the formulas with your answers for Item 1.

b) Revisit Item 2 and determine each distance using your formulas from Item 3. Substitute: $k = 100$; $l = 2$; $m = 300$; $p = 212$. Compare your answers using the formulas with your answers for Item 2.

5. In Item 3, you developed an algebraic formula for determining the horizontal distance between a particular pole and the vanishing point. Confirm your results through simulation as outlined below.

First, build a physical model. Place five equally-spaced objects in a row on a table. (The objects should have some resemblance to telephone poles. You may want to insert drinking straws or pencils in bases that will hold them upright. The bases could be clay or cookie dough or spools.) Space the objects equally—about 12 inches apart. Make sure all the objects are the same height.

Note that your formula in Item 3 was developed assuming the plane of vision is perpendicular to the line of poles and assuming that the viewer is somewhat to the side of the line of poles. Also, the eye height should probably be somewhere between the tops and bottoms of the poles. Select such a viewing position and record the following measurements.

Step away from the model and view the blocks in a manner similar to that used in Lesson 2, Activity 3. Measure the distance from your eye to the ruler in your extended hand. This is the distance from your eye to the picture plane and is the value of l in your formula. Measure the distance (m) between the picture plane and the first object. Measure the distance (k) between your eye and the imaginary line that passes through the objects; this is also the distance between the objects and the center line. The letter p represents the distance between the objects; in this case 12 inches.

a) Use your measurements from this set-up and your formulas from Item 3 to calculate the distances between the center line and each pole.

b) Use a ruler and the artist's method (see Activity 3) to determine the horizontal spacing, in your plane of vision, between each pole and the first pole. Record these measurements. (Remember that horizontal spacing in the plane of vision must be measured with the ruler *in* the plane of vision—perpendicular to the line formed by the poles.)

c) Compare the calculated results from part (a) with your observations in part (b). Do the results agree? Explain any differences.

INDIVIDUAL WORK 6

In Items 1 through 5, you have determined distances between images in a line of objects based on proportions calculated from a top view.

Now think back to your study of scale in Lesson 3. Distances related to scale include: distance between the artist and the object, the eye level of the artist, the distance between the artist's eye and the picture plane, the distance between the bottom of the image and the picture's horizon line, the size of the image, and the size of the object.

6. Suppose you are drawing a series of equally-spaced poles and you make the image of the first pole in your drawing 150 mm in length and situated so that the bottom of the pole is 225 mm below the picture's horizon. The actual height of the pole is 12 meters.

   a) Calculate the scale of the first pole.

   b) What is the eye level of the viewer? Show the proportions you use.

   c) How far, in the real world, is the first pole from the artist? Assume the picture plane is 50 cm from the eye of the artist.

7. Suppose the second pole is 90 mm tall in your drawing and the distance from the bottom of the pole to the horizon is 135 mm.

   a) Calculate the scale of the second pole.

   b) Use the measurements for the second pole to determine the eye height of the viewer.

   c) How far, in the real world, is the second pole from the artist?

8. Sketch a perspective view of a picture illustrating the two poles described in Items 6 and 7. Separate the images of the two poles by a horizontal distance of 20 mm in the drawing. Use the results of Items 6 and 7 to determine the distance (k) between the eye of the artist and the imaginary line joining the two poles. (Refer to Figure 1.85 for variable identifications.)

Remember:

- The distance between the artist's eye and the picture plane is 50 cm or 500 mm. Substitute this number for l.

- The distance from the artist to the first pole (measured along the line of poles) is your answer to 6(c). Subtract the distance from the artist's eye to the picture plane, 50 cm, from this answer and substitute for m.

- The distance between the artist's eye and the second pole is your answer to 7(c). Subtract the distance m from your answer to 7(c) to obtain the value of p.

Substitute for *m, l,* and *p* and determine the value for *k* that produces a distance of 20 mm between the images of Pole 1 and Pole 2.

9. Draw a picture of a series of three poles which meets the following specifications (see **Figure 1.86**):

• The actual height of each pole is 5 meters.

• The distance from the artist to the first pole, measured along the line of the poles, is 10 meters. The distance between poles is 15 meters.

• The distance between the artist's eye and the plane of vision is 60 cm.

• The eye height of the artist is 150 cm.

• The eye of the artist is a distance of 5 meters from the imaginary line connecting the series of poles.

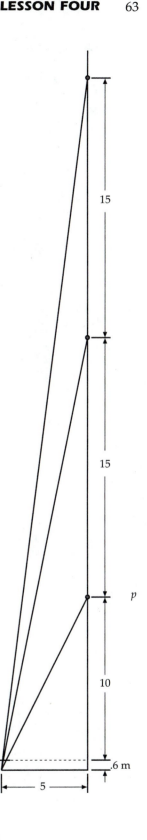

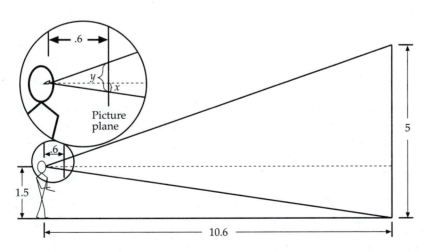

Figure 1.86.
Top view and side view of series of three equally-spaced poles. (Not to scale.)

INDIVIDUAL WORK 6

10. You have examined image size and image placement, each separately. How are these two kinds of measurements related? Answering that question is the purpose of this item.

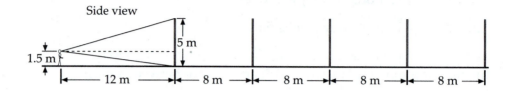

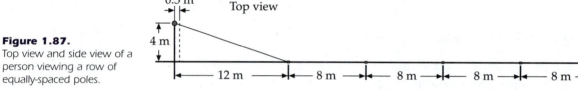

Figure 1.87.
Top view and side view of a person viewing a row of equally-spaced poles.

a) Use proportions to calculate the image height of each pole based on the information in **Figure 1.87**. Then calculate the distance from the center line to the image of each pole. Record your values in a copy of **Figure 1.88**.

Pole number	Picture distance from center line	Image height
1		
2		
3		
4		

Figure 1.88.
Table of locations and heights.

b) Graph the relationship between the image heights of successive poles and their distances from the vanishing point. What pattern, if any, do you notice? If there is a pattern, write an equation to represent the pattern.

VANISHING TELEPHONE POLES

In Individual Work 6, you produced an algebraic method for determining the horizontal picture distance between poles receding into the distance. This activity demonstrates the steps of a geometric construction of such distances.

Telephone poles, like all lines that are parallel to the viewing plane, appear in the image parallel to one another. In a perspective view, the poles may diminish in size as they converge toward a vanishing point, but they remain parallel to one another. Connect the tops of the poles with a line and the bottoms of the poles with a line and you see a series of adjacent trapezoids that diminish in size (see **Figure 1.89**).

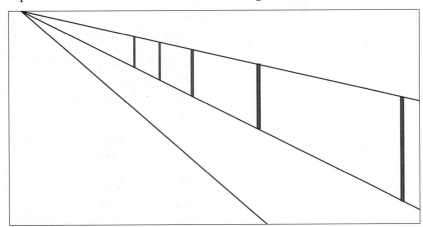

Figure 1.89.
Perspective view of poles with connecting lines that form trapezoids.

This activity is in two parts. The key idea is illustrated in **Figure 1.90**. The diagonals of a rectangle intersect at a point midway between opposite sides. A line drawn through the point of intersection and parallel to the sides of the rectangle divides the rectangle into two equal rectangles

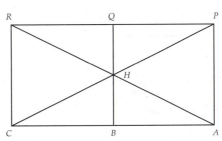

Figure 1.90.
Rectangle with center determined by intersecting diagonals.

ACTIVITY

VANISHING TELEPHONE POLES

7

adjacent to one another. In Part 1, the problem is simplified to the nonperspective case; the line of poles is parallel to the picture plane. Part 2 moves to the perspective case. The result is a pair of adjacent, identical rectangles. Of course, their perspective images are neither identical nor rectangular.

PART 1:

Non-perspective view.

To solve the separation problem in a plane parallel to the view plane, begin by drawing two poles an arbitrary distance apart (see **Figure 1.91**).

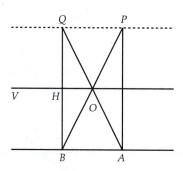

Next, draw diagonals to locate the center, *O*, of rectangle *ABQP*. Draw horizontal line *VO* (see **Figure 1.92**). Point *H* is therefore the midpoint of pole *BQ*.

Figure 1.91.
Poles spaced at an arbitrary distance.

1. Look back at Figure 1.90. Copy Figure 1.92 on your paper and draw a line from *P* through *H* intersecting the line through *A* and *B* at a point you label *C*.

2. Draw a line segment from *C* parallel to *BQ* and ending on *PQ* (extended). Call the new point *R*.

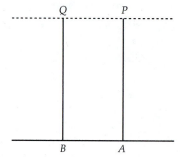

3. a) How does the length of *CR* compare to *AP* and *BQ*?

   b) How do *AB* and *BC* compare? Why?

Figure 1.92.
View of intersecting diagonals.

ACTIVITY

VANISHING TELEPHONE POLES

7

4. Repeat the construction to draw another pole to the left of *CR*.

Note that two ideas were crucial in the construction you just completed. First, the diagonals of a rectangle meet at a point halfway between top and bottom. Second, once the midheight is found at *one* place, a horizontal line through that point can be used to mark that height *everywhere*.

PART 2:

Perspective view

This same construction can be used for the poles drawn in perspective. To get started, draw on your own paper two poles in perspective (see **Figure 1.93**) or use Handout H1.11, supplied by your teacher.

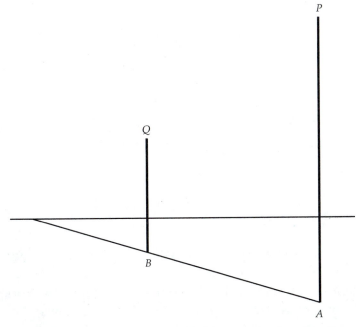

Figure 1.93.
Perspective view of the vertical sides of the "rectangle."

5. Determine the location of the vanishing point for this figure. Explain what the vanishing point represents.

6. Draw in diagonals *AQ* and *BP* to establish the center of rectangle *ABQP* in correct perspective.

ACTIVITY

7

VANISHING TELEPHONE POLES

7. In Item 6, you found the midheight of a pole at one location. Now you need a horizontal line through that point, in the plane of the poles, to assist in the rest of the construction. Add the appropriate line to your figure. (Hint: Look back at your answer to Item 5(b).)

8. Apply the ideas you used in Part 1 to establish the location of the next pole in proper perspective. Explain why your method is correct.

9. Continue your process for another two poles.

10. Telephone poles frequently are supported by guy-wires. (A guy-wire is a cable from the top of the pole to the ground.) From the side, a pole with a guy-wire might look like **Figure 1.94**. In perspective it might look like **Figure 1.95**.

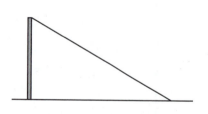

Figure 1.94.
Side view of guy-wire to support a telephone pole.

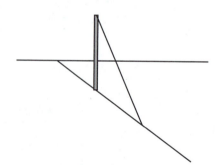

Figure 1.95.
Perspective view of the guy-wire.

To protect people from accidentally running into the guy-wire, the phone company would like to hang small markers at the midpoint and at the 1/4 and 3/4 points of the cable. By working with both the perspective and the non-perspective views, show how these points can be constructed.

Under Construction

1. Suppose you work for an architect and a client wants a plan for a
   series of equally-spaced flagpoles along the side of a road. Repeat the
   telephone pole construction on the road in **Figure 1.96**. The horizon,
   the vanishing point, and the first pole have been placed for you.
   Copy the figure on your own paper, or obtain handout H1.12 from
   your teacher.

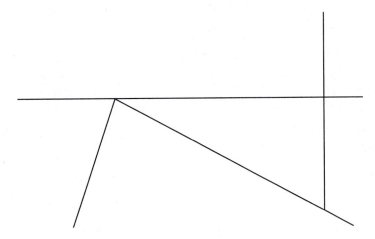

Figure 1.96.
Beginning view of flagpole
construction.

2. A landscape architect wants to remodel a walkway by alternating
   rows of bricks with rectangular concrete panels. Construct the proper
   placement, in a perspective view, of the panels and lines of bricks
   given the placement of the first two in **Figure 1.97**. Copy the figure,
   or use Handout H1.13.

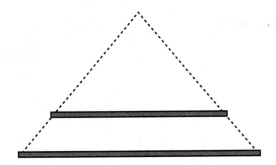

Figure 1.97.
Beginning view of the
remodeled walkway.

INDIVIDUAL WORK 7

3. Prove the construction method for rectangles guarantees equal spacing of poles.

4. Make a copy of a photograph or drawing that shows a perspective view of equally-spaced objects (streetlights, railroad ties, fence posts, trees, telephone poles, light poles).

   a) Measure the lengths of the images of the objects. Measure the distance between the bottom of each object and the horizon. Measure the horizontal distance between each image and the vanishing point. Determine whether your formulas from Individual Work 6 are confirmed by the photograph.

   b) On the copy of the image, draw a line connecting the tops of the objects and one connecting the bottoms. Draw the diagonals between the first and third objects, second and fourth objects, third and fifth objects, and fourth and sixth objects. Determine whether the geometric construction confirms the perspective view in the image.

5. You have constructed accurate representations of equally-spaced poles in perspective drawings. Poles are one-dimensional objects. Consider ways to represent two-dimensional signs and three-dimensional buildings that are equally spaced in the real world.

   a) Revisit the video game challenge from Activity 2 (see Figure 1.16). Use geometric construction or your algebraic formulas to draw the three square signs described in Activity 2.

   b) Explain how to draw a perspective view of a series of identical, equally-spaced rectangular buildings.

6. Observe the series of rectangular buildings in **Figures 1.98 and 1.99**.

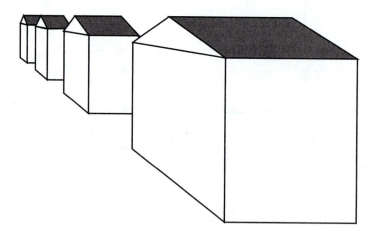

Figure 1.98.
Perspective view of a series of
rectangular buildings.

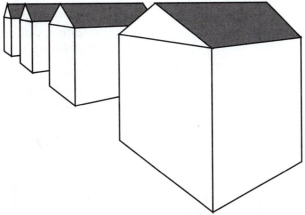

Figure 1.99.
Another perspective view of a series of rectangular buildings.

a) Describe the location of the vanishing point for Figure 1.98.

b) How many vanishing points appear in Figure 1.99? Describe the location of each vanishing point.

c) How is it possible to have more than one vanishing point in a perspective view of a scene? What view of the cube produces this effect?

7. Optical illusions may be created when you violate the principle of diminution or the principle of convergence.

a) Describe the effect of not reducing the height of a series of objects and not reducing the spacing between the objects as other objects converge to the vanishing point or points (see **Figure 1.100**).

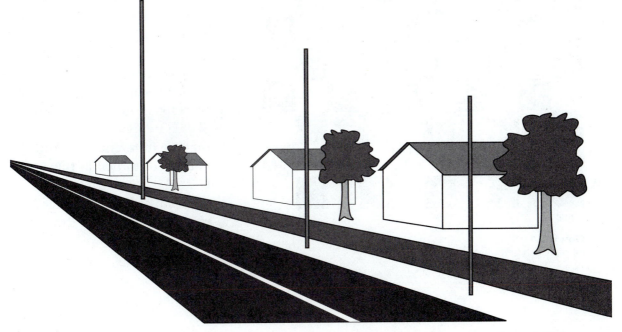

Figure 1.100.
Drawing for 7(a).

INDIVIDUAL WORK 7

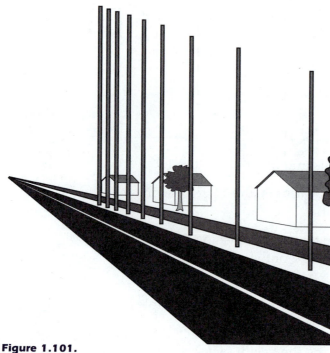

Figure 1.101.
Drawing for 7(b).

1 foot

1 foot

Figure 1.102.
Top view of a tiled floor.

b) Describe the effect of not reducing the height, but allowing the spacing between the objects to agree with principles of perspective (see **Figure 1.101**).

c) Explain how the B.C. cartoon (see Figure 1.15) in Lesson 2 violates a principle of perspective drawing.

8. **Figure 1.102** shows a top view of a tiled floor. Draw a perspective view of this tiled floor.

9. In Lessons 2–4, you have viewed images based on a cube with one face parallel to the plane of vision. Only one set of lines—the lines associated with the edges of the cube perpendicular to the plane of vision—have been affected by diminution and convergence. The modeling decision to draw cubes parallel to the plane of vision and parallel to the ground has simplified the development of principles and skills. The real world is more complicated. Sketch two views of a cube that are different from any you have studied in this unit. Describe how each view is different and what makes it more challenging to draw.

LESSON FIVE

The View From The Edge

KEY CONCEPTS

Convergence

The Image Bank

Figure 1.103.
Scene with two vanishing points.

PREPARATION READING

Double Extensions

*T*hroughout your work in this unit, you have examined features of images of a cube. You have not moved. The cube has not moved. Until now you have viewed the cube so one face is parallel to the plane of vision.

In the process of modeling, you have worked with a constant object, the cube, and changed the location and distance from which that object is viewed. Each change has led to new methods or principles for representing three-dimensional objects on a two-dimensional plane.

What happens when no face is parallel to the picture plane? Try it for yourself. Find a cube-like object. Again, for simplicity, hold it at eye level. Rotate it so all edges remain parallel or perpendicular to the ground, but one vertical edge is closer to you than the others. Compare what you see to the sketch in **Figure 1.104** on the following page.

PREPARATION READING

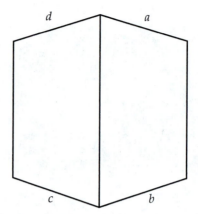

Figure 1.104.
View of the cube looking
directly at a vertical edge.

How is the principle of convergence apparent in the rotated view of the cube in Figure 1.104?

If you extend parallel edges *a* and *b* to the right, what do you notice? The edges converge toward a vanishing point.

If you extend parallel edges *c* and *d* to the left, what do you notice? These edges also converge toward a vanishing point, but it is a different vanishing point. There are two vanishing points!

Where do you find examples of two vanishing points in the real world?

Look at a rectangular building from the front, and then walk part of the way around the building until you can see two faces of the building at the same time. Sketch what you see. Are there two vanishing points in your sketch?

Figure 1.103 is a photograph of a scene with two vanishing points. How can you tell from a picture that there is more than one vanishing point?

In this lesson, you will study conditions that lead to more than one vanishing point, and you will develop methods and techniques for representing such scenes accurately.

CONSIDER:

1. Find a solid cube or a rectangular object and view it from several different positions. Sketch each view. How many different ways are there are to view the cube? How many faces of the cube can you observe simultaneously? Experiment by observing the rotated cube up-close and at a distance.

2. In the preparation reading for this lesson, you noticed that the view of a rotated cube can reveal two vanishing points (see Figure 1.104). Why is there more than one vanishing point in that figure? Why are there not more than two vanishing points?

3. The vanishing point is on the horizon for horizontal lines that increase in distance from the viewer. If there can be two vanishing points in a picture, can there be two horizons?

4. Can you have more than two vanishing points? If yes, what conditions lead to more than two vanishing points? If no, why not?

THE CORNER STORE

ACTIVITY

8

In this activity, you develop ways to create drawings with two vanishing points.

1. **Figure 1.105** shows two roads meeting at an intersection. Your client wants to build a store at the corner opposite where the viewer is standing. Draw Figure 1.105 on your own paper, or use Handout H1.14 provided by your teacher, and make a detailed drawing showing what the store will look like when it is constructed. Include windows, doors, and a sign on the building. For an extra challenge, try drawing a sloped roof rather than a flat roof.

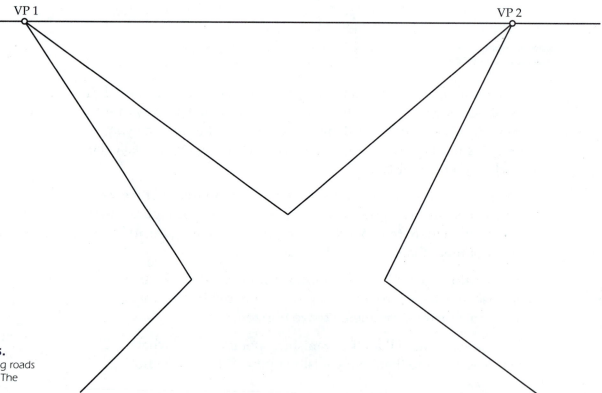

Figure 1.105.
Two intersecting roads and the site of The Corner Store.

2. Create a dynamic version of this activity using a geometric drawing utility. Make sure you can move the vanishing points along the horizon without moving the horizon itself.

3. What is the effect if the vanishing points are brought closer together or moved farther apart? Draw sketches to illustrate your description.

4. What would have to change in the context to increase the apparent distance between the vanishing points?

Two Point Perspective

1. a) Locate the vanishing points and the horizon in each of **Figures 1.106** and **1.107**. Use the coordinates that surround each picture frame, or draw the vanishing points and horizon on Handout H1.15 provided by your teacher.

Vin Catania

Figure 1.106.
Photograph for Item 1.

   b) How many vanishing points are there? Why?

   c) Assume the plane of vision for the painting (see Figure 1.107) is 24 inches from the viewer and the eye level is 3 feet because the viewer is sitting in a chair. Determine the scale of at least one object in the painting. Show the proportions you use.

   d) Approximate the distance between the artist and the object selected in (c).

Figure 1.107.
Painting for Item 1.

©Bridgeman Art Library, International, Ltd.

INDIVIDUAL WORK 8

2. Revisit the painting by William Hogarth in Activity 1 (see Figure 1.3). How many vanishing points do you observe in this painting? Explain your answer.

3. Figure 1.108 shows the front view of a cottage. Draw the cottage in perspective with two vanishing points.

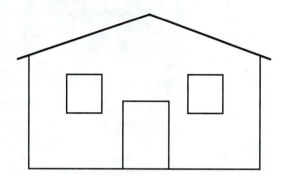

Figure 1.108.
Front view of a cottage.

4. The following drawing was created by a child (see **Figure 1.109**). It does not adhere to the principles of perspective. Draw the same scene on your own paper using principles of perspective and two vanishing points.

Figure 1.109.
Child's drawing that does not conform to principles of perspective.

Jackson Barber, Age 8

5. Practice drawing a rectangular box using two vanishing points. Use pencil and paper or a geometric drawing utility. Begin with a drawing that looks similar to **Figure 1.110**. Notice the box is drawn entirely below the horizon.

   a) Why does edge *e* appear to converge to the same vanishing point as edges *a* and *b*?

   b) Why does edge *f* appear to converge to the same vanishing point as edges *c* and *d*?

   c) In Figure 1.110, you see two sides and the top of the box. Why is the artist able to see the top of the box in this figure but not able to see the top of the cube in Figure 1.103?

   d) What, in the context, would have to change so the artist could see the bottom of the box instead of the top?

   e) Describe what happens to the drawing of the box when you bring the two vanishing points closer together.

   f) Describe what happens to the drawing of the box when you move the two vanishing points farther apart.

6. a) **Figure 1.111** shows a top view of a series of equally-spaced cubes. Each cube has one face parallel to the plane of vision. Each individual distance is 0.75 cm. Make a perspective drawing in which you can see two sides and the top of each cube. How many vanishing points should there be?

   b) **Figure 1.112** shows another top view of a series of equally-spaced cubes. Now none of the faces of the cubes are parallel to the plane of vision (though four of the edges are). Make a perspective drawing of this scene in which you can see two sides and the top of each cube. How many vanishing points should there be now?

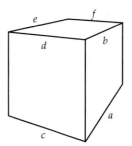

Figure 1.110.
Perspective drawing of a box using two vanishing points.

Figure 1.111.
Top view of a series of four cubes for Item 6(a).

Figure 1.112.
Top view of a series of four cubes for Item 6(b).

7. **Figure 1.113** is a top view of a scene with two roads intersecting at right angles. The rectangular object is a building, and the circles represent light poles. Make a perspective drawing with two vanishing points to illustrate this scene. Choose realistic measurements for key distances.

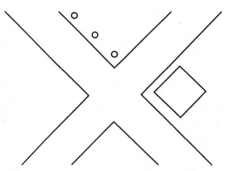

Figure 1.113.
Top view of intersecting roads.

8. Revisit your drawing from Item 8 of Individual Work 1. Draw a new version of the same scene. Utilize what you have learned about perspective drawing.

9. A certain cube measures 24 cm on each edge. It is to be drawn so the scale of the edge of the cube closest to the viewer is 1:20. How tall should you make the image of the closest edge of the cube? What if the scale were 1:4 instead of 1:20?

10. A university is planning to build a new post office for students. The architect wants an artist to draw a perspective view of the building. The architect provides the following specifications for the drawing (see **Figure 1.114**): Note that all distances are measured perpendicular to the plane of vision.

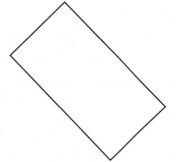

Figure 1.114.
Top view of rectangular building.

- The closest vertical edge of the building is 15 meters from the artist.

- The next closest vertical edge is 19.2 meters from the artist.

- The third vertical edge is 24 meters from the artist.

- The eye level of the artist is 150 cm.

- The picture plane is 60 cm from the eye of the artist.

a) Find the scale for each vertical edge.

b) Find the image height for each edge of the building if the actual heights will be 8 meters.

c) How far below the horizon is the bottom of the closest vertical edge? The second closest vertical edge? The third closest visible vertical edge?

11. Figure 1.106 (Item 1) shows a perspective image with two vanishing points. The eye level of the artist is 60 inches. The distance from the viewer to the plane of vision is 27 inches.

a) Determine the scale for the part of the building closest to the viewer. Show the proportion you use to determine the scale.

b) Determine the scale for the visible part of the building farthest from the viewer. Show the proportion you use to determine the scale.

c) Suppose you want to draw a square sign on the right face of the building. The actual height of the sign is 10 feet. Find the picture height of the sign. Show the proportion you use to determine the height.

12. **Figure 1.115** is a perspective drawing of a house. Suppose you want to double the scale of the house. Explain how to use a vanishing point, like the centerpoint of a dilation, to double the size of the house. How is the dilation affected when there are two vanishing points?

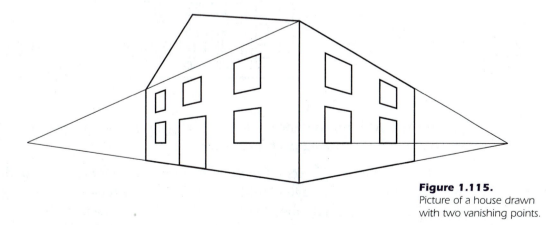

Figure 1.115.
Picture of a house drawn with two vanishing points.

13. Do the locations of the vanishing points affect the scales of objects in a drawing? That is, if you prepare a perspective drawing using a geometric drawing utility and decide to move the horizon line up or down, or to move the vanishing points farther apart, will it change the scales of the objects? Conduct an investigation. Prepare to report your findings to the class.

14. Draw a cube or rectangular building using three vanishing points— one to the right of your page, one to the left of your page, and one at the bottom of your page. How would you have to view a real cube to see this image?

15. Brunelleschi's Peep Hole

As you read in Individual Work 1, an Italian metal-worker/architect named Filippo Brunelleschi is credited with the invention of the rules of scientific perspective some time before 1413. Among other things, he painted a picture of an octagonal baptistery that looked remark- ably real, particularly when viewed from the same position at which Brunelleschi was standing when he painted it **(Figure 1.116)**.

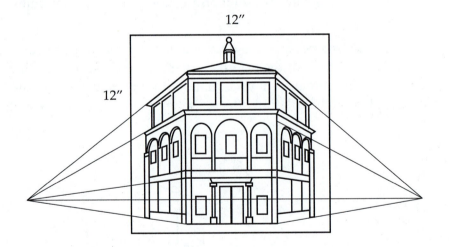

Figure 1.116.
Brunelleschi's Baptistery of St. John, Florence, Italy.

Brunelleschi forced viewers to view the picture from the correct posi- tion by the following peep-hole trick:

He drilled a small hole in the picture, which was painted on wood, at the point where his eye would have focused when he was painting it and looking straight ahead at the horizon. (Remember, the horizon is always at eye level). Then he placed a mirror in front of the picture and had viewers look through the picture from the back at its reflec- tion in the mirror. (See **Figure 1.117**.)

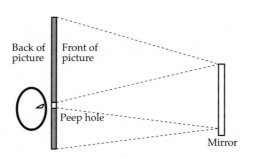

Figure 1.117.
Side view of Brunelleschi's
Peep-Hole.

Using the reproduction of the picture of the Baptistery in Figure 1.116, reconstruct Brunelleschi's experiment. For the purpose of this activity, assume Brunelleschi's eye was 5 feet above the ground and 40 yards from the front of the building. Use this information to determine the scale of the picture, thus to determine how far his eye was from the canvas. (Remember that the distance to the mirror will be half the eye-to-canvas distance. See the diagram in Figure 1.117.)

16. The key question for this unit is: How do you represent three-dimensional objects accurately on a two-dimensional plane? You started the modeling process in Lesson 2 by simplifying the object to be drawn. The cube was chosen because all the edges and faces are parallel and perpendicular to one another. In Lesson 2, you also simplified the *way* the cube is viewed. The cube appears to be a two-dimensional square when viewed at eye level with the one visible face parallel to the picture plane. In Lesson 3, you developed the principle of convergence by viewing an invisible version of a cube with one face parallel to the picture plane. In Lesson 5, you kept the horizontal edges of the cube parallel to the ground and you rotated the cube so no face was parallel to the picture plane, resulting in two distinct vanishing points for the cube. What are the next steps in the modeling process for representing three-dimensional scenes on a two-dimensional plane? Discuss several options.

17. a) **Figure 1.118** shows the perspective view of a cube as seen in Lesson 2 where it was viewed face-on. Sketch views from the top and the right side.

Figure 1.118.
Perspective view of a cube
with edges parallel and perpendicular to both the picture plane and the ground.

b) **Figure 1.119** shows the perspective view of a cube as seen in Lesson 5 where it is viewed edge-on. Sketch views from the top and the right side of this image.

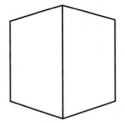

Figure 1.119.
Perspective view of a cube as seen in Lesson 5.

18. In Lesson 6, you will continue your study of perspective by once again varying the view of a cube. This time, you will consider the corner-on view caused by tilting the cube at an angle to the plane of vision. This means you need to be able to deal with the geometry associated with different angles. You may recall the characteristics of some special angles from Course 2, Unit 4, *The Right Stuff.*

a) Draw a right triangle with an angle of 30°. Measure the lengths of the two legs of the triangle. Use the Pythagorean Theorem to determine the length of the hypotenuse. Measure the hypotenuse and compare with the length predicted by the Pythagorean Theorem.

b) Draw a right triangle with an angle of 45°. Measure the lengths of two sides of the triangle. Use the Pythagorean Theorem to determine the length of the third side. Measure the third side and compare with the length predicted by the Pythagorean Theorem.

c) Suppose you wish to draw a 30°-60°-90° right triangle with a hypotenuse of length 2.5 cm. Determine the lengths of all three sides of the triangle.

LESSON SIX

Foreshortening

KEY CONCEPTS

Angle

Trigonometric
ratios

The Image Bank

PREPARATION READING

Tilt

Start with a simple cube. Zoom in or zoom out and you observe the effects described by the principle of diminution. Make the cube transparent and you observe the principle of convergence. Rotate the cube and convergence produces two vanishing points. Raise or lower the cube to a position above or below your eye level and you may see three faces simultaneously.

In all these cases, four edges of the cube have remained vertical, thus parallel to the picture plane. But what do you see when you tilt a cube?

Try it for yourself. Hold a cube so the closest face is parallel to the picture plane. Then change the way you view the cube by tilting it away from you, so the horizontal edges of the front face remain parallel to the ground, but the closest face is at an angle to the picture plane. It looks similar to the side view of the rotated cube.

How do you draw the tilted cube accurately? In general, how do you represent accurately three-dimensional objects tilted at an angle to a two-dimensional picture plane?

One approach is to start with a simpler task. One simplification you can make is to draw a one-dimensional object, such as a pencil, tilted at an angle to the picture plane, instead of tilting a general three-dimensional shape.

By the definition of a plane of vision, a 6-inch pencil standing up in your plane of vision looks like a 6-inch pencil (see **Figure 1.120**).

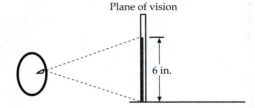

Figure 1.120.
Pencil in plane of vision.

But the same pencil lying down on the table does not look that long (see **Figure 1.121**).

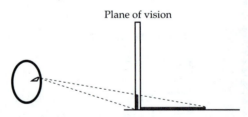

Figure 1.121.
Pencil laying flat on a table.

This phenomenon illustrates a special case of the principle of foreshortening. **Foreshortening** occurs when lines or surfaces perpendicular to the line of sight appear increasingly shorter as they are rotated away from the observer. In this case, the shorter appearance of the pencil is a result of the fact that the plane of vision intersects a smaller angle between the two lines of sight when the pencil lies flat on its side.

Suppose your eye level is 5 feet above the floor and a pencil
6 inches long is lying on a table 3 feet high and 2 feet away
from you (see **Figure 1.122**).

Plane of vision

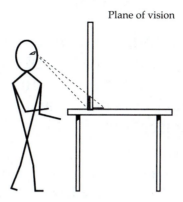

Figure 1.122.
Pencil viewed from an angle.

An abstract geometrical picture of this might look like **Figure 1.123**.

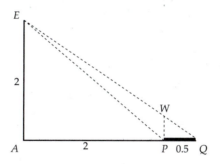

Figure 1.123.
The geometry of viewing a
pencil.

Here *E* is your eye, *PQ* is the pencil, and *WP* is the image of the pencil
on the plane of vision. For situations such as this, in which everything is
either parallel or perpendicular to the plane of vision, you may use
methods from earlier lessons to determine the proper size of the image.
However, many objects are tilted at an angle to the plane of view. But
how can you use mathematics to represent accurately the length of such
objects in other situations?

In this lesson, you will solve this problem by building on what you
already know about similarity. The new mathematics dealing with
understanding angles is called trigonometry.

ACTIVITY

9

PERPENDICULAR VIEW

Begin your investigation of foreshortening with the simplest situation. Determine the length of the image for a one-dimensional object, a pencil, that is perpendicular to the plane of vision along its center line.

1. Use the information provided in the Preparation Reading, "Tilt," (see Figure 1.123) along with what you know about similar figures to find the apparent length, *WP*, of the pencil.

2. In **Figure 1.124**, two 6-inch pencils are lined up point-to-eraser on a table.

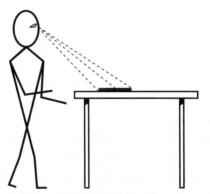

Figure 1.124.
Figure for Item 2.

a) Draw a geometric model of this situation. Label all the lengths in your model.

b) Determine the length of the projection of the first pencil on the picture plane.

c) Determine the length of the projection of the second pencil on the picture plane.

PERPENDICULAR VIEW

3. a) **Figure 1.125** and Handout H1.16 show a famous painting by Mantegna called *Dead Christ*. Its original dimensions are about 27 inches high by 32 inches wide. If the figure in the painting was 5 feet, 10 inches (70 inches) tall and the eye of the painter was 36 inches above the height of the platform on which the figure was lying, how far away from the platform was the painter standing if the figure's feet were touching the plane of the picture?

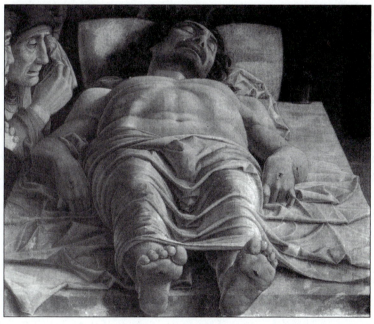

Figure 1.125.
Mantegna, *Dead Christ*.

©*Bridgeman Art Library, International, Ltd.*

b) Based on your answer to (a), if you want to view the image in the handout to see the picture as the artist did, where should you hold the handout? (Hint: Because this reproduction is a smaller version of the original painting, you will have to hold the smaller picture closer to your eye to produce a view similar to the artist's view.)

INDIVIDUAL WORK 9

Grounded

*I*n this individual work, you will practice finding the foreshortened image length for objects perpendicular to the picture plane.

1. Suppose you are running down the beach and come upon your best friend lying flat on the sand. Your friend is 6 feet tall, and you are looking at him feet first from 8 feet away. Your eye level is at 5 feet, 4 inches as you look down upon your friend.

    a) Draw a picture, to scale, of this situation and label all important distances. Be sure to include your lines of sight. State the scale you use.

    b) How long is the projection of your friend on your plane of vision if you assume that the plane of vision goes through his feet?

2. A murder has been committed in a closed room and the victim is lying on the floor with his head toward a locked door 10 feet from the body. You are 2 feet from the door, looking through a window in the door. At your eye level, which is 5 1/2 feet, the victim appears, according to his projection on the window, to be 3 2/3 inches long.

    a) Draw a geometric model of this situation, labeling all the important distances.

    b) How tall is the victim?

    c) Suppose you just estimated that the victim was lying 10 feet from the door. How could you make such an estimation?

    d) Suppose your estimation of distance is off by 6 inches. How far off could the calculations of the height be?

    e) What would be the effect if your measurement of 3 2/3 inches was off by 1/6 inches?

    f) How reliable is this method for determining the length of the body?

3. Repeat Item 2 of Activity 9 changing the eye level of the viewer to 3 feet above the table instead of 2 feet.

    a) Determine the length of the projection of the first pencil.

    b) Determine the length of the projection of the second pencil.

4. a) Extend Item 2 of Activity 9 to find the image lengths for the third, fourth, fifth, sixth, and seventh pencils (the eye level of the viewer is 2 feet above the table). Predict the apparent length of the eighth pencil.

   b) Graph the relationship between image length, y, and number of pencils, x.

5. a) Extend Item 2 of Activity 9 to find the distances from the horizon line to the ends of the first, second, third, fourth, fifth, sixth, and seventh pencils farthest from the viewer (the eye level of the viewer is 2 feet above the table). Predict the distance below the horizon to the near end of the eighth pencil.

   b) Graph the relationship between distance, y, below horizon line and number of pencils, x.

   c) Generalize your work from either Item 4(a) or Item 5(a) to produce a formula that can be used for any number of pencils.

   d) Explain why you selected the particular problem to generalize.

   e) Revisit Item 8 of Individual Work 7 in Lesson 4. Use your generalization to locate the rows of tiles properly. Be sure to state your assumptions about tile size, viewer location, etc.

6. Suppose you are looking at a single pencil from a vantage point 2 feet above the table (as in Item 1 of Activity 9). Tilt the pencil away from the plane of vision so that it makes an angle of 45° with the table (see **Figure 1.126**).

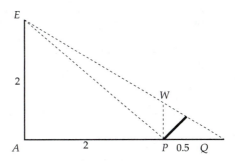

Figure 1.126.
Side view of pencil tilted 45° away from the viewer.

   a) Estimate the length of the image of the pencil.

   b) Draw a scale drawing of the side view to match the measurements in Figure 1.126. Use graph paper to make it easier to draw a pencil at a 45° angle. Measure the length of the pencil in your drawing.

INDIVIDUAL WORK 9

7. a) Predict the angle of tilt that makes a pencil appear to be half its original length when the lower end is at eye level.

   b) To check your prediction, draw a scale picture of you viewing the pencil held vertically (see **Figure 1.127**).

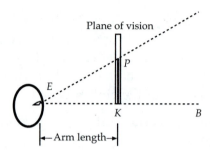

Figure 1.127.
Side view of person viewing a vertical pencil.

   The pencil will look half as long if the line of sight to its tip bisects line segment *KP*. Find midpoint *W* on your scale drawing, and draw in the line of sight through that point.

   c) The base of the pencil stays at point *K*, but the top will rotate down and away from your eye. When the top intersects line *EW*, the pencil will look half its length. To draw the tilted pencil exactly, take your compass and put the point at *K*. Open the compass so that the pencil point is at *P* and draw an arc that meets line *MW*. Call that point *Q*. Draw line *KQ* and measure angle *PKQ*.

   d) When $WP = (1/2)KP$, does angle $PKQ = 1/2$ angle PKB?

Due to foreshortening, horizontal objects look shorter than their real length, even when one end is at the plane of vision. However, your knowledge of similarity has served well to compute such lengths. But what about tilted objects? What is the relationship between the angle of tilt and the apparent length of an object in the plane of vision? One way to examine an unknown relationship is through data from a simulation, that is, to actually look at objects and record what you see. That's the idea in this activity.

There are many variables that affect the apparent length of an object in a drawing. In previous lessons, you have studied the relationship between distances from your eye to the plane of vision and to the object. In this activity, the explanatory variable will be the angle of tilt. You will keep the base of an object at a constant distance from the plane of vision and tilt it away from your view so the object is at an angle to the plane of vision. You will explore how the angle of tilt affects the apparent length of the object. You used pencils in the last few investigations because they were essentially one dimensional. This activity takes the same approach, but with a bigger "pencil."

You need a pole or rod a foot or two long, a meter stick to measure the length of images in your plane of vision, and a clinometer (or a level and protractor) to measure the angle the pole makes with the ground. Work with at least two partners in the following data-collection activity.

1. To simplify the experiment, have one partner hold the pole vertically so its base is at eye level. (For example, place the bottom of the pole on a table, and match your eye level to the level of the table.) Have another partner measure the height of the pole.

2. Hold the meter stick vertically at arm's length, and position yourself so your eye is level with the base of the pole, and the bottom of the meter stick in your hand actually touches the pole your partner is holding. The meter stick you are holding

ACTIVITY

LEAN TO THE LEFT

10

measures the apparent height of the pole in your plane of vision. (Right now, of course, the apparent height is exactly the same as the actual length.) Have a partner measure the distance from your eye to the meter stick.

3. Now have your partner tilt the pole at an angle away from the plane of view (here, 0° means vertical, or no tilt). Have the other partner measure the angle of tilt. Use your meter stick to measure the new apparent height of the pole in the plane of vision. Record the angle and apparent height in a table similar to that in **Figure 1.128**. Repeat this step for at least 8 different angles, including angles of 0°, 30°, 45°, and 60° and four more angles of your choosing. Be sure to record units, too.

Figure 1.128.
Sample table for Item 3.

Angle of tilt (degrees)	Apparent Length

4. a) Make a scatter plot showing the relationship between the angle of tilt and the apparent length of the pole. Explain your choice of axis labels.

   b) Is it linear? If not, what is it?

5. Sketch a smooth curve along your scatter plot data. Select three other angles that you have not yet observed. Use your graph to predict the apparent heights for those angles, then check your results using direct observation.

INDIVIDUAL WORK 10

Tilt the Scales

*I*n Activity 10, you solved the problem of predicting apparent height from the angle of tilt. There are two main drawbacks to that solution: First, because it was completed by brute force, it is only approximate—subject to errors in measurement by each of the members of the group. Second, it applies only to the specific set of numbers you used for viewing distance and pole length, but it's a start.

1. Suppose you have a pole 20 feet in height. The distance from your eye to the plane of vision is 2 feet. The scale for the vertical pole is 1:50, and the base of the pole is at eye level.

   a) How far away is the pole?

   b) What is the apparent height if the pole is vertical?

   c) What is the apparent height if the pole is tilted at an angle of 35° back from vertical?

2. Suppose you have a pole 20 feet in length and your plane of vision is 1.5 feet from your eye. Your partner is holding the pole at an angle so its base is at your eye level and in the plane of vision. The top of the pole is actually 5.18 feet above your eye level and quite a bit beyond the plane of vision.

   a) How far back from the plane of vision is the top of the pole?

   b) What is the scale for objects at the same distance away as the top of the pole?

   c) Recall that scale also can be measured using distances from the horizon line. Explain where the horizon line must be in this situation.

   d) Use your answer to (b) and the actual height of the pole to determine its apparent height in the plane of vision.

3. Rework Item 2, this time with the base of the pole 10 feet from the view plane.

4. In each of Items 1-3, information about scale is equivalent to information about the distance from your eye to the object, provided you also know the distance to the plane of vision. For the following questions, assume you know where the plane of vision is, and that the base of the object is at eye level.

   a) Explain how to compute the scale at the top of an object when you know the horizontal distance to that point in reality.

   b) Explain how you could determine the actual height of the top of a tilted pole if you knew its actual length and the horizontal distances to both its top and base.

   c) Explain how knowing the answers to (a) and (b) helps solve the problem of drawing a foreshortened image. Why is the assumption that the base of the object be at eye level important?

5. Look back at Item 1(c). What information would allow you to find an exact solution to that problem?

SPECIAL ANGLES

Return once more to the general problem of foreshortening. Suppose a pencil of length l is held in your plane of vision, a distance of d from your eye (see **Figure 1.129**). In this case, the length of the image is identical to the length of the pencil; there is no foreshortening.

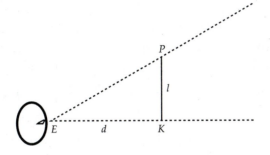

Figure 1.129.
Side view of pencil.

If the pencil is rotated away from your eye at an angle of θ from vertical, then the apparent length of the pencil shortens (see **Figure 1.130**).

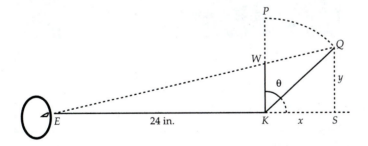

Figure 1.130.
Side view of tilted pencil.

EQ is a line of sight from the eye to the tip of the pencil in the rotated position. PK is the plane of vision. WK represents the image of the tilted pencil.

The general foreshortening problem in this context is to find the length of WK in terms of the angle, θ, of rotation. As you saw in Individual Work 10, WK is just the scaled image of length y, so

ACTIVITY

SPECIAL ANGLES

11

being able to determine the length of x will allow you to find the scale and, in turn, y and WK.

If you know the values of x and y, you can find the length of WK. Thus, the problem of determining the length of WK has been replaced with the problem of determining the lengths of x and y from the length of the pencil and its angle of tilt.

In this activity, you will review the ratios and proportions related to 45°-45°-90° right triangles and 30°-60°-90° right triangles. You may have studied these special right triangles in Course 2, Unit 4, *The Right Stuff*. Those properties will allow you to determine the image length, WK, for rotations of 30°, 45° and 60°.

1. Review relationships in 45°-45°-90° right triangles:

   a) Carefully draw five or six isosceles right triangles of different sizes. Measure the lengths of all three sides for each triangle. Record your results in a table similar to that in **Figure 1.131**. Specify your units of measure. Be sure one of the triangles has a leg with a length of 1 unit.

One leg of right triangle (units)	Second leg of the right triangle (units)	Hypotenuse of the right triangle (units)
1		

Figure 1.131.
Table for recording lengths of triangle sides.

   b) Use the Pythagorean Theorem to confirm the accuracy of your measurements.

SPECIAL ANGLES

2. Review relationships for 30°-60°-90° right triangles:

   a) Repeat Item 1, this time for 30°-60°-90° right triangles.

   b) Draw an equilateral triangle, *ABC*. Bisect angle *B* to create two equal adjacent triangles. Explain how the resulting figure relates the length of the hypotenuse to the shortest side of a 30°-60°-90° right triangle.

   c) Use the Pythagorean Theorem and your conclusion from (b) to determine the length of the second leg in terms of the length of the shorter leg. Generalize your work as a formula.

   d) Compare this analytic result with your measured results. Show your work.

3. a) Using a straightedge and a protractor, make careful drawings of three right triangles of different sizes, each of which has one 40° angle. Call the 40° angle *A*.

   b) Measure the third angle of each triangle.

   c) For each of your triangles, measure the hypotenuse and the length of side *a*, the side opposite angle *A*. Find the ratio of *a*: hypotenuse.

   d) Suppose the hypotenuse of a right triangle is 10 feet long and one of its angles is 50°. How long are the legs? Use your answer from (c) and the Pythagorean Theorem.

INDIVIDUAL WORK 11

A Vision of Angles

1. In **Figure 1.132**, the measure of angle *A* is 30°.

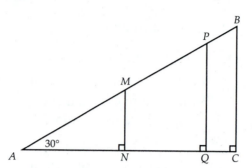

Figure 1.132.
Figure for Item 4.

a) How are triangles *AMN*, *APQ*, and *ABC* related? Explain.

b) Measure the lengths of *AM*, *AN*, and *MN*, and find the ratios *MN:AM* and *AN:AM*.

c) Measure *AP*. Using (b) and properties of similar triangles, find the lengths of *PQ* and *AQ* without measuring them directly.

d) Measure the length of *AB*. Using the properties of similar triangles, find the lengths of *BC* and *AC* without measuring them.

e) What can you conclude about the ratio of the side opposite the 30° angle to the hypotenuse?

f) Explain why the value you calculated in (b) could be called a shape ratio for 30°-60°-90° triangles.

g) Look back at Item 3 of Activity 11. What is a possible shape ratio for 40°-50°-90° right triangles?

2. **Figure 1.133** shows a right triangle similar to the ones you used in Activity 11, where *Q* can rotate on the dotted circular arc as the size of θ (so, also, of α) changes.

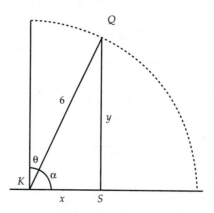

Figure 1.133.
Figure for Item 6.

a) Use your results from Items 1 and 2 of Activity 11 to complete a copy of **Figure 1.134**. The length of the pencil is still 6 inches.

alpha	x	y
0°		
30°		
45°		
60°		
90°		

Figure 1.134.
Table for Item 6.

b) Carefully plot the *y* values (response variable) versus the angles (explanatory variable) from the table in Figure 1.134. Use a graph similar to **Figure 1.135**. Connect the points with a smooth curve.

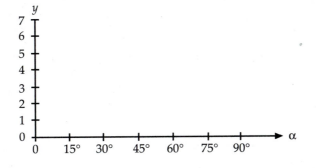

Figure 1.135.
Model of graph to use for Item 6(b).

c) Use the graph to find an approximate value of *y* when $\alpha = 75$.

3. a) In Figure 1.130, what is the relationship between triangle *EWK* and triangle *EQS*? Explain.

   In (b)–(e), assume the base of the object is in the picture plane at eye level and that the picture plane is 2 feet in front of the eye.

   b) Apply the results from Item 1 of Activity 11 to determine the apparent length of a 6-inch pencil held at eye level and tilted at a 45° angle back from vertical.

   c) Find the image length for a pole with a height of 8 feet that is tilted 45° back from vertical.

d) Find the image height for a sign 10 feet by 10 feet square and tilted back at an angle of 45°.

e) Find the image height of one face of a cube tilted back 45°. The height of each side of the cube is 4 inches.

f) In general, if *d* is 24 inches, and the object is tilted back at 45°, write a proportion relating *x*, *y*, 24 and *WK*. Solve the proportion to write a formula for *WK*.

4. In each of the following questions, assume the base of the object is at eye level and in the plane of vision, which is 2 feet in front of the eye.

a) Determine the apparent length of a 6-inch pencil tilted 30° back from vertical.

b) Determine the length of the pencil image for an angle of tilt equal to 60°.

c) Which angle comes closest to making the image half its original length: 30°, 45°, or 60°?

FOLLOW THE SINES

In Activity 11 and Individual Work 11, you
worked with three specific right triangles: one
with an acute angle of 45°, one with an acute
angle of 30°, and one with an acute angle of 40°. In each case, you
knew the size of one acute angle and the length of one side.
Using that information, you were able to find the lengths of the
other two sides.

The mathematics that deals with the relationships between the
sizes of angles and the lengths of line segments in right triangles
is a topic in trigonometry, a field of mathematics that was first
developed in ancient times to aid in navigation and surveying.

The word trigonometry comes from the Greek *trigonon*, which
means triangle, and *metria*, which means measure.

Because there is such an important relationship between an acute
angle in a right triangle and the ratio of the side opposite it to the
hypotenuse, that ratio is given a name: the **sine** of the angle
(from the Latin *sinus*, which means curve). See **Figure 1.136**.

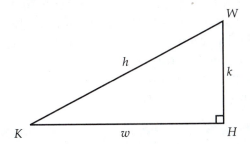

Figure 1.136.
Illustrating that the sine of
angle *K* is the ratio of *k* to *h*.

The sine is abbreviated sin. The relation in Figure 1.136 is written
as $\sin(K) = \dfrac{k}{h}$.

1. a) In **Figure 1.137**, what is the sine of angle *T*? The sine of angle *R*?

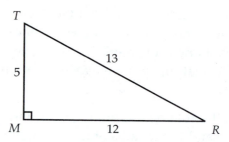

Figure 1.137.
Figure for Item 1(a).

b) In Item 1 of Individual Work 11, you found that the sine of 30° is 1/2. You may write sine of 30° as sin(30°). Based on your measurements from Item 3 of Activity 11, what is the approximate value of sin(50°)?

c) Use a ruler and protractor or a geometric drawing utility to draw several right triangles. Vary the sizes of the acute angles among the triangles you draw. Vary the sizes of the triangles. Include some triangles that are similar to each other. For each triangle, measure one acute angle, the length of the side opposite the measured angle, and the length of the hypotenuse. Copy **Figure 1.138**, and record these measurements and the value of the sine of the measured angle as computed directly from the definition of sine and your side measurements.

Angle measure	Side opposite	Hypotenuse	Sine

Figure 1.138.
Table for recording the sine of an angle.

FOLLOW THE SINES

12

d) Examine sets of similar triangles among your data. Why is it possible that such triangles are of different size, but have the sine of the angle remain the same?

2. a) Use a scientific calculator or a graphing calculator and check the accuracy of your answers for the sine of the angles in Figure 1.138. Make sure your calculator is in degree mode.

  b) Prepare a graph of the sine of an angle versus the measure of the angle. If you use a graphing calculator and graph $y = \sin(x)$, you will need to make sure the MODE is set to degree measure. Restrict your domain from 0° to 90° angles.

  c) Draw the graph or describe its shape.

3. The **trigonometric ratios** you have studied are ratios of the lengths of two sides of only right triangles. Sometimes **helping lines** are added to create right triangles where none exist. Add a helping line to triangle *RST*, and then use the given information to find the length of side *ST*. (See **Figure 1.139**. Note, however, that the figure is *not* drawn to scale.)

Angle *SRT* = 110°

Angle *RST* = 25°

Side *SR* = 10 units

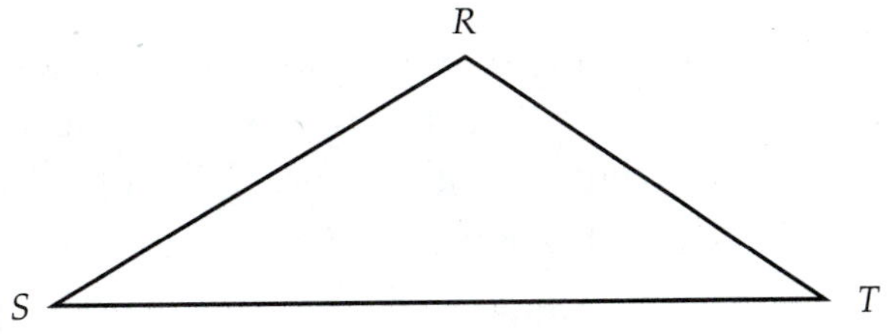

Figure 1.139.
Figure for Item 3.

ACTIVITY

FOLLOW THE SINES

12

The sine ratio is one of three right triangle trigonometric (or trig, for short) ratios commonly used to solve problems. The cosine and tangent ratios are the other two. The **cosine** of an acute angle of a right triangle is defined as the ratio of the length of the adjacent side to the length of the hypotenuse. The **tangent** is defined as the ratio of the side opposite to the side adjacent. Cosine is abbreviated as cos, and tangent as tan. As formulas, these ratios are:

$$\cos(\text{angle}) = \frac{\text{side adjacent}}{\text{hypotenuse}}, \quad \text{and}$$

$$\tan(\text{angle}) = \frac{\text{side opposite}}{\text{side adjacent}}.$$

Figure 1.140.
Illustrating the cosine and tangent ratios.

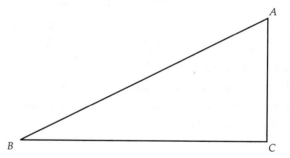

For example, in **Figure 1.140**, triangle *ABC* is a right triangle with angle *C* being the right angle. Side *a* is opposite angle *A* and is adjacent to angle *B*. Side *b* is opposite angle *B* and adjacent to angle *A*. Then,

$$\sin(A) = \frac{a}{c} \qquad \cos(A) = \frac{b}{c} \qquad \tan(A) = \frac{a}{b}$$

$$\sin(B) = \frac{b}{c} \qquad \cos(B) = \frac{a}{c} \qquad \tan(B) = \frac{b}{a}.$$

Remember, these definitions for the trig ratios apply *only* in right triangles.

FOLLOW THE SINES

Angle (degrees)	Tangent (tan)	Cosine (cos)	Sine (sin)

Figure 1.141.
Table for Item 4.

4. a) Draw five right triangles that are not similar. (You may use triangles drawn for earlier work.) Measure the lengths of all three sides of each triangle. Use the Pythagorean Theorem to check the accuracy of your measurements. Then use your measurements to determine the tangent and cosine ratios for the ten acute angles in your five triangles. Record your answers in a table similar to that in **Figure 1.141**.

b) Use your calculator's built-in trig functions to verify the accuracy of your ratios.

c) Graph $y = \sin(x)$ and $y = \cos(x)$ and $y = \tan(x)$ using the values in the table (Figure 1.141) or using a graphing calculator. Again, make sure your MODE is set to degrees and you restrict your domain from 0° to 90°.

d) Describe the similarities between the graphs of the cosine and sine functions.

e) Why does the tangent graph behave oddly near 90°?

ACTIVITY

12

FOLLOW THE SINES

5. a) Graph $y = \sin^2(x)$ and $y = \cos^2(x)$ in the window
   $[0, 90] \times [-1.5, 1.5]$. If you use a calculator, be sure you are
   in degree mode. Describe the relationship between the two
   graphs. (Note: $\sin^2(x)$ means $[\sin(x)] \times [\sin(x)]$. Most calculators require that you enter the equation as $y = (\sin(x))^2$.
   Cosine is treated similarly.)

   b) Select five x-values of your choice. Use your graph to
   determine the corresponding values of $\sin^2(x)$ and $\cos^2(x)$.
   Comment on how $\sin^2(x)$ and $\cos^2(x)$ appear to be related.

   c) If you did not try it in (b), add corresponding y-values for
   the two functions you graphed in (a), at the x-values you
   selected. For example, if you selected $40°$, then compute
   $\sin^2(40°) + \cos^2(40°)$. Describe any pattern you find in these
   sums.

   d) Use your answer to (c) to predict what the graph of
   $y = \sin^2(x) + \cos^2(x)$ will look like. Explain your answer.
   Then graph it to check your prediction.

   e) Suppose the hypotenuse of a right triangle is 1. Write an
   expression for the sine of angle A and an expression for
   the cosine of angle A, each in terms of a, b, and 1.

   f) Explain how the Pythagorean Theorem and (e) prove the
   conclusions you reached in (b)-(d).

   g) Substitute your expressions from (b) into the expression
   from (c) to obtain a formula illustrating the relationship
   between the sine and cosine of an acute angle.

INDIVIDUAL WORK 12

SOH-CAH-TOA

1. Draw three right triangles or use a geometric drawing utility. Vary the acute angles so the triangles are not similar to one another. Measure the lengths of the opposite sides and the hypotenuse. Write the ratio of the side opposite to the hypotenuse. Use your calculator to compare your answer with the sine of the angle. Show all of your work and ratios.

2. Use the information in (a)-(e) to find the lengths of all sides and the measures of all angles in right triangle *FGH* (see **Figure 1.142**). In each case, angle *G* is the right angle.

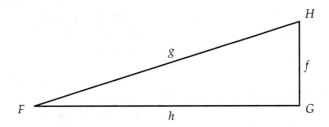

Figure 1.142.
Figure for Item 2.

   a) $F = 37°$ and $f = 6$ units.

   b) $F = 52°$ and $h = 12$ units.

   c) $F = 20°$ and $g = 15$ units.

   d) $f = 8$ units and $g = 12$ units.

   e) $H = 72°$ and $g = 20$ units.

3. a) Charlotte places a 22-foot ladder against her house with 2 feet extending beyond the roof edge. The ladder makes an angle of 75° with the ground. How far is the base of the ladder from the house?

   b) How high is the roof?

INDIVIDUAL WORK 12

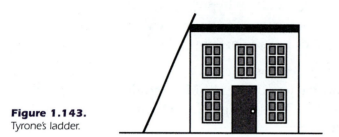

Figure 1.143.
Tyrone's ladder.

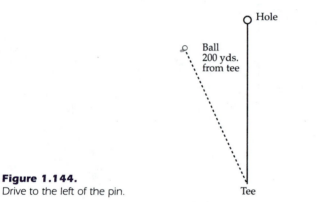

Hole

Ball
200 yds.
from tee

Figure 1.144.
Drive to the left of the pin.

Tee

4. Tyrone plans to use a ladder to get on his roof to clean out his gutters. The ladder will lean against the house, and his wife, Tyra, will hold the bottom of the ladder. Even with someone holding the ladder, Tyrone is afraid he will fall and wants the ladder to be held at an angle between 65° and 85° with the ground. If Tyrone's ladder is 22 feet long and, for safety's sake, it must extend at least 2 feet above the edge of the roof, what are the possible heights of his roof? (See **Figure 1.143**.)

5. The tee at the tenth hole of the golf course is 220 yards from the hole. Ingrid, the club golf pro, hooked her drive at a 15° angle. Her drive went 200 yards from the tee, but to the left of the hole. How far is she from the hole? (See **Figure 1.144**.)

6. Suppose you are flying a kite on a 200-foot string. You are holding the end of the string 6 feet above the ground, and the string makes an angle of 55° with the horizontal. How high is the kite flying (if you disregard the sag in the string)? See **Figure 1.145**.

200 ft.

55°

6 ft.

Figure 1.145.
Kite on a string.

7. Suppose triangle *ABC* is a right triangle, with angle *C* the right angle. Use sin, cos, and tan to find each length from the additional information below. Remember that side *a* is opposite angle *A*, side *b* is opposite angle *B*, and side *c* is the hypotenuse.

   a) Angle *A* = 23°. Side *c* = 7.5 cm. Find angle *B*. Find lengths *a* and *b*.

   b) Angle *B* is 58°. Side *b* is 3.84 meters. Find angle *A*. Find lengths *a* and *c*.

   c) Side *a* = 27 and side *c* = 42. Find side *b*. Find angles *A* and *B*.

8. a) Angela flies an airplane. She descends at a rate of 1000 feet in elevation for every horizontal mile along the ground. What is the angle of descent?

   b) Rohan is flying at an altitude of 12,000 feet. He is 19 miles from the airport. At what angle should he descend if he wants to make a steady descent?

9. A radio tower is 30 feet tall. Chloe wants to attach cables to the top of the tower and tether the other ends to the ground to hold the tower perpendicular to the ground (right angle). She wants the angle between the ground and each cable to be 75°. Calculate the length of each cable.

10. When the sum of two angles is 90° then these angles are called **complementary angles**. Thus the angles measuring 32° and 58° are complements. Likewise, angles measuring 40° and 50° are complements.

    a) Describe the relationship between the sine of an acute angle and the cosine of its complement. Investigate for several pairs of complementary angles. (Your data from Item 4 of Activity 12 may be helpful here.)

    b) Explain the reason for the relationship you noticed in (a).

11 a) Describe the relationship between the tangent of an acute angle and the ratio of the sine to the cosine for the same acute angle.

    For example, find tan(50°), sin(50°), and cos(50°). Take the ratio $\frac{\sin(50°)}{\cos(50°)}$ and compare your answer to tan(50°). Repeat the comparison for several other acute angles.

    b) Explain the reason for the relationship you noticed in (a).

ACTIVITY

TRIGONOMETRIC TILT

13

Now, back to the original problem of this lesson, which was to find the apparent length, *WK*, of a pencil that has been tilted away from the plane of vision. The geometric picture looks like **Figure 1.146**.

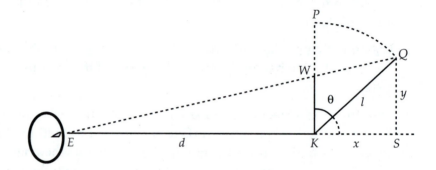

Figure 1.146.
Labeled side view of tilted pencil.

Earlier in this lesson, you found the length *WK* when θ was 45° or 30°. Because of the special properties of right triangles with these acute angles, you were able to solve for *x* and *y* without trigonometry.

Try the problem again, this time with a tilt that requires the use of trigonometry. First solve this specific case, then solve the general case as outlined below.

1. To make things a little simpler, suppose you are holding a 1-foot ruler 3 feet from your eyes, tilted back at 40°. Then $d = 3$, $l = 1$ and $θ = 40°$. Find the values of *x* and *y*.

2. A general solution for *WK* gives a formula for the apparent length of the pencil if you know its actual length, the distance from its nearest point to the viewer, and the angle of rotation. Assume the lower point is at eye level in the center of the plane of vision.

Work with your group, and apply the method of generalization to your work in Item 1 to find an expression for the length *e* (the apparent length of the pencil) in terms of θ and *l*. (See Figure 1.146)

INDIVIDUAL WORK 13

Aquarium Window

1. Check your formula by comparing its answers to measured results from Activity 10 and Individual Work 11.

2. Confirm your formula by reconstructing the activity using a geometric drawing utility.

3. An aquarium exhibit is being designed to allow visitors to watch the activity of fish around a coral reef. The reef will be wedge-shaped (see **Figure 1.147**) and the tilted surface will make an angle of 38° with the bottom. The tilted surface is to be 10 feet long. The sharp bottom edge will be flush against the bottom of the viewing window and at eye level. It is expected that some visitors will stand with their noses pressed to the glass, but because of crowding, many will be standing as far back as 8 feet from the window.

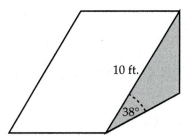

Figure 1.147.
Wedge-shaped reef.

a) How tall is the back of the aquarium reef?

b) How high should the window be so even those in the back will be able to see the top of the reef?

c) Suppose that, because of water pressure, the window cannot be more than 2 feet high. How much shorter should the reef be made?

Wrapping Up Unit One

1. a) Revisit the Hogarth painting (see Figure 1.3) in Activity 1. Summarize violations of perspective based on terms defined in the unit.

   b) Analyze a perspective drawing from a magazine or painting to determine if it is consistent with the principles of perspective. Check for vanishing points and consistent spacing. Provide a copy of your picture and explain your findings.

   c) Produce a drawing that illustrates convergence.

   d) Produce a drawing that violates a principle of perspective drawing. Challenge someone else to find the mistake.

2. Find each measure using proportions. In each case, suppose a ruler is held at arm's length so the plane of vision is 27 inches from the eye of the viewer.

   a) You are 100 yards away from the goalpost on a football field. The image height of the goalpost is 1.6 inches. How high are the goalposts?

   b) How wide is the lake? On the opposite side of the lake is a tower that is 50 feet tall. The image height is 1 inch.

   c) A certain basketball player stands 86 inches tall. You are standing under the basket and he is attempting a free-throw, which means he is about 18 feet from you. How tall is his image?

3. Determine the scale of each of two objects in the painting shown in **Figure 1.148**. Select two objects that are at different distances from the artist.

Figure 1.148.
Perspective view for Item 3.

4. Suppose you observe a 120-foot tall building from a higher position in a nearby building. Using the artist's method for measuring, you determine the distance between the horizon and the top of the image for the building to be 2 inches in your plane of vision. Your plane of vision is 27 inches from your eye. The total image height for the nearest edge of the observed building is 6 inches.

    a. How far horizontally are you from the building?

    b. What is your height in the other building?

    c) Draw your view of the other building using two-point perspective.

5. Explain the relation between dilations (as studied in Course 1, Unit 3, *Landsat*, for example) and projections of perspective drawings onto image planes.

6. Recall the characteristics of trapezoids, parallelograms, rectangles, rhombuses, and squares.

    a) For which figures are opposite sides equal?

    b) For which figures are opposite angles equal?

    c) For which figures do diagonals bisect one another?

    d) For which figures are diagonals perpendicular to one another?

    e) For which figures are diagonals equal in length?

7. a) Which angles in **Figure 1.149** are equal in measure to angle 5?

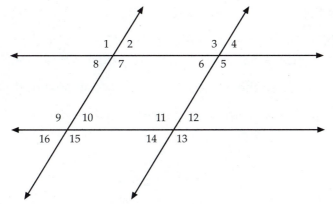

Figure 1.149.
Two parallel lines intersected by two parallel lines.

    b) If the measure of angle 12 is 65°, what is the measure of angle 1? Of angle 9? Of angle 16?

8. Produce a perspective drawing of equally-spaced objects. Describe your method. Show the steps you use to assure that the objects appear to be equally spaced in your perspective view.

9. Suppose triangle *ABC* is a right triangle, with angle *C* the right angle. Use the definitions for sine, cosine, and tangent to determine the lengths of the indicated sides of the triangle under the given conditions. Remember that side *a* is opposite angle *A*, side *b* is opposite angle *B*, and the hypotenuse is opposite angle *C*.

   a) Suppose angle *A* is 13.5° and side *c* is 8.9 mm. Find the lengths of *a* and *b*. Find the measure of angle *B*.

   b) Suppose side *a* is 14 feet and angle *B* is 68°. Find the lengths of *b* and *c* and the measure of angle *A*.

10. Suppose you want to use a ramp to move objects from ground level to the back of a furniture truck. The length of the ramp is 8 feet. It is difficult to move objects up the ramp if the ramp makes an angle of more than 35° with the ground. What is the maximum height for the back of the truck given the 35° restriction?

11. The angle between eye level and the line of sight to the top of a mountain is 14°. The distance from the eye to the plane of vision is 24 inches. The horizontal distance to the top of the mountain is 10 miles. Calculate the height of the image and estimate the actual height of the mountain (above the horizon).

12. The height of a rectangular sign is 15 feet. Suppose the sign is tilted away from vertical at an angle of 25° from the picture plane. What is the apparent height of the sign if the lower edge of the sign coincides with the picture plane at eye level?

13. In this unit, the key question is this: How do you represent three-dimensional objects accurately on a two-dimensional plane?

   a) Summarize the modeling process (decisions) in this unit.

   b) Discuss the possible next steps in the modeling process.

Mathematical Summary

The unit combines the precision of geometry with principles of perspective drawing to represent accurately three-dimensional objects on a two-dimensional plane.

The three major principles of perspective drawing addressed in this unit are diminution, convergence, and foreshortening. In this unit, each principle is associated with the development or review of a key mathematical topic.

The mathematics of similar triangles and proportions is central to the idea of diminution. The geometry of parallel lines guides the study of convergence. Relationships between the sides and angles of right triangles, a major topic in trigonometry, are necessary to quantify the principle of foreshortening.

SIMILAR TRIANGLES AND PROPORTIONS

The phenomenon that objects appear smaller as their distance from the viewer increases is called diminution. The mathematics of similar triangles and proportions is useful in relating size, distance, and scale— the key elements of diminution.

To help identify parts of a triangle and compare relationships between triangles, the following conventions are used:

   a) Vertices of triangles are labeled with capital letters.

   b) A side of a triangle is labeled with the same letter (but in lower case) as its opposite angle.

For example, in **Figure 1.50**, side *a* is opposite angle *A*.

Two triangles are similar if the three angles of one are equal to the three angles of the other. When you identify two triangles as similar, the order in which you write the letters is significant. For example, if triangle *ABC* is similar to triangle *FED*, then you imply that angle *A* = angle *F*, angle *B* = angle *E*, and angle *C* = angle *D*. The order in which the vertices are written is crucial when identifying corresponding sides and angles.

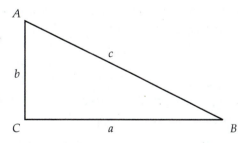

Figure 1.50.
Triangle to illustrate how to label angles and sides.

You can use similar triangles and proportions when three of the following measurements are used to find the fourth (see **Figure 1.151**):

1. The horizontal distance (*a*) between the viewer's eye and the picture plane.

2. The horizontal distance (*b*) between the viewer and the object.

3. The size (*c*), in the picture plane, of the image of the object.

4. The size (*d*) of the object.

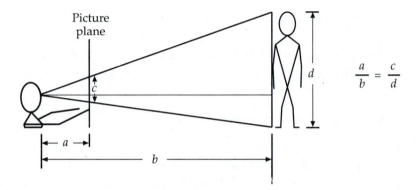

Figure 1.151.
Proportions and perspective drawing.

From this context (see Figure 1.151) comes the mathematical definition of the scale of an object in a picture:

$$\text{Scale} = \frac{\text{height in picture}}{\text{actual height}} = \frac{c}{d}.$$

From the figure it is also clear that

$$\text{scale} = \frac{\text{horizontal distance from eye to picture plane}}{\text{horizontal distance from eye to object}} = \frac{a}{b}.$$

When the concept of horizon is combined with scale, another ratio may be added to these representations of scale:

$$\text{Scale} = \frac{\text{distance in picture from horizon to place where object meets ground}}{\text{eye-level of viewer}}.$$

Proportions may also be used to determine the correct spacing, in the perspective view, between objects that are equally-spaced in the real world.

For example, suppose the distance between poles is *p* units and the distance between the picture plane and the first pole is *m* units. The distance from the viewer to the plane of view is *l* units. The eye of the artist is *k* units to the left of the imaginary line connecting the poles. The letter *a* represents the horizontal distance in the plane of vision between the image of Pole 1 and the imaginary center line connecting the eye to the vanishing point for the line of poles (see **Figure 1.152**).

Then $\dfrac{a}{l} = \dfrac{k}{l+m}$. In general, if the horizontal distance from the image of pole number n to the vanishing point is d, then $\dfrac{d}{l} = \dfrac{k}{l + m + (n-1)p}$.

PARALLEL LINES AND RELATED FIGURES

The principle of diminution guarantees that parallel lines that are horizontal in reality and increase in distance from the viewer must appear to converge to a point at the eye level of the viewer. The notion that parallel lines drawn into the distance will appear to meet is called convergence.

One consequence of convergence is that a rectangle with two vertical sides looks like a trapezoid in the perspective view.

The diagonals of rectangles and trapezoids are key features of constructions that ensure the equal spacing of objects. The constructions rely on the facts that, (1) the diagonals of a rectangle bisect one another and are equal in length, and (2) the diagonals of trapezoid do the same in a perspective view.

Figure 1.153 shows how the diagonals of a rectangle may be used to divide the rectangle into two equal parts. Therefore, the diagonals of a trapezoid representing the perspective view of a rectangle divide the rectangle into equal parts in the perspective view (see Figure 1.153).

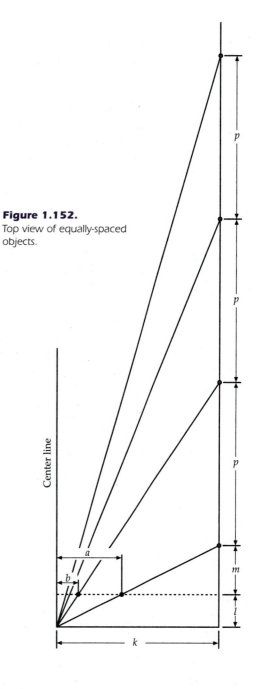

Figure 1.152.
Top view of equally-spaced objects.

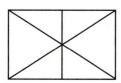

The diagonals of the rectangle divide the larger rectangle into two equal parts.

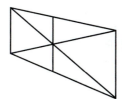

The diagonals of the rectangle in the perspective view divides the larger "rectangle" into two "equal" rectangles.

Figure 1.153.
Diagonals bisect a rectangle in a side view and a perspective view.

RIGHT TRIANGLE RELATIONSHIPS

Foreshortening is a result of the fact that the plane of vision intersects a smaller angle between the two lines of sight when an object is tilted at an angle to the plane of vision.

Figure 1.154 shows the relationship between the foreshortened image of an object and a right triangle with horizontal and vertical sides x and y and hypotenuse defined by the object itself.

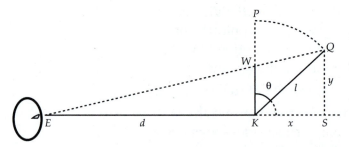

Figure 1.154.
Side view of an object tiled at an angle from the picture plane.

The relationships between the sides and the acute angles of a right triangle are described by trigonometry. For the right triangle ABC shown in **Figure 1.155**, a is the side opposite angle A and b is the side adjacent to angle A. Angle A actually has two adjacent sides, b and c, but since triangle ABC is a right triangle, we can avoid confusion by referring to c as the hypotenuse, not as a side. The shorter sides are usually called legs.

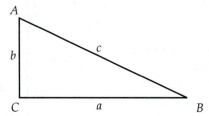

Figure 1.55.
Right triangle ABC.

The sine ratio is one of three right triangle trigonometric ratios commonly used to solve problems. The cosine and tangent ratios are the other two. These ratios are defined by the equations:

$$\sin(\text{angle}) = \frac{\text{side opposite}}{\text{hypotenuse}},$$

$$\cos(\text{angle}) = \frac{\text{side adjacent}}{\text{hypotenuse}}, \quad \text{and}$$

$$\tan(\text{angle}) = \frac{\text{side opposite}}{\text{side adjacent}}.$$

For example, in triangle ABC, $\sin(A) = \dfrac{a}{c}$, $\cos(A) = \dfrac{b}{c}$, $\tan(A) = \dfrac{a}{b}$,

$\sin(B) = \dfrac{b}{c}$, $\cos(B) = \dfrac{a}{c}$, and $\tan(B) = \dfrac{b}{a}$.

In an isosceles right triangle, the two acute angles each measure 45°, and the two legs are of equal length. The hypotenuse measures $\sqrt{2}$ times the length of a leg. See **Figure 1.156**. Therefore, $\sin(45°) = \cos(45°) = \dfrac{1}{\sqrt{2}}$, or about 0.7071, and $\tan(45°) = 1$.

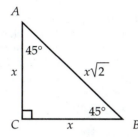
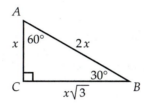

Figure 1.156.
Two special right triangles.

In a 30°-60°-90° right triangle, the hypotenuse is twice the length of the shorter leg. The longer leg is $\sqrt{3}$ times the shorter leg. Thus, $\sin(30°)$ $= \cos(60°) = \dfrac{1}{2} = 0.5$; $\sin(60°) = \cos(30°) = \dfrac{\sqrt{3}}{2}$, or about 0.8660;

$\tan(30°) = \dfrac{1}{\sqrt{3}}$, or about 0.5774, and $\tan(60°) = \sqrt{3}$, or about 1.7321.
One consequence of the Pythagorean Theorem is the fact that $\sin^2(A) + \cos^2(A) = 1$, no matter what the measure of angle A.

Trigonometric ratios help in calculating the length of a foreshortened image when the amount of tilt is known.

Glossary

COMPLEMENTARY ANGLES:
Two angles the sum of which is 90°.

CONVERGENCE:
Artistic principle asserting that lines or edges of objects that in reality are parallel appear to come together (that is, converge) as they recede from the observer.

CORRESPONDING ANGLES:
Angles in corresponding (analogous) positions within similar figures. Corresponding angles are equal in measure.

COSINE:
In a right triangle, the ratio of the length of the side adjacent to an acute angle to the length of the hypotenuse.

DILATION:
A scaling transformation of the plane in which the directed distance to every point's image is exactly k times its original directed distance from some specified, fixed point. The fixed point is called the center of the dilation; k is the scale factor for the dilation. Informally, think of a dilation as a stretching away from the center by a factor of k.

DIMINUTION:
The phenomenon by which objects appear smaller as their distances from the observer increases.

FORESHORTENING:
The phenomenon that occurs when lines or surfaces perpendicular to the line of sight show their maximum length, but as they are rotated away from the observer, they appear increasingly shorter.

HELPING LINES:
Lines added to figures to create right triangles where none exist.

HORIZON LINE:
The imaginary line on the plane of vision (or picture plane) containing the vanishing points of all horizontal (in reality, parallel to the ground), converging lines. It is always on the same level as the observer's eyes (the eye level).

LINES OF SIGHT:
Any of the imaginary lines between the viewer's eye and the top and bottom of the three-dimensional object being observed.

ONE-POINT PERSPECTIVE:
Occurs with only one family of horizontal parallel lines not parallel to the plane of vision; all the lines converge to a single vanishing point located on the horizon line.

OVERLAPPING:
A technique achieving a sense of depth and space in drawings by showing which objects are in front and which are in back.

PERSPECTIVE:
The technique of representing objects in three-dimensional space in a two-dimensional plane.

PLANE OF VISION (OR PICTURE PLANE):
An imaginary plane between the observer and the three-dimensional object(s) being viewed. The image of the object is projected onto the plane. In this unit, the picture plane is always vertical.

PYTHAGOREAN THEOREM:
A formula relating the lengths of the three sides of a right triangle: $a^2 + b^2 = c^2$ where c is the length of the hypotenuse and a and b are the lengths of the other two sides (legs).

SCALE:
The ratio of an image size (height or width) in a picture to the actual size of the object.

SCALE FACTOR:
In a dilation, the ratio of the new lengths to the old lengths. The number by which each linear dimension of an object is multiplied in a dilation or scale drawing.

SCALING:
A mathematical technique for representing depth and distance by enlarging or reducing objects represented in a drawing. The amount of enlargement or reduction depends on the scale factor.

SINE:
In a right triangle, the ratio of the length of the side opposite an acute angle and the length of the hypotenuse.

TANGENT:
In a right triangle, the ratio of the length of the side opposite an acute angle and the length of the side adjacent to the acute angle.

TRANSVERSAL:
A line that intersects two or more parallel lines.

TRIGONOMETRIC RATIO:
A ratio of the lengths of two sides of a right triangle.

TWO-POINT PERSPECTIVE:
Occurs with exactly two families of horizontal parallel lines not parallel to the plane of vision; all the lines converge to one of two vanishing points located on the horizon line.

VANISHING POINT:
The imaginary point to which lines parallel to one another appear to converge.

UNIT

2

Fairness and Apportionment

In earlier courses of *Mathematics: Modeling Our World*, mathematics was used to help make social decisions, such as selecting people to run our governments. In this unit, mathematics is once again called upon to help make fair decisions. Sometimes, it is impossible to find perfect solutions to the problem of dividing indivisible objects among people or groups of people. In those instances, solving equations and inequalities helps to optimize fairness. Here, you will learn about rational functions and about how they can be used to model apportionment problems to help to solve the real-world problems of fair division.

PEACE OVER THE PIECES

Decisions about dividing objects, or groups of objects, fairly among family members and friends are often made without too much thought. Later, after the objects or pieces of objects have been distributed to the people involved, hurt feelings and second thoughts about the fairness of the distribution may arise. In this unit, you will find that, with a little forethought and mathematical knowledge, it is possible to minimize the perceived unfairness and help to reduce the conflict and unhappiness experienced in such cases.

The mathematics of fairness also plays a large part in solving larger problems. The fair allocation of teachers and computers to schools, or of congressional districts to states involves similar reasoning. Solving these more global problems is important to our democratic society.

LESSON ONE
Heir Today, Gone Tomorrow

KEY CONCEPTS

Fair division

Algorithms

Tabular reasoning

Measuring fairness

Paradox

The Image Bank

PREPARATION READING

Getting Your Fair Share

This unit is about fairness. Even at an early age, people are concerned about being treated fairly. Children often complain, "It's not fair! Johnny got a bigger piece of pizza than I did!" or "She got to stay up later than I did!" or "How come she gets a better bike than I do?" But the question of dividing things fairly goes far beyond sharing a pizza. It is a continuous concern to people of all ages and can be very serious. For example, several roommates may need to share their telephone bill fairly, or the heirs named in a will may need to divide an estate fairly. Areas of our world, such as the Middle East, continually struggle with decisions about fair land division. Even the United States House of Representatives has had difficulties in apportioning a fair number of seats to the states.

When two children want to share M & M®'s, it is simple: "One for you, one for me," and they can flip a coin for the last one if there is an odd number. Without realizing it, they are using a simple algorithm for fair division. But in more complicated division situations, it may be hard to find an algorithm. In fact, it is often hard to say what fairness means. Even with the best of intentions, people may not be able to share things in a way that satisfies everyone.

In this lesson, three heirs need to divide an estate. Since the estate consists of a car, a dog, a stereo system, and some cash, a fair division is not obvious. In fact, the heirs may not agree on the values of the non-cash items, so it is not even clear what fair share means! Nevertheless, the estate must be divided. How would you divide the estate fairly?

ACTIVITY

1

DIVIDING THE ESTATE

An **estate** is everything of value that a person possesses at the time of his or her death. People who wish to specify how their estates will be handled after their deaths prepare wills. A **will** is a legal document stating how a person wishes his or her estate to be disposed of after death. Anyone who inherits any part of the estate of a person who has died is called an **heir**.

Every day families and estate lawyers face the question of how to divide an estate among heirs. Unfortunately, real problems of this type are often too large and complex for our investigation. In order to simplify the problem for study, an artificial situation has been chosen for your exploration.

1. Read the Montoff will (see **Figure 2.1**), and describe the method you would use to divide the estate fairly among the three children.

   a) Is your method fair to all three heirs? Why or why not?

   b) What criteria did you use to make your judgment of fairness?

2. Generalize your method so it will solve any estate-division problem. Write an algorithm (step-by-step procedure) for carrying out your method for the distribution of any estate among several heirs. Such an algorithm will be called an **estate-division algorithm**.

The Last Will & Testament of...

Myra M. Montoff

To my three children, I bequeath my entire estate consisting of my car, my stereo system, my dear dog, Lappa, and $18,000 in cash. These items are to be divided equally among the heirs.

signed
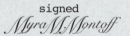

Figure 2.1.
The Montoff will.

CONSIDER:

1. Suppose one of the heirs really wanted all three of the items and the other two heirs didn't care about the items but they still wanted their fair share of the estate. Does your estate-division algorithm apply to this situation? If not, how would you solve this problem?

2. How are the values of items in an estate determined? Is that fair to all heirs?

3. If the will forbids the sale of any of the items in an estate, how might the estate be divided so that it is fair to all of the heirs?

INDIVIDUAL WORK 1

Making Good Decisions

1. Talk with a parent and/or friend about settling estates containing objects that can't be cut into pieces. Tell them about the method you used to divide the Montoff inheritance and ask them for additional ideas. Record their suggestions.

2. Use a newspaper, catalog, local expert, or other means to help you determine what *you* would consider to be a fair value for each of the items in the Montoff estate. The information you find will help you determine your sealed bids for these items in Activity 2.

ITEM	VALUE
1. Blue Honda Civic (3 years old)	?
2. Sony stereo system (1 year old)	?
3. Purebred Irish Setter dog (female, 2 years old)	?
4. $18,000	?

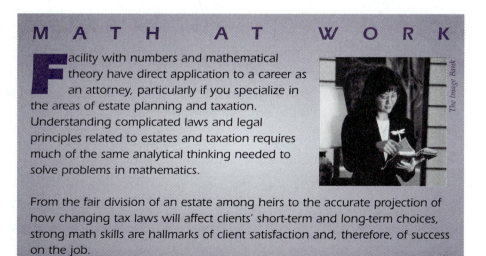

M A T H   A T   W O R K

Facility with numbers and mathematical theory have direct application to a career as an attorney, particularly if you specialize in the areas of estate planning and taxation. Understanding complicated laws and legal principles related to estates and taxation requires much of the same analytical thinking needed to solve problems in mathematics.

The Image Bank

From the fair division of an estate among heirs to the accurate projection of how changing tax laws will affect clients' short-term and long-term choices, strong math skills are hallmarks of client satisfaction and, therefore, of success on the job.

ACTIVITY

2

DETERMINING THE WORTH OF THE ESTATE

In Activity 1, you developed an algorithm for dividing an estate fairly. In this activity, you are given an estate-division algorithm and asked to role play the division of the Montoff Estate.

In order to play out the situation, form a group of three people to represent the three heirs. One person needs to play the part of Marty, one the part of Robin, and the third to play the part of Carrie.

1. Working independently, use your information from Individual Work 1, Item 2, along with the additional information given below, to determine your bid (in your character's role) for the items in the estate. You are *not* to discuss your bid with other members of your group.

    Additional information about each heir:

    Marty: You've always loved foreign-made cars, and your favorite color is blue.

    Robin: You love music and pets. Lappa, the Irish Setter, has always liked you.

    Carrie: You are allergic to house pets.

    a) Write the values to you for the car, the stereo, the dog and the cash.

    b) According to your figures in Item 1(a), what do you feel is the total value to you of the entire estate?

    c) Assuming there are three heirs to the estate and all are to receive an equal share, what is the value of what you should receive?

DETERMINING THE WORTH OF THE ESTATE

An Estate-Division Algorithm

1. Without seeing anyone else's bid, each heir submits a sealed bid recording the value to him or her of each item in the estate. Those values may be affected by an heir's sentimental attachment. If cash is part of the estate, its worth is determined by its face value.

2. A fair share is determined for each heir by finding the sum of his or her bids and dividing this sum by the number of heirs.

3. Each item in the estate is given to the heir who bid the highest on that item.

4. Each heir is given an amount of cash from the estate that is equal to his or her fair share of the entire estate (Step 2) less the amount that the heir bid on the objects he or she received. If this net amount is negative, the heir pays that amount back to the estate.

5. The remaining cash in the estate is divided equally among the heirs.

Figure 2.2.
An estate-division algorithm.

2. Return to your group. Use the estate-division algorithm shown in **Figure 2.2** to divide the estate, and complete Handout H2.2. An organized report form similar to the one in the handout is helpful in solutions to problems of this type.

3. In Item 1(c), you determined what you considered to be your fair share of the estate. After you divided the estate in Item 2, how much did you actually receive? (Don't forget to add your values for the items and cash you received.)

4. Was this more or less than what you felt should be your fair share of the estate?

CONSIDER:

1. Why do you think it is important that the heirs keep their bids secret?

2. A **paradox** is something that happens in a situation that runs counter, or against, a person's intuition. Does it seem to be a paradox that every heir receives more than what they think is their fair share? Why or why not?

INDIVIDUAL WORK 2

Estate Division

*I*n your Activity 2, you used an algorithm to divide the Montoff estate among its three heirs. Use that same algorithm to divide the estates in Items 1 and 2 below.

1. When Ed's final will was read, Les, Mary, and Ned found they had inherited a sailboat, an old baseball card, a diamond ring, and $30,000 in cash. Their bids for these items are listed in **Figure 2.3**.

	Les	Mary	Ned
Boat	$6000	$7500	$500
Card	$30	$1000	$850
Ring	$8500	$5300	$500

Figure 2.3.
Bids by Les, Mary, and Ned.

	Alan	Bev	Carol
Piano	$2000	$3000	$2700
Cabin	$5000	$4500	$4500
Kayak	$700	$200	$600
Ring	$300	$4500	$400

Figure 2.4.
Bids by Alan, Bev, and Carol.

Use a report form such as the one in Handout H2.2 to help organize your work.

2. Alan, Bev, and Carol have received word they are the sole heirs of their long-lost uncle's estate consisting of a piano, a log cabin, a kayak, a ring, and $4800 in cash. The bids made by each are shown in **Figure 2.4**.

Determine a fair distribution of the estate.

3. a) Handout H2.2 provides a logical organization of data used in estate-division problems. A computer spreadsheet can make the corresponding calculations very quickly. Set up a spreadsheet to solve the fair division problem for three heirs. Use Items 1 and 2 to check your output.

   b) Return to Item 2. Use your spreadsheet to determine the fair distribution of the estate if Carol's bid for the piano changes from $2700 to $3200.

LESSON TWO

More Estate Division

KEY CONCEPTS

Fair division

Measuring fairness

Fractional parts

Rounding

Algorithms

The Image Bank

PREPARATION READING

Decisions, Decisions, Decisions

*I*n Lesson 1, you discussed methods of dividing an estate fairly among a number of heirs. The estate consisted of several different assets, such as a house, a car, a TV, and some cash.

Sometimes it is necessary to divide a collection of things that cannot be cut into pieces, but also may not be sold or exchanged for cash. Collections of pearls, watches, or gold coins might give rise to such a situation. For example, suppose three people, *A*, *B*, and *C*, want to divide 100 identical gold coins, where *A*'s share is 25%, *B*'s share is 30%, and *C*'s is 45%. No problem: *A* gets 25 coins, *B* gets 30, and *C* gets 45. But if there are 101 coins, nothing comes out even. Who gets the extra coin? How do you decide what is fair?

Similar problems arise frequently in real life. For example, at a certain college all students live in dorms. There are rooms for exactly 1270 students. The college wants to maintain a balance in the dorms among students from each of the different schools in the college. They want 33% of the rooms to be filled by students in liberal arts, 25% in science, 16% in education, 11% in engineering, 9% in architecture, and 6% in pharmacy. A decision must be made on how many rooms to allot to students from each school. How should this be done?

ACTIVITY

3

DIVIDING ANOTHER ESTATE

In Lesson 1, you explored a situation that was a simplified version of a real-life division of an estate. The allocation of a number of objects, or some fixed amount of "stuff," among several entities or recipients is called **apportionment**. You examined methods of your own along with an algorithm that was given to you. In each case, you asked the all-important question, "Is this division fair to all heirs?"

In this lesson, you continue to explore apportioning estates, but the rules change slightly.

Figure 2.5 shows the will to the Chasten estate.

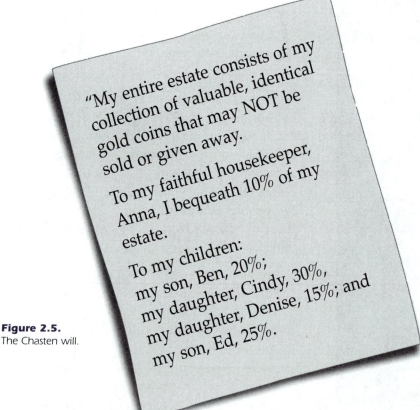

Figure 2.5.
The Chasten will.

"My entire estate consists of my collection of valuable, identical gold coins that may NOT be sold or given away.

To my faithful housekeeper, Anna, I bequeath 10% of my estate.

To my children:
my son, Ben, 20%;
my daughter, Cindy, 30%,
my daughter, Denise, 15%; and
my son, Ed, 25%.

DIVIDING ANOTHER ESTATE

1. Suppose there are 77 coins in the Chasten estate. Divide the coins among the five heirs according to the will. Write an algorithm for using your fair division method.

2. The will specifies the exact fraction of the estate each heir should receive. If fractional coins were permitted, the resulting allocation would give all heirs their **ideal shares**—the exact amount or number of items they should each receive as a result of an apportionment. Many times, though, ideal shares involve fractions of objects, which is not allowed. Thus, the amount or number of items the heirs eventually do receive as a result of the apportionment are their **actual shares**.

   a) According to the Chasten will, what are the ideal shares of the heirs?

   b) According to your division method, what is the actual share each heir receives?

3. What criteria for fairness did you use in deciding on your method?

4. Which of the heirs will most likely feel treated unfairly? Why?

5. Oops, another gold coin has been found. Now there are 78. Use your algorithm to apportion these 78 coins according to the Chasten will.

   a) What is each heir's actual share now?

   b) How good is your algorithm with 78 coins?

INDIVIDUAL WORK 3

Creating a Fair Scheme

1. Suppose your school has 200 freshmen, 170 sophomores, 160 juniors, and 145 seniors, and also has 100 free tickets for the championship basketball game.

   a) What is the ideal share of tickets each class should get? Ideal share of an apportionment is usually called **quota**. (Remember, rarely are quotas whole numbers.)

   b) Since tickets cannot be split usefully into fractional parts, what is the actual share of tickets that should be allotted to each class in a fair distribution?

2. Suppose that Chasten (Activity 3) had decided on a different split of his estate: Anna, 5%; Ben, 15%; Cindy, 20%; Denise, 25%; and Ed, 35%. If the estate consists of 77 coins, how would you distribute the coins among the 5 heirs? What if there were 78 coins?

3. In Activity 3, the percentages of the estate given to the heirs were 10, 20, 30, 15, and 25 respectively. One fair-division algorithm says Anna should receive 8 of the 77 coins. Suppose, however, Anna dies before the will is executed.

   a) Denise proposes an easy fix: just distribute the 8 coins evenly among the 4 remaining heirs. Cindy claims that isn't fair. Why do you think Cindy objects? Is she right? Why or why not?

   b) Assuming Cindy is justified in claiming Denise's way is not fair, how would you distribute the 8 coins fairly? Explain why your distribution is more fair than just giving 2 coins to each of the 4 remaining heirs. Support your reasoning numerically.

4. At a certain college, all students live in dorms. There are rooms for exactly 1270 students. The college wants to maintain a balance in the dorms among students from each of the different schools in the college. They want 33% of the rooms to be filled by students in liberal arts, 25% by students in science, 16% by students in education, 11% by students in engineering, 9% by students in architecture, and 6% by students in pharmacy.

   a) What is the quota or ideal share of rooms for each school in the college?

   b) Give the results of a fair apportionment (actual share) of rooms for each school in the college. Explain the apportionment method you use.

LESSON THREE

Apportionment: The Unfairness of Fairness

KEY CONCEPTS

Fractional parts

Measuring fairness

Rounding

Hamilton method of apportionment

Paradox

Proportional reasoning

Algorithms

Minimizing unfairness

Rational expressions

The Image Bank

PREPARATION READING

Making the Best of It

Suppose a school district is trying to distribute a number of computers among several schools. They find they cannot apportion the computers in a way everyone would agree is perfectly fair. Your job is to help them make the best of the situation. Generally, you will not be able to apportion the computers exactly; no matter what method you use, some schools will get more than their fair share and some will get less.

The goal is to find a distribution with the least amount of unfairness. But that depends on what you mean by unfairness. How do you measure it? Is there a way of assigning a number that measures the unfairness of a distribution? Is there more than one way?

Apportionment problems are not limited to sharing computers. A famous example is the apportionment of the U.S. House of Representatives. Since states are very concerned about their numbers of seats in the House, there have been political battles over this since the country began. In fact, the first presidential veto involved an apportionment method.

Mathematicians have shown that no method of apportionment is perfect. Whatever method you use, unexpected things happen occasionally. You will see examples of some surprising results in this lesson.

THE DISTRICT'S DILEMMA

The Preparation Reading described a commonly-occurring situation dealing with apportioning computers in a school district. Suppose the district has three schools, *A*, *B*, and *C*, and each school has requested computers. School *A* has 217 students, school *B* has 288, and school *C* has 395 for a total of 900 students. The superintendent orders 90 computers, which is all the district can afford.

1. Suggest a way that seems fair for the superintendent to distribute, or apportion, the 90 computers among the 3 schools.

2. Which school got the best deal? Which got the worst?

3. Find a numerical measure to determine how good or how bad was each school's deal.

4. Try to make the deal fairer by taking one computer from the school that got the best deal and giving it to the school that got the worst deal. Use your numerical measure from Item 3 to decide whether the swap really makes the distribution of computers fairer.

5. In Item 3 you defined a school-by-school measure of unfairness. Describe how you would measure the *overall* amount of fairness or unfairness in a given apportionment.

Reprinted by permission of United Feature Syndicate, Inc.

INDIVIDUAL WORK 4

Sharing the Computers

R eturn to the situation of Activity 4. School *A* has 217 students, school *B* has 288, and school *C* has 395, making a total of 900 students. The question is how to apportion 90 computers among the 3 schools. Use this situation as a starting point from which to consider the additional circumstances described.

1. The principal of school *A* says there are 3 schools, so each should receive 1/3 of the computers, that is, 30. The principal of school *C* complains this is not fair. In order to prove his point, principal *C* uses **Figure 2.6**. Copy and complete it for him.

   How does Figure 2.6 show that principal *C* is right?

	A	*B*	*C*
Population	217	288	395
Computers assigned	30	30	30
Students per computer			

Figure 2.6.
Principal C's information.

2. The superintendent based the total of 90 computers on 10 students per computer.

   a) If there were *exactly* 10 students to each computer, what is the exact fair share of computers for school *A*? school *B*? school *C*? Remember, this is the quota for each school.

   b) The quota is an ideal that cannot be achieved in this case. Why?

   c) Under the circumstances, what do you think is the fairest division? Indicate your answer to this item by completing a copy of **Figure 2.7**.

   d) How does the actual number of students per computer reveal which school got the best deal and which got the worst?

3. To make things fairer, the superintendent is thinking of taking one computer from the school with the best deal and giving it to the school with the worst deal. Modify Figure 2.7 to show what would happen if this exchange took place. Would the distribution be more fair? Why or why not?

	A	*B*	*C*
Population	217	288	395
Ideal number of students/computer	10	10	10
Ideal number of computers (quota)			
Number of computers assigned			
Actual number of students/computer			

Figure 2.7.
Fairness information.

4. After she decided on a fair apportionment, the superintendent planned to order 90 computers. By that time, however, the district was short of money and could afford only 79.

a) What is a fair way of apportioning these 79 computers? Modify your copy of Figure 2.7 and use it to make your decision.

b) Which of the three schools is treated unfairly by this apportionment?

c) Which school gets the best deal?

d) Assign a single number that measures the amount of unfairness in the entire distribution. (Hint: Use numbers from your chart.)

e) Try to make the distribution more fair by taking a computer from one of the schools and giving it to another school. Use your measure of unfairness to decide whether this exchange makes things fairer or not.

The **Hamilton method** of apportionment is named for the American statesman Alexander Hamilton, who suggested its use. To use this method, first calculate quotas and give each class a number of representatives equal to the integer part of its quota. If too few representatives are assigned, arrange the classes in descending order of the fractional parts of their quotas. Assign the remaining delegates in that order until all are assigned.

5. Suppose your school has 256 seniors, 372 juniors, and 372 sophomores, and assigns student council representatives by the Hamilton method. The student council has 25 delegates.

a) Discuss the common features among the problems of distributing gold coins, assigning computers, and apportioning representatives. In particular, what corresponds to computers, schools, and students?

b) Compute the Hamilton apportionment of the 25 representatives for the classes.

c) Suppose the classes agreed to measure unfairness in the apportionment as the differences between the actual ratio of students per representative to the ideal ratio for the classes. Discuss the fairness of the Hamilton apportionment.

6. For the situation in Item 5, the principal sees there is no absolutely fair apportionment of 25 delegates. He decides to break tradition and enlarge the council to 26 delegates, hoping the addition of an extra delegate will lead to a fairer apportionment.

a) Use a copy of **Figure 2.8** to record the Hamilton apportionments for 25 delegates, then for 26 delegates.

	25 Delegates			26 Delegates		
	Srs.	Jrs.	Soph.	Srs.	Jrs.	Soph.
Population	256	372	372	256	372	372
Ideal number of students/delegate						
Ideal number of delegates (quota)						
Number of delegates assigned						

Figure 2.8.
Apportionment of student council delegates.

b) Compare the apportionment of delegates in the first case (25) with the apportionment in the second case (26). Describe what happened when the extra delegate was added to the council.

c) Do you think any of the classes will be upset with the result after adding an additional delegate? Why or why not?

d) Recall from Lesson 1 that when something happens in a situation that runs counter to a person's intuition, it is known as a paradox. Why do you think the results in Items 6 (a and b) could be called a paradox?

ACTIVITY

5

SOME U.S. HISTORY

FYI

**Article 1,
Section 2, of the
U.S. Constitution**

"Representatives and direct Taxes shall be apportioned among the several States which may be included within this Union, according to their respective Numbers... The actual Enumeration shall be made within three Years after the first Meeting of the Congress of the United States, and within every subsequent Term of ten Years, in such Manner as they shall by Law direct. The Number of Representatives shall not exceed one for every thirty thousand, but each State shall have at least one Representative."

During the first part of this unit, many different methods of apportioning coins, computers, and student council representatives have been explored. Since we live in a country that values representative government, our Congress strives to make the votes of citizens bear equal weight by apportioning representatives according to state populations. The basis for apportionment in the United States is found in Article 1, Section 2, of the Constitution.

During the past two centuries, the search for the optimal method of finding how many seats should be in the U.S. House of Representatives and which states should get them has been an interesting, and often heated, debate.

In 1880, the U.S. House of Representatives was using the Hamilton method to apportion seats among the states. Just as in Individual Work 4, the method was based on the size of an ideal ratio, namely the ideal congressional district size:

$$\text{Ideal district size} = \frac{\text{U. S. population}}{\text{Number of seats in Congress}}.$$

Then for each state,

$$\text{Ideal number of seats} = \text{quota} = \frac{\text{State population}}{\text{Ideal district size}}.$$

After the census of 1880, a new apportionment was needed. At that time the size of the House was not fixed. As they considered sizes between 275 and 350, a problem affecting the state of Alabama drew much attention. If the house size increased from 299 to 300 seats, Alabama's number of seats would have gone from 8 to 7! How could this have happened when there were more seats available?

This unexpected discovery showed that Hamilton's method has a flaw: a state can lose a seat even though the total number of seats increases! This undesirable possibility is now known as the **Alabama paradox**.

SOME U.S. HISTORY

1. Based on Article 1, Section 2, of the U.S. Constitution, is there a largest or smallest legal district size? Explain.

2. a) In Individual Work 4, how does the student council activity in Item 6 illustrate the Alabama paradox?

   b) What element in Item 6 corresponds to the ideal district size for the House of Representatives? What corresponds to the ideal number of seats for a state?

3. You have seen that the Hamilton method, which seems so reasonable, has a serious flaw. There's more bad news: the method has another flaw known as the **population paradox**. See if you can discover it by examining this situation.

   Suppose that 100 seats are to be assigned to three states in 1980 and again in 1990. The populations of the states are shown in **Figure 2.9.**

State	1980 Population	1990 Population
A	6,470,000	6,500,000
B	2,470,000	2,550,000
C	1,060,000	1,050,000

Figure 2.9.
Population paradox.

   a) Use Hamilton's method to find the apportionment of the 100 seats in 1980 and in 1990.

   b) What is paradoxical about the results?

For Better or Worse

1. A school district has three schools, *D*, *E*, and *F*, with student populations of 280, 350, and 560 respectively.

	D	E	F
Population	280	350	560
Ideal number of students/computer			
Ideal number of computers (quota)			
Number of computers assigned			
Actual number of students/computer			

Figure 2.10.
Computer apportionment.

a) Use the Hamilton method to apportion 95 computers among them. Summarize your work in a copy of **Figure 2.10.**

b) Which school gets the best deal? Which one gets the worst?

c) Suppose the school with the best deal gives one computer to the school with the worst deal. Would that make the apportionment fairer? Why or why not? Be sure to indicate exactly how you measure unfairness.

2. In another school district, schools *J*, *K*, and *L* have student populations of 453, 442, and 105 respectively.

a) Use the Hamilton method to apportion 100 computers among them. How many computers would each school receive?

b) Suppose that an additional computer is available. Compute the Hamilton apportionment of the 101 computers. Would you expect all of the schools to be happy with the new apportionment? Why or why not?

c) What is the name of the situation causing the unhappiness noted in part (b)?

3. Suppose the student populations of schools *A*, *B*, and *C* are represented by P_A, P_B, and P_C respectively, and the number of computers to be distributed is *H*.

a) Write an expression for *P*, the total number of students in all three schools. What does *P/H* represent?

b) Suppose that the numbers of computers assigned to the three schools are *a*, *b*, *c*, respectively. What do the expressions P_A/a, P_B/b, and P_C/c represent?

c) Write expressions that represent the amount of unfairness in each school's share.

LESSON FOUR
Other Methods

KEY CONCEPTS

Algorithms

Apportionment Methods (Webster, Jefferson, Adams)

Measuring fairness

Tabular reasoning

Fractional parts

Rounding

Proportional reasoning

Minimizing unfairness

Rational functions

Solving equations

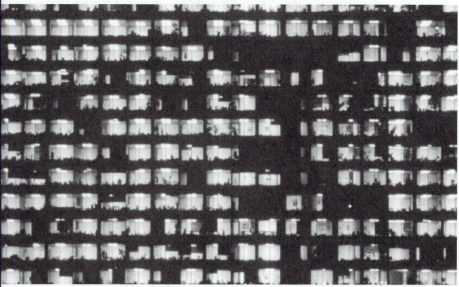

The Image Bank

PREPARATION READING

Many More Questions

In previous lessons, you examined how to apportion objects that couldn't be split up. You looked at a simple rounding method and a method (Hamilton method) of giving out extra coins, computers, or seats according to the sizes of the fractional parts of the fair share (quota).

Both of these methods have flaws. Some of the flaws are so surprising that we called them paradoxes, as in the cases of the Alabama paradox and the population paradox when using the Hamilton method.

In this lesson, you will examine other methods of apportionment—the **Jefferson**, **Adams**, and **Webster** methods. Whenever you find a new method of apportionment, several questions come to mind. Are these new methods better? Will they apportion things so the distribution is closer to the ideal ratio? How is closeness measured, anyway? Will these new methods give rise to new paradoxes? What method is currently being used to apportion the U.S. House seats? What method(s) have been used in the past? Historically, why has our government not chosen one method and stuck with it?

Some of these questions will be answered in this lesson, while others will be examined in Lesson 5.

ACTIVITY

6

THE JEFFERSON METHOD

When the proposed distribution of the 90 computers was announced in Lesson 3, school C, the largest school, realized it had received the worst deal and began looking for another way to divide the computers among the three schools. The situation is shown in **Figure 2.11.**

	A	*B*	*C*
Population	217	288	395
Ideal ratio (*I*) of students/computer	10	10	10
Quota ($q_s = P_s / I$)	21.7	28.8	39.5
Hamilton Apportionment (s)	22	29	39
Actual number of students/computer (P_s / s)	9.86	9.93	10.13

Figure 2.11.
Hamilton apportionment of 90 computers.

The Image Bank

Thomas Jefferson
(1743–1826),
of Virginia, served as the third president of the United States. The Jefferson method of apportionment, which tends to favor large states, was named after him.

School C agrees to begin by giving each school the integer part of its quota. So *A* gets 21, *B* gets 28, and *C* gets 39. This accounts for 88 computers and leaves 2 computers to give away.

In the Hamilton method, the extra computers were given to the schools with quotas having the largest fractional parts. Instead of doing that, school C suggested using a divisor method. A **divisor method** is a method of apportionment that determines quotas by dividing the populations by an ideal ratio or an adjusted ratio, then applying a specific rounding rule. In this method, the quotas are adjusted in such a way that the integer parts add up to 90.

How do you do that? Recall that the quotas were obtained by dividing each school's population by 10—the ideal student per computer ratio. Now try a different divisor, some number *x*, which will be either slightly larger or smaller than 10. Using *x*, obtain a new, adjusted quota, and use just the integer part.

THE JEFFERSON METHOD

Quota for school $S = \dfrac{\text{School population}}{\text{Students / Computer}} = \dfrac{P_S}{I}$.

Adjusted quota for school $S = \dfrac{\text{School population}}{\text{Adjusted (Students / Computer)}} = \dfrac{P_S}{x}$.

The challenge is to find an x so the sum of these integer parts of the three adjusted quotas totals 90 computers.

1. Examine the information in the table in **Figure 2.12.**

School	Size	Quota	Integer part of of quota
A	217	21.7	21
B	288	28.8	28
C	395	39.5	39
Total	900	90	88

Figure 2.12.
Apportionment information.

Using the ideal ratio of 10 as a divisor, the integer parts of the quota only sum to 88. Do you think you need to divide by a number larger or smaller than 10 to get the integer parts of the quotient to total the desired 90? Why?

ACTIVITY

6

THE JEFFERSON METHOD

2. Choose a new divisor, then compute the adjusted quotas and their integer parts. Keep adjusting the divisor and re-computing the adjusted quotas until the sum of the integer parts of your adjusted quotas is 90. Keep a record of your trial divisors, adjusted quotas, and apportionment totals in a table similar to **Figure 2.13.**

Attempt number	Adjusted divisor (x)	P_A/x	P_B/x	P_C/x	Apportionment total
1					
2					
3					
...					

Figure 2.13.
Record of trial divisors, adjusted quotas and totals.

3. What adjusted divisor produced the desired apportionment for your group? Compare that number with the final divisors of other groups in your classroom. Do you all have the same divisor? Why or why not?

The **Jefferson method** of apportionment is one of many divisor methods, and differs from other divisor methods only in the way the quotients are rounded after the divisors have been adjusted. It rounds by dropping all fractional parts of the quota.

4. The method of apportionment proposed by school C is known as the Jefferson method, one of several divisor methods. Calculate a measure of unfairness for each school and an overall measure of unfairness for the apportionment. Use your measure to compare the amount of unfairness in this apportionment to that from the Hamilton method. Do you think this method produced the results desired by school C? Why or why not?

INDIVIDUAL WORK 6

To the Biggest Belong the Spoils

The Jefferson method of apportionment was the first method used by our government in 1790 to apportion the U.S. House of Representatives. President Washington selected this method over the Hamilton method when he vetoed a bill that called for the Hamilton method to be used in apportioning the U.S. House. (This was the first presidential veto in U.S. history.) The Jefferson method continued to be the method of choice until 1840.

Decisions on how to apportion the seats of the U.S. House have often been surrounded with heated debates occurring between states: large v. small, northern v. southern, and agricultural v. industrial. Keep in mind our Constitution says only that the representatives shall be apportioned according to the respective populations of the states. It does not specify the number of seats in the House or the method by which those seats are divided among the states. Since apportionment determines the power of the states in the Congress, arguments have raged, political battles have been fought, and laws have been passed and repealed. As this unit proceeds, you will revisit our country's past and learn about our present system.

As you noticed in Activity 6, each time you change the adjusted divisor, you get a new set of adjusted quotas. In fact, the relationship between the adjusted divisor and the adjusted quota defines a function (adjusted quota = P_S/x). This function may be used and analyzed just as any other function you have studied (e.g. you can make tables, graph it, solve it for particular circumstances, etc.). In Individual Work 6, your study of this function continues.

1. **Figure 2.14** shows relevant facts about a desired apportionment. Use its information to complete items (a)–(d).

   a) What is the value of P_A in this problem?

   b) What is the value of P?

   c) What is the value of H (the number of seats to be distributed)?

State	Population	Quota P_s/I	Adjusted quota	Final apportionment
A	561			
B	338			
C	101			
Total	1000	40	....	40
Adjusted divisor used:				

Figure 2.14. Jefferson apportionment of 40 seats.

d) What is the value of I (the ideal ratio or ideal **district size**)?

e) Determine the Jefferson apportionment. Apportion 40 seats among three states—A, B, and C—using the Jefferson method. Keep a record, as you did in Activity 6, of all the divisors you use and the resulting apportionments. Record your final divisor and apportionment in a copy of Figure 2.14.

f) Find the Hamilton apportionment for the states in Figure 2.14.

$A =$ $B =$ $C =$

g) Do the two methods apportion the seats the same way?

h) One state measures unfairness as the largest absolute difference between ideal district size and actual district size. A second state measures unfairness as the largest absolute difference between ideal quota and final apportionment. Compare their assessments of the apportionments in parts (e) and (f).

2. a) To help understand what happens when you try various divisors x, use a calculator or spreadsheet to complete a table of adjusted quota functions like the one shown in **Figure 2.15.**

x	A $561/x$	B $338/x$	C $101/x$
25			
24.9			
24.8			
24.7			
24.6			
24.5			
24.4			
24.3			
24.2			
24.1			
24			

Figure 2.15.
Changing the divisor.

b) As the divisor x decreases, what do you notice about the amount of growth (first differences) in the adjusted quota of state C (population 561) compared to the amount of growth in the adjusted quota of the states with populations of 338 and 101?

c) If all three states had begun with the same fractional remainder, which one would have reached the next higher integer first?

d) It seems that some states are favored here. Are the larger or smaller states receiving the unfair advantage? Why do you think this is true?

3. Look at the problem in Item 1 once more. Another way of looking at an apportionment is as a coding scheme. That is, you wish to change one list of numbers (the populations: 561, 338, 101) into another list of numbers (the apportionment: ?, ?, ?). Of course, not just any change will be fair; you would like to do it in such a way that the two sets of numbers are spaced the same. To guarantee this spacing condition, you need to use a multiplication code or stretch cipher, multiplying each number by the same constant.

a) Plot the numbers (561, 338, 101) on a number line. On a separate number line (using a different scale if you wish), plot the results of coding these numbers using a "multiply by 1/25" code. The multiplier is based on the ideal district size. Geometrically, the two number line arrangements are similar. Compare your results to those you obtained in your first row of Figure 2.15.

b) Repeat part (a) using a "multiply by 2/25" code. How do the three plots compare as you look at them?

c) Rounding down in the list you found in part (a) results in a total less than 40, so it's not valid. Part (b) shows that changing multipliers just rescales the plot, but spacing stays the same. A multiplier other than 1/25 is needed, one that raises exactly one of the numbers in part (a) past the next largest integer. How much does 4.04 have to be stretched (multiplied) to reach the next integer?

d) What multipliers get the other two values from part (a) past their next integers?

e) The original multiplier was 1/25. Combine it with the appropriate value from parts (c) and (d) to get a valid apportionment without trial and error.

4. a) Find the Jefferson apportionment for the information in Figure 2.16.

State	Population	Quota	Adjusted quota	Jefferson apportionment
A	466			
B	1142			
C	8392			
Total	10,000			

Figure 2.16.
Jefferson apportionment.

b) Suppose that for some state S, the integer part of its quota is n. Then you would expect an apportionment to give the state either n or $n + 1$ seats. When that happens, the apportionment for the state is said to agree with quota. If a state is given a number of seats that is not equal to the integer part of its quota or 1 more than that, the apportionment is said to **violate quota**. According to the calculation of state A's quota (P_A / I), it should get either 4 or 5 seats. What about B and C?

c) In the final apportionment, what state(s) got the extra two seats? Discuss this result in terms of quota and fairness.

5. Are you tired of all this trial and error? Algebra to the rescue! There are easier ways to find a divisor x for which the adjusted quotas sum to H. Here's a hint for one way to do it:

For each state A and each value x: $\dfrac{P_A}{x}$ = adjusted quota.

Think about what you know in this equation and what you want to happen. Try to find a short-cut for finding some divisor x that will give you the desired adjusted quotas. This equation, some simple algebra, and a few simple calculations will do it. Then apply your method to check your results in Items 1 and 4.

MORE DIVISOR METHODS

In the first two lessons of this unit, you may
have tried using a traditional rounding method
to model the situation of estate division. In some
cases, it worked and in other cases, it didn't. The failure of this
model occurred because the method had no way to guarantee
the apportionment would assign the total number of items that
needed to be divided among the heirs. This lesson will help you
solve that problem.

Now that you are familiar with the Jefferson method and some
of its shortcomings, like bias and violation of quota, many other
divisor methods of apportionment are within your reach.

1. Before examining any new divisor methods, write an algorithm for the Jefferson method. When your group has completed the algorithm, share it with others in your class to produce one algorithm that everyone agrees is good.

The **Webster method**, like the Jefferson method, is a divisor
method of apportionment. The only difference is in the way it
rounds off the fractional parts of the quota. The Jefferson method
rounds every quota down, dropping the fractional parts. The
Webster method rounds in the traditional manner—when the
fractional part is 0.5 or greater it rounds up, and when the
fractional part is smaller than 0.5 it rounds down. Other than
that, the two methods work in the same way.

One of the problems you found with the Jefferson method was
that it seemed to favor large states. Nobody was more aware of
this issue than the smaller states in the union. In 1840, with this
concern in mind, the U.S. House of Representatives changed
from the Jefferson to the Webster method of apportionment.

The Image Bank

Daniel Webster
(1782–1852),
great American
statesman, orator,
Congressman, and
Senator is credited
with proposing
another divisor
method of
apportionment.

MORE DIVISOR METHODS

2. Use the information in **Figure 2.17** to find a Webster apportionment of 50 seats to the three states listed. (Hint: Use the algorithm you wrote for Item 1. Change only the way you round the fractional parts of the adjusted quotas.)

State	Population	Quota	Rounded quota	Adjusted quota	Webster result
A	284,000				
B	488,000				
C	228,000				
Total	1,000,000				

Figure 2.17.
Webster apportionment.

John Quincy Adams
(1767–1848)
served as the sixth President of the United States. In the hopes of avoiding the flaw of quota violation found in the Jefferson method, he proposed the method of apportionment that is now named after him.

The Image Bank

3. Do you think it is possible to violate quota with the Webster method? Why or why not? Do you think the population paradox might occur with this method? Why or why not? Include examples to support your answers.

A third divisor method, known as the **Adams method**, has historically been favored by small states. Even though it has never actually been used to apportion the U.S. Congress, it was proposed in 1830 as a method to help keep New England's representation from falling. Again, the Adams method differs from the other two divisor methods only in the way it rounds. In this method, all fractional parts are rounded up to the next integer. For example, if a quota is 17.02, the number of seats given is 18 (rounded up).

MORE DIVISOR METHODS

4. Explore the Adams method for the data shown in **Figure 2.18**, assuming that the number of delegates to apportion is 25.

Class	Population	Quota	Rounded quota	Adjusted quota	Adams apportionment
10th	450				
11th	345				
12th	205				
Total	1000				

Figure 2.18.
Adams apportionment.

5. Why does the Adams method seem to favor small states? Remember the only difference between the Jefferson and Adams methods is the rounding rule. How do they affect the initial apportionment before adjustment? How does the adjustment process move things? Refer back to Individual Work 6, Item 3, which discusses stretching quotas.

6. How does violation of quota for the Adams method differ from violation of quota with the Jefferson method? What might you conjecture about all divisor methods?

INDIVIDUAL WORK 7

Fair, Fairer, and Fairest

1. In Activities 6 and 7, you examined the Jefferson, Webster, and Adams methods of apportionment and found that all three methods could be classified as divisor methods. Find the Jefferson, Webster, and Adams apportionments to complete a copy of **Figure 2.19.** Assume there are 20 representatives to apportion among the four precincts, *W*, *X*, *Y*, and *Z*.

	Population	Quota	Jefferson method	Webster method	Adams method
Precinct *W*	145				
Precinct *X*	1310				
Precinct *Y*	290				
Precinct *Z*	255				
Total	2000				

Figure 2.19.
Jefferson, Webster, and Adams apportionments.

2. Use some measure of unfairness to examine the three different apportionments in Item 1. Based on those results, which of the three methods appears to be the fairest for this situation?

LESSON FIVE
Measuring Unfairness

KEY CONCEPTS

Measuring fairness

Tabular reasoning

Apportionment (Hill, Webster)

Rounding

Minimizing unfairness

Rational expressions

Rational functions

Solving equations

Solving inequalities

The Image Bank

PREPARATION READING

Not Without Flaws

*I*n the preceding lessons, you considered several methods of apportionment and found all of them were unfair in one way or another. In fact, as you may have suspected, there is no method of apportionment that avoids all types of inequities. Around 1980, two American mathematicians, Michael L. Balinski and H. Peyton Young, produced what is known as the Apportionment Impossiblity Theorem. This theorem proves no method is free of flaws; it either violates quota or produces paradoxes, for example the Alabama or population paradox.

In past lessons, you learned to use a method of apportionment and then examined its fairness. In this lesson, you will do just the opposite. You will examine two different mathematical measures of unfairness. These, in turn, will lead you to two different apportionment methods. One leads to the Hill method, which is currently used to apportion the U.S. House of Representatives. The other leads to the Webster method, which you examined in Lesson 4.

ACTIVITY

THE CLOSER YOU GET

8

When examining the amount of unfairness in an apportionment, looking at how much two schools differ in the number of computers per student or how much two congressional districts differ in the number of people per representative may not give you the best picture of the situation. Answering the following items will help you discover better ways of quantifying unfairness.

1. Suppose you want to lay out a football field. Its length should be 100 yards, or 300 feet, but your measurement is not quite accurate. You are off by 1 foot.

   Suppose also that you want to build a square frame that is 12 x 12 inches, but your measurement is off by 1/4 inch.

   Certainly your measurement error of 12 inches is much larger than your error of 1/4 inch. Yet, in a way, you were more accurate when measuring the football field than when you measured the frame. Explain why that is so, and support your explanation with numbers.

2. In the presidential election of 1844, James K. Polk defeated Henry Clay by a margin of 38,000 votes: 1,337,000 to 1,299,000. In 1960, John F. Kennedy defeated Richard M. Nixon by a margin of 108,000 votes: 34,227,000 to 34,109,000. Yet, despite the much larger margin of victory, the 1960 election is considered closer than the 1844 election. Explain; support your argument with numbers.

3. Suppose that seats in the U.S. House of Representatives are apportioned in such a way that state A has an average district size (N_A) of 500,000 people per seat, and state B has a district size (N_B) of 450,000 people per seat. This is unfair to state A. One way of measuring the unfairness to state A is to say that each of state A's representatives has to represent 50,000 people more than those of state B. (Note: the average district size of a state S (N_S) is equal to the population of the state divided by the total number of state S's representatives. $N_S = P_S/s$.)

THE CLOSER YOU GET

Now suppose for state C, $N_C = 150{,}000$ people per seat while for state D, $N_D = 100{,}000$. Since the difference is 50,000 in both cases, you could say the unfairness is the same as in the case of states A and B. Still, somehow the unfairness to C relative to D seems worse than the unfairness to A relative to B. Explain.

4. In Item 3, assign a single number to measure the unfairness to A relative to B. Assign a single number to measure the unfairness to C relative to D.

5. Suppose states A and B have congressional districts of N_A people per district and N_B people per district. If $N_A > N_B$, the apportionment is unfair to A. Reasoning as you did in Item 4, assign a number to measure the relative unfairness to A. In other words, write a formula for the relative unfairness.

6. Find examples of district size N_A and N_B for which the relative unfairness is 1.0, 0.5, 0.2, and 0.1.

7. Think about the fraction N_A/N_B. If $N_A/N_B = 1$, what does that say about relative unfairness? What if $N_A/N_B > 1$? In that case what does the number $N_A/N_B - 1$ represent?

8. Suppose ten seats in the House are to be apportioned between states A and B (see **Figure 2.20**).

The ideal congressional district has size $1000/10 = 100$. Dividing the population by the ideal district size of 100 gives the quotas shown in Figure 2.20. Start by giving seven seats to A and two seats to B. Now the question is: who gets the extra seat? (Define $N_A/N_B - 1$ as the relative unfairness to A.)

State	Population	Quota
A	714	7.41
B	259	2.59
Total	1000	10

Figure 2.20.
Populations and quotas for states A and B.

a) Compute the relative unfairness to A if B gets the extra seat, and the relative unfairness to B if A gets the extra seat. This is to show that whichever state gets the seat, it will be unfair to the other state. Then determine which state should get the extra seat so the relative unfairness is least.

b) Who would get the extra seat if the populations of A and B were 754 and 246 respectively?

INDIVIDUAL WORK 8

More States

For the items below, define the unfairness to state A relative to state B as

$$\frac{N_A - N_B}{N_B}.$$

State	Population	Quota
A	432	4.32
B	231	2.31
C	337	3.37
Total	1000	10

Figure 2.21.
Populations and quotas for states
A, B, and C.

State	Population	Quota
A	367	3.67
B	265	2.65
C	368	3.68
Total	1000	10

Figure 2.22.
Populations and quotas for states
A, B, and C.

1. Use the data in **Figure 2.21** to examine the apportionment of ten seats among three states.

   a) Suppose you begin by giving four seats to A, two seats to B, and three seats to C. That's nine seats. Assign the remaining seat so the relative unfairness is as small as possible. (Hint: If the remaining seat goes to A, you should compute the relative unfairness to B and to C. If it goes to B, you should compute the relative unfairness to A and to C. Finally, if the last seat goes to C, you should compute the relative unfairness to A and to B. This requires computing six measures of unfairness.)

   b) The process you used to answer Item 1(a) involves many computations, and things can get worse! If there were four states, how many computations of relative unfairness would be needed? How about ten states? 50 states?

2. If this weren't bad enough, there is another possible complication. Consider the situation in **Figure 2.22.**

   In this case, three seats are assigned to A, two to B, and three to C. That makes eight seats, so there are two seats left over. In order to decide who gets the ninth seat, you need six computations of unfairness. After the ninth seat is assigned, you need six more computations to see who gets the tenth seat. Just imagine what would happen if there were 50 states and 20 seats left over. That would require an enormous number of computations. How many computations would be needed?

ONE AT A TIME

After calculating how many computations it will take to examine all possible values of unfairness if 20 seats need to be apportioned among the 50 states, you must be thinking that there has to be a better way! And there is—the power of algebra once again comes to the rescue. With algebra, you can greatly reduce the number of computations needed.

To see how this works, start with just two states, A and B, with populations P_A and P_B. Suppose A has already been assigned a seats and B has been assigned b seats. Recall that N_A and N_B denote the respective district sizes of states A and B with this allocation. Assume that no matter how the next seat is assigned, it will be unfair to one of the states.

If an extra seat needs to be allocated, the next seat goes to A if:

> relative unfairness to A   relative unfairness to B
> (if next seat goes to B) $>$ (if next seat goes to A)

1. Use the measure of unfairness defined in Individual Work 8 to rewrite this inequality in terms of the variables P_A, P_B, a, b. (Hint: Remember, if the next seat goes to A, then A will have $a + 1$ seats. Similarly, if the next seat goes to B, then B will have $b + 1$ seats.)

2. Using the inequality from Item 1, separate your variables by state. From that simplified inequality, what can you conclude about who gets the next seat?

3. The situation can be summarized nicely by using algebraic notation. Let S stand for either A or B. Let s be the number of seats assigned to S. (So $s = a$ when S represents state A, and $s = b$ when S represents B.) Then the next seat is assigned to that state S for which $\dfrac{P_S}{\sqrt{s(s+1)}}$ is larger.

ONE AT A TIME

This number will be called the index value for the measure of unfairness defined by $\dfrac{N_A - N_B}{N_B}$.

A quantity, computed for each state, that determines a state's eligibility for the next seat to be allocated is called the **Index.**

It is related to the relative unfairness to state S if the next seat is given to another state. Notice this index depends not on the other state but only on how many seats S already has.

a) When there are more than two states, this index really pays off. For example, if there were four states, A, B, C, and D, then the next seat would go to the state corresponding to the largest of the numbers

$$\frac{P_A}{\sqrt{a(a+1)}}, \ \frac{P_B}{\sqrt{b(b+1)}}, \ \frac{P_C}{\sqrt{c(c+1)}}, \ \frac{P_D}{\sqrt{d(d+1)}}.$$

Explain why this is so.

b) Note that for four states, you have to compute only four quantities. How many quantities would you have to compute otherwise?

c) How many computations did you need to make in order to apply the measure of unfairness directly (without using the index) to the allocation of one seat among 50 states? How many are needed if you use the index?

THE HILL METHOD

Since the first U.S. census, several different methods have been used to apportion the U.S. House of Representatives. The current method used, the **Hill method** (also called the Method of Equal Proportions), was adopted in 1941 following the census of 1940. This method is based on the index of relative unfairness you investigated in Activity 9.

The Constitution requires all states to have at least one representative, so the Hill method begins by assigning one seat to each state. After that, it assigns one seat at a time, minimizing the unfairness at each step, until all 435 seats are assigned.

1. To illustrate the Hill method, examine a simpler problem of four states, A, B, C, and D with populations

$$P_A = 11,950 \quad P_B = 8100 \quad P_C = 4620 \quad P_D = 3660$$

Suppose the Hill apportionment has just started and each state has been given one seat. Then a decision must be made as to which state gets the next seat, and which state gets the seat after that, and the seat after that.

The Hill Method

FYI

Joseph A. Hill was a statistician for the U.S. Census Bureau, and in 1911, he and Edward V. Huntington, Harvard mathematics professor, proposed a method of apportionment now known as the Hill (or Hill-Huntington) method of apportionment. This method has been used to apportion the House of Representatives since 1941. The Hill method is a divisor method of apportionment that rounds according to the geometric mean. If a quota (q) is between two integers s and s + 1, it is rounded up when q is greater than or equal to the geometric mean of s and s + 1; it is rounded down when q is less than the geometric mean.

ACTIVITY

THE HILL METHOD

10

In order to carry out the Hill method efficiently, it helps to make a table of index values similar to the one in **Figure 2.23.**

Seats currently held	$\sqrt{s(s+1)}$	$P_A = 11{,}950$ Index: $\dfrac{P_A}{\sqrt{s(s+1)}}$	$P_B = 8100$ Index: $\dfrac{P_B}{\sqrt{s(s+1)}}$	$P_C = 4620$ Index: $\dfrac{P_C}{\sqrt{s(s+1)}}$	$P_D = 3660$ Index: $\dfrac{P_D}{\sqrt{s(s+1)}}$
1	$\sqrt{1 \times 2}$	8449.93	5727.56	3266.83	2588.01
2	$\sqrt{2 \times 3}$	4878.57	3306.81	1886.11	1494.19
3	$\sqrt{3 \times 4}$	3449.67	2338.27	1333.68	1056.55

Figure 2.23.
Index values for Hill apportionment.

Figure 2.23 shows unfairness index values, $P_s / \sqrt{s(s+1)}$, for each state. In the first row, each state *already* has one seat so $s = 1$ and each population is divided by $\sqrt{1 \times 2} = \sqrt{2}$. In the second row, $s = 2$ and each population is divided by, $\sqrt{2 \times 3} = \sqrt{6}$. In the third row, each population is divided by $\sqrt{3 \times 4} = \sqrt{12}$.

a) Assuming each state has just been given one seat, use this figure to determine how the Hill method would assign the next six seats. (Thus, a total of 10 seats will have been apportioned.)

b) Extend the table using a spreadsheet program or a calculator table and determine how the next ten seats would be assigned by the Hill method (for a total of 20 seats).

Recall the divisor methods you encountered in Lesson 4. In each one, you divide each state's population by the ideal divisor (ideal district size). Then you round each adjusted quota in some specified manner and give each state that many seats. If too many (or not enough) seats have been allocated, you adjust the divisors until the sum of the rounded adjusted quotas equals the required number of seats.

THE HILL METHOD

The Hill method can also be viewed as a divisor method. However, it rounds off quotas in an unusual way.

For example, a quota q between 6 and 7 is rounded down to 6 if $q < \sqrt{6 \times 7} = \sqrt{42} \approx 6.481$ and rounded up to 7 if $q \geq \sqrt{42}$. In general, a quota q between an integer s and the next integer $s + 1$ is rounded down to s if $q < \sqrt{s(s+1)}$ and q is rounded up to $s + 1$ if $q \geq \sqrt{s(s+1)}$.

Here's how this applies to Item 1. There were four states—A, B, C, and D—with respective populations

$$P_A = 11{,}950 \quad P_B = 8100 \quad P_C = 4620 \quad P_D = 3660.$$

Each state starts with one seat. In order to earn a second seat, a state will need a quota $\geq \sqrt{1 \times 2} \approx 1.414$. Start with a divisor, x, slightly smaller than 11,950. This value was chosen because a divisor of 11,950 will assign only one seat to the state with the largest population. Make sure you don't start with a divisor that is too small because it could cause more than one seat to be allocated.

Gradually lower the divisor until some state has an adjusted quota $\geq \sqrt{2}$. Then round that quota up to 2 and award that state its second seat.

2. a) What is the largest value of your divisor x when that happens? Which of the four states gets the seat?

   b) Next, lower the divisor until another seat is assigned. (Remember: the state that won the last seat now has two seats and so will need an adjusted quota of at least $\sqrt{2 \times 3} = \sqrt{6} \approx 2.449$ before it gets another seat. The other states have one seat, so they will need an adjusted quota of at least $\sqrt{2} \approx 1.414$. Which state gets the next seat? For what divisor does this happen?

THE HILL METHOD

c) Repeat the process to determine which state wins the next seat. For what divisor does this happen? (Remember: if the same state got both of the last two seats, then that state would now have three seats, so it would need an adjusted quota of at least $\sqrt{3 \times 4} = \sqrt{12} \approx 3.464$ to earn the next seat.)

d) Compare the divisors that appeared in assigning these three seats with the table of indices you created in Item 1. Explain how the process of assigning seats using that table agrees with the method of lowering divisors and rounding off according to $\sqrt{(s(s+1))}$.

THE WEBSTER METHOD REVISITED

In Activity 10, you developed the Hill method from a measure of unfairness, then showed that it could also be obtained as a divisor method. Now look at the Webster method from the point of view of unfairness. It works very much like the Hill method except that it uses a different measure of unfairness.

Webster considers the number of seats per person in each state, that is, s/P_S. If state A has more seats per person than state B does, that is unfair to B. Webster measures the unfairness to B by the difference $1/N_A - 1/N_B$, or $\dfrac{a}{P_A} - \dfrac{b}{P_B}$.

Now suppose that A has a seats and B has b seats and one more seat is to be assigned. Just as in the Hill method, the question arises: is it less unfair to give the seat to A or to B?

Once again, if an extra seat needs to be allocated, it is assigned to A if:

$$\begin{matrix} \text{unfairness to } A \\ \text{(if next seat goes to } B\text{)} \end{matrix} \quad > \quad \begin{matrix} \text{unfairness to } B \\ \text{(if next seat goes to } A\text{)} \end{matrix}$$

1. Rewrite this inequality in terms of P_A, P_B, a, and b. Separate your variables by state. Then find a single index in terms of any state S that could be used to determine the order in which seats are given away in a Webster apportionment.

2. Return to the example of the four states A, B, C, and D with respective populations

$$P_A = 11{,}950 \quad P_B = 8100 \quad P_C = 4620 \quad P_D = 3660$$

Assume each state has been given its initial seat. Make a table similar to the one you made for the Hill method. This time use the index that you found in Item 1 and assign the 20 seats according to the Webster method. A spreadsheet or calculator table may prove helpful.

INDIVIDUAL WORK 9

Two Means

1. In the Hill and Webster methods, unfairness is related to the numbers $P_S/\sqrt{s(s+1)}$ and $P_S/(s + 1/2)$, respectively. Compare the values of $\sqrt{s(s+1)}$ and $s + 1/2$ for $s = 1, 2, 3, 5, 10,$ and 20. Which is larger? What happens as s gets larger?

2. Check that $\sqrt{s(s+1)}$ is always less than $s + 1/2$ by squaring the two formulas and comparing the results.

3. The **geometric mean** of two positive numbers is the square root of their product. For two positive numbers a and b, their geometric mean is $\sqrt{ab}$ and their arithmetic mean (average) is $(a + b)/2$. Verify the statement $ab = \left(\dfrac{a+b}{2}\right)^2 - \left(\dfrac{a-b}{2}\right)^2$.

   How does it follow that the geometric mean is less than or equal to the arithmetic mean? When can they be equal? This general result is known as the Arithmetic Mean - Geometric Mean inequality, or AM-GM inequality for short.

4. Use the AM-GM inequality to show that $\sqrt{s(s+1)} < s + 1/2$ for all positive values of s.

5. If the perimeter of a rectangle is 100 ft., use the AM-GM inequality to explain why its area is at most $25^2 = 625$ ft.^{2}. Can its area be exactly 625 ft.^{2}? If so, what are the dimensions of the rectangle for which this occurs? If not, why not? In general, for a given perimeter, what rectangle has the largest area?

6. A school has four computer rooms. Room A has space for 21 students, room B has room for 16, room C for 13, and room D for 10. Each room now has one computer. Using the Hill method, how should ten more computers be apportioned among the rooms? 15 more? 20 more? How many computers must be assigned before D gets its fourth computer?

7. Answer Item 6 using the Webster method. Compare the apportionments with those given by the Hill method.

8. (For those who used spreadsheets or calculator tables to answer Items 6 and 7.) How could you tell in advance that the numbers in these spreadsheets, especially in the lower rows, would be similar? Check your spreadsheets to see that this is so.

Wrapping Up Unit Two

1. When Alan, Beth, and Cathy were told it was their responsibility to divide up the remaining items and $2,500 in cash from their grandparents' estate, they decided to use the Estate-Division Algorithm from Lesson 1. Their sealed bids are given in **Figure 2.24.**

	Alan	Beth	Cathy
Handmade quilt	300	500	200
Antique dresser	800	1200	1000
Riding lawn mower	50	250	490
Canoe	700	500	750

Figure 2.24.
Estate bids.

Determine a fair distribution of the estate.

2. How does the distribution of items and cash change in Question 1 if Cathy decides she wants all of the items and tries to outbid everyone else with bids of $700, $1500, $500, and $1000 for the quilt, dresser, lawn mower, and canoe respectively?

3. When asked about dividing items in an estate settlement, a family lawyer gave this advice: "Each party should prepare a list of items he or she wants, compare lists, and determine the items both want. Then a coin should be tossed with the winner taking first pick of the items wanted by both. The coin toss loser gets second pick. This process is continued until all items are given away."

   Keeping in mind criteria for judging fairness, is this a fair method? Why or why not?

4. As in many families, the Wallace children receive a weekly allowance. In 1991, when the three children were ages 5, 7, and 10, their mother apportioned $22 among them according to their ages.

   a) If the mother based her apportionment of the allowance on ages, and she only had one-dollar bills to give the children, how much would each child receive? Explain your reasoning.

   b) In 1993, two years later, the total amount of the allowance had not increased. Making the same assumptions as in Item 4(a), use the Hamilton method to reapportion the allowances.

c) Keeping in mind the 1991 apportionment, would your 1993 apportionment seem fair to all three children? Why or why not?

5. Create an apportionment problem in which a certain number of pieces of hard candy must be divided among a given number of children based on some criteria other than age. Your problem should involve at least 4 children and the quotas (amount of candy/child) should not be integers. Make sure you show a solution to your problem.

6. Last year Savannah High School had 100 free Six Flags Theme Park tickets to give away to its students. To allot the tickets fairly, the student council decided to give each grade level a portion of the tickets and allow the class officers in that grade to give them away. **Figure 2.25** shows the respective class sizes.

a) Use **Figure 2.26** and the Hamilton method to assign tickets to each class.

Figure 2.25.
Number of students per class.

Class	Sophomore	Junior	Senior
Number in class	583	222	95

Figure 2.26.
Tickets assigned to each class last year.

Class	Sophomore	Junior	Senior
Quota			
Number of tickets			

b) Later in the year, the high school was again given 100 free tickets. Since the first method of assigning tickets worked well, the student council decided to use it again. Find the assignments for these tickets. See **Figure 2.27**.

Figure 2.27.
Tickets assigned to each class this year.

Class	Sophomore	Junior	Senior
Number in class	584	230	94
Quota			
Number of ticket			

c) After comparing the results of this latest apportionment with the earlier one, the sophomores complained. Why did the sophomores protest? What do you think the seniors thought about this latest distribution?

7. In the August 10, 1997, issue of *Parade Magazine*, a reader wrote to the "Ask Marilyn" column with the following question:

My roommate and I pay a total of $850 per month for rent. The two bedrooms in the apartment are of significantly different quality, so we decided that the one who has the nicer bedroom should pay more. We decided that my roommate would pay $450, and I would pay $400. However, she has become unhappy with this arrangement recently. She feels she is paying $50 per month more, and this is too much. My argument is that she is only paying $25 per month more than if we each paid half the rent: $425. In the same way, I am only paying $25 per month less. What view do you think more accurately describes the situation?

Write your response to the reader.

8. A six-region area of the Midwest has an educational consortium with 450 representatives. **Figure 2.28** shows the population of each of the regions.

a) Show that the Hamilton, Jefferson, Webster, and Adams methods produce different apportionments.

b) Which apportionment do you think is the fairest? Explain why.

c) Do any of the methods violate quota?

9. Devise an apportionment problem in which at least two of the four apportionment methods (Hamilton, Jefferson, Adams, and Webster) yield different results. (Use at least five different populations.)

Region	Population
A	2,636,800
B	9,228,800
C	243,200
D	3,312,800
E	948,000
F	1,630,400
Total population	18,000,000

Figure 2.28.
Populations for regions A–F.

10. The result of the first census of the United States (1790) taken after the adoption of the U.S. Constitution is shown in **Figure 2.29.** The number of seats in the House of Representatives was set at 105.

State	Population
Connecticut	236,841
Delaware	55,540
Georgia	70,835
Kentucky	68,705
Maryland	278,514
Massachusetts	475,327
New Hampshire	141,822
New Jersey	179,570
New York	331,589
North Carolina	353,523
Pennsylvania	432,879
Rhode Island	68,446
South Carolina	206,236
Vermont	85,533
Virginia	630,560
Total	3,615,920

Figure 2.29.
State populations in 1790.

a) Use the Jefferson method to find the apportionment for the first U.S. House of Representatives.

b) If President Washington had not vetoed the bill to use the Hamilton Method, what apportionment would have resulted?

c) Compare the two apportionments. Which state(s) do you think preferred the Jefferson method? the Hamilton method?

11. **Figure 2.30** shows four states, their populations based on the 1990 Census, and the number of representatives they each received in the 1991 apportionment of Congress.

State	Apportionment population	Size of state delegation
California	29,839,250	52
Missouri	5,137,804	9
North Dakota	641,364	1
Washington	4,887,941	9

Figure 2.30.
Populations and number of representatives for four states.

Of these four states, which state do you think is most happy with the apportionment? Which would be the least happy? Explain your reasoning.

12. In the 1991 apportionment of the Congress, Iowa had a population of 2,787,424 and was given 5 representatives. Nebraska's population was 1,584,617 and was given 3 representatives.

   a) What was the average district size of each state? Which state had the worse deal?

   b) What was the relative difference in the district size?

   c) Suppose one of Nebraska's 3 seats was given to Iowa. What would be the relative difference in the district size then?

   d) Should Nebraska give up a seat to Iowa? Why or why not?

13. Another way to think about the geometric mean is to think about it geometrically. To do so, sketch a rectangle whose sides are lengths of A and B. Thus its area is AB. Then sketch a square whose side is S. Its area is S^2. If the area of the rectangle is equal in measure to the area of the square, then S is said to be the geometric mean of A and B.

   a) Sketch a rectangle with dimensions 2 and 8. What would be the length of the side of the square whose area is equal in measure to the rectangle's area?

   b) Sketch a rectangle of width s and length $s + 1$. Find the length of the side of the square whose area is equal in measure to that of the rectangle.

14. A state has five major highways of varying lengths: Route *A*, 335 miles; Route *B*, 277 miles; Route *C*, 210 miles; Route *D*, 154 miles; and Route *E*, 95 miles. These highways are patrolled by state police cars: Route *A* by seven cars, Route *B* by five cars 5, Route *C* by four cars, Route *D* by two cars, and Route *E* by two cars. The state is planning to add eight more cars to its highway patrol. Assign the new cars using the Hill method of apportionment.

15. Suppose you make a table like the one you made for the Webster method except that you use P_S/s instead of $P_S/(s + 1/2)$. What apportionment method would result?

Mathematical Summary

This unit focuses on fairness. Fairness is an issue whenever anyone wishes to divide objects or groups of objects among several people.

Dividing estates among heirs is one such situation. If the estate is being divided equally among n heirs, all heirs want at least $1/n$th of the estate. In reality, however, individual heirs are often dissatisfied with their share of the estate. Heirs often feel that they don't receive their fair share. Individuals sometimes value things differently. Items often are not divisible and can't be sold. Some people simply do not want particular items. And the list goes on.

A second fair division situation is the problem of dividing identical things that cannot be split up, like computers or seats in Congress. Solving that apportionment problem involves adjusting non-integer quotas (ideal shares) to form integer shares in some fair manner.

One apportionment scheme, known as the Hamilton method, rounds all quotas (ideal shares) down. When the adjusted shares add up to fewer objects than what is to be allocated, the remaining objects are assigned to people, schools, or states whose quotas have the largest fractional parts. This method is simple and easy to use, but as you have seen, it is flawed.

As you searched for fairer methods, you discovered a group of methods known as divisor methods. All divisor schemes are similar in their initial approach to the problem. If the goal is to apportion representatives in a governmental body, begin by dividing the total constituent population by the total number of seats. This gives the ideal ratio (divisor). Quotas are then calculated by dividing state populations by the ideal ratio. The quotas are then rounded up or down according to the rounding method specified by the particular apportionment method being used. **Figure 2.31** summarizes standard rounding methods and their associated apportionment type.

Apportionment type	Rounding method
Jefferson	Rounds down, dropping all fractional parts
Webster	Rounds up when the fractional parts are 0.5 or greater; rounds down when fractional parts are less than 0.5.
Adams	Rounds all fractions up to the next integer.
Hill	Rounds up when the fractional parts are greater than or equal to the geometric mean of the two integers between which the quota lies. Otherwise, it rounds down.

Figure 2.31.
Summary of rounding methods.

After the rounding process is complete, the total of the rounded quotas is examined. If the total is too large, the divisor must be adjusted upward to decrease the total number of seats. If the total is too small, the divisor must be adjusted downward. The adjustment of the divisor continues until the total of the rounded quotas is the desired number of seats.

For each divisor, x, there is a corresponding number of seats allocated. This defines a function, P_S/x, for each state, and permits both graphical and tabular implementation of divisor methods. Again, however, divisor methods are fairly easy to use, but they also have flaws.

In your final attempt to find a flawless method, you derived models by minimizing measures of unfairness. These schemes, including the Hill method, turn out to be just other ways to define divisor methods. Thus, they have the same flaws as the others.

In the final analysis, no method is without flaws. The key is to use mathematics to try to find the method(s) that produce the fairest results for the populations with which you are working.

Glossary

ACTUAL SHARE:
The amount or number of items one gets as a result of an apportionment.

ADAMS METHOD:
A divisor method that rounds all fractions up to the next integer.

ALABAMA PARADOX:
An unexpected situation that occurs when the size of a legislative body increases and an individual state loses a seat even though there are no population changes in any of the states.

APPORTIONMENT:
The parceling out of a number of objects among several entities.

DISTRICT SIZE (U.S. HOUSE OF REPRESENTATIVES):
The average number of people in a state who are represented by one representative in the House. It is equal to the state population divided by the number of representatives for that state.

DIVISOR METHOD:
A method of apportionment that determines quotas by dividing the populations by an ideal ratio or an adjusted ratio, then applying a specified rounding rule.

ESTATE:
Everything of value that a person possesses at the time of his or her death.

ESTATE-DIVISION ALGORITHM:
A step-by-step procedure for distributing an estate among several heirs.

GEOMETRIC MEAN:
The geometric mean of two positive numbers is the square root of their product.

HAMILTON METHOD:
A method of apportioning identical objects when the quotas are not whole numbers. Each person is first given the integer part of his or her quota. The remaining objects are given (in order) to the persons whose quotas have the largest fractional parts.

HEIR:
One who inherits all or part of the estate of a person who has died.

HILL METHOD:
A divisor method of apportionment that rounds according to the geometric mean. If a quota (q) is between two integers s and $s + 1$, it is rounded up when q is greater than or equal to the geometric mean of s and $s + 1$ and down when q is less than the geometric mean.

IDEAL SHARE:
The exact amount or number of items a person should receive as a result of an apportionment.

INDEX:
A quantity, computed for each state, that determines a state's eligibility for the next seat to be allocated. An index for a state depends only on that state's data and the measure of unfairness being used.

JEFFERSON METHOD:
A divisor method of apportionment that rounds by dropping all fractional parts of the quota.

PARADOX:
An occurrence in a situation that runs counter, or against, a person's intuition.

POPULATION PARADOX:
An unexpected situation in which a state with a population gain loses a seat to a state with a population loss, even though there is no change in the size of the legislative body.

QUOTA:
An ideal fair share in an apportionment.

VIOLATION OF QUOTA:
An apportionment method is said to violate quota if a state is given a number of seats that is not equal to the integer part of its quota or 1 more than that.

WEBSTER METHOD:
A divisor method of apportionment that rounds up quotas when the fractional parts are 0.5 or greater and rounds them down when the fractional parts are less than 0.5.

WILL:
A legal document stating how a person wishes his or her estate to be disposed of after his or her death.

Glossary of Notation

P = total population of all states

H = total number of seats (House size)

I = ideal district size (= P/H)

P_S = population of state S

q_s = quota for state S (= P_S/I)

s = number of seats for state S

N_S = district size for state S (= P_S/s)

UNIT

3

Sampling

In this unit, you will design and administer a sample survey and then analyze the results. In the process, you will consider several methods used to obtain a sample. Also, you will learn how data from a sample can be used to provide information about the population from which the sample was taken. You will adapt these techniques to the problem of estimating the size of a wildlife population using mark-recapture methods.

Percentages, reference distributions, confidence intervals, proportional reasoning, and graphical representations of data are useful tools in your analyses of survey and mark-recapture data.

CRYING WOLF

Wolves used to roam the Great Northern Woods, but settlers saw them as a threat. Paying bounty hunters for dead wolves was common practice on and off from 1630. By 1960, the gray wolf, also called the timber wolf, was virtually eliminated in America; Minnesota had the only breeding population. Michigan gray wolves were not given protection until the passage of the Federal Endangered Species Act of 1973.

In the early 1980's, the Michigan Department of Natural Resources began monitoring the wolves after tracks were discovered. In 1992, the Department appointed a wolf recovery team. Their plan included monitoring the number of wolves, as well as the wolf-prey population, in Michigan, Minnesota, and Wisconsin. Also, because humans were the primary threat to wolves, the team designed a survey to monitor public opinion on wolf restoration in Michigan.

In this unit, you will design and conduct a sample survey to discover students' opinion on many topics. Also, you will analyze mark-recapture data to estimate the size of an animal population.

LESSON ONE
It's All in the Question

KEY CONCEPTS

Questionnaire design

Bias

The Image Bank

PREPARATION READING

Crying Wolf

A 1990 survey of Michigan residents found considerable support for restoring the wolf population in the Upper Peninsula. Study data were obtained through surveys mailed to a random sample of 300 Upper Peninsula and 300 Lower Peninsula residents, and to special samples of 150 Michigan deer hunters, 150 trappers, and 150 farmers. Most respondents cited the wolf's existence and ecological values as reasons for wanting to restore wolves. The deer hunters were found to be the most supportive of the wolf's restoration and the farmers the most apprehensive.

Upper peninsula

Michigan

Lower peninsula

Although a majority of the respondents supported restoration of the resident wolf population, they did not support a program in which wolves from other states were captured and released in Michigan. Most groups agreed that if the wolf population were re-established in Michigan, government officials should do all they could to keep the wolves from being killed or mistreated. On the other hand, all the sample groups supported limiting the number of wolves in the Upper Peninsula if they became too numerous.

CONSIDER:

1. Why do you think each of the five different groups was targeted to receive surveys?

2. How do you think wildlife managers might estimate the size of a wolf population?

ACTIVITY

1

QUESTIONABLE QUESTIONING

Was the Michigan survey described in the preparation reading a reliable survey? The answer to this question depends on many factors, including the wording and ordering of the survey questions. Consider, for example, the questions in **Figure 3.1,** which appeared as part of a national Harris poll conducted in February of 1995.

Please circle your answer to each of the following questions.

Q1. Do you think the government should be doing more or less than it does now to protect and restore endangered species such as salmon and wolves?

 Doing more   Doing Less   Doing about what we are now   Not sure

Q2. How willing would you be to pay somewhat higher taxes to the government if you knew the money would be spent to protect and restore endangered species such as the salmon or the wolves?

 Very willing   Somewhat willing   Not very willing   Not willing at all   Not sure

Q3. How willing would you be to spend $5 more per month for electricity or 5 cents per pound of potatoes if you knew that this money would be spent to protect and restore endangered species such as the salmon or the wolves?

 Very willing   Somewhat willing   Not very willing   Not willing at all   Not sure

---

Figure 3.1.
Survey questions related to endangered species.

CONSIDER:

1. Do you think a higher percentage of people would respond "Doing more" to Q1 or "Very willing" to Q2? State reasons for your answer.

2. Suppose the order of the questions was changed, with Q1 interchanged with Q3. Do you think this change in question ordering would affect people's responses? If so, how?

ACTIVITY

QUESTIONABLE QUESTIONING

1

To obtain reliable information, pollsters must be very careful how they word their questions and how they structure their questionnaires. Otherwise, the survey results may give a very misleading picture of how the respondents feel about the issues being surveyed. In addition, pollsters can, if they so choose, manipulate the responses on a survey.

At the end of this lesson, you will design a questionnaire to collect information on topics of interest to you. (You may or may not want to include questions soliciting student opinions on endangered species in your state.) But before you design your questionnaire, you need to be aware of some pitfalls that could slant your results. In the Consider questions, for example, you no doubt decided that changing the order of the questions would influence people's responses. When you write your survey questions, you'll have to consider how each of the following might influence responses:

- the order of your questions

- the wording of questions

- the order of wording within questions

- background information provided with questions.

Sometimes, as illustrated by Items 1 and 2 of Activity 1, the order of the questions (in particular, the addition of preface questions) or the order of wording within questions can be used to manipulate people's responses. Sometimes the effects of ordering can be subtle and, at other times, blatantly manipulative. Consider, for example, the survey questions in **Figure 3.2.**

ACTIVITY

1

QUESTIONABLE QUESTIONING

Q4. Are there more television programs now that include too much violence and brutality?

    Yes   No

Q5. Should big advertisers demand higher standards of program quality?

    Yes   No

Q6. Should networks be required to provide educational programs for children?

    Yes   No

Q7. Should federal funding for public TV be increased, remain the same, or be cut?

    Increased   Remain the same   Cut

Figure 3.2.
Survey questions related to support for public television.

1. Survey Q4–Q7 are based on a poll commissioned by the Public Broadcasting Service in response to a threat from Congress in 1995 to cut or eliminate federal funding for public broadcasting.

   a) What effect do you think including Q4–Q6 had on the responses to Q7?

   b) Do you think the Public Broadcasting Service intended to manipulate public opinion with this poll? Why or why not?

   In the actual Public Broadcasting Service survey, the question on funding was preceded by 19 questions, some of which were worded to illustrate deficiencies in commercial broadcasting. The result was that 49% of the respondents favored an increase in funding for public television, 35% favored funding at the current level, and only 16% voted for cutting. However, a Los Angeles Times poll taken earlier in the same year found that 63% of respondents favored cutting federal spending for public television and radio. This highlights the fact that the Public Broadcasting Service was successful in designing a sequence of questions that triggered the survey responses they wanted to hear.

ACTIVITY

QUESTIONABLE QUESTIONING

1

2. The order in which comparisons are made can affect people's responses. Consider, for example, the questions in **Figure 3.3.**

Q8. Does this country have health care problems or a health care crisis?

   Problems   Crisis

Q9. Does this country have a health care crisis or health care problems?

   Crisis   Problems

Q10. Which is more exciting:

   Tennis   Soccer

Q11. Which is more exciting:

   Soccer   Tennis

Figure 3.3.
Survey questions related to health care and sports.

a) What is the difference between Q8 and Q9? How do you think this difference might affect the responses?

b) How do you think the difference in the order of response choices in Q10 and Q11 might affect the responses?

c) When Q8 was given to one group of people and Q9 was given to another group, 55% of those answering Q8 responded Crisis, and 61% of those answering Q9 circled Problems. Similarly, when question Q10 was given to one group and Q11 was given to another group, 65% of those answering Q10 selected Soccer and 77% of those answering Q11 responded Tennis. What do these results suggest about the order of response choices?

d) Suppose you were in charge of television programming and wanted to conduct a survey to ascertain viewers' preferences for tennis versus soccer. What would you do to assure that the responses to your questionnaire were not due to the ordering of the response choices?

ACTIVITY

QUESTIONABLE QUESTIONING

1

3. One thousand and thirty-one people responded to a *Reader's Digest* survey that included both questions in **Figure 3.4.**

Figure 3.4.
Survey questions related to support for public television.

> Q12. I would be disappointed if Congress cut its funding for public televi-sion.
>
>   Yes   No   No Opinion
>
> Q13. Cuts in funding for public television are justified as part of an overall effort to reduce federal spending.
>
>   Yes   No   No Opinion

Responses

Question	Yes	No	No opinion
Q 12	54%	40%	6%
Q 13	52%	37%	10%

Figure 3.5.
Responses to Q12 and Q13 by the same 1031 people.

a) How do you think the wording of the questions might have influenced the responses?

b) **Figure 3.5** displays the actual responses to Q12 and Q13. Draw a graphical display that would be useful in comparing the responses to these two questions. Interpret the information contained in your display. How did the wording of the questions affect the responses?

4. You can influence responses by writing a question slanted toward a particular viewpoint. Which of the questions in **Figure 3.6** is slanted toward a particular viewpoint?

Figure 3.6.
Survey questions related to capital punishment.

> Q14. Do you favor the use of capital punishment?
>
>   Yes   No
>
> Q15. Do you favor or oppose the use of capital punishment?
>
>   Favor   Oppose

Sometimes the information you choose to include or exclude from a question can influence the responses. Deciding what background infor-mation to include with a question can be tricky. Sometimes the back-ground information is necessary for the respondent to make an informed choice. Other times, the background information adds **bias**, or a slanted

ACTIVITY

QUESTIONABLE QUESTIONING

1

point of view, to the content of the question because it influences the results by suggesting how the respondent should answer. Items 5 and 6 illustrate one method of manipulating responses.

5. In the fall of 1995, President Clinton announced that he would be sending troops to Bosnia. A Gallup survey reported that Americans approved sending the troops to Bosnia by 46 to 40 percent. However, a CBS/*New York Times* poll got the opposite reaction—a 58 to 33 percent disapproval rate. The only difference between the questions asked by these two polling organizations was that one of them reported 20,000 American troops would be going to Bosnia.

   a) Which poll mentioned the number of troops? How do you know?

   b) Was the background information that 20,000 American troops would be sent to Bosnia intended to manipulate the responses or to help the respondents make informed choices?

6. A survey appearing in *Parade* magazine (see **Figure 3.7**) asked readers to send in their responses. The survey questions began as follows:

Many defense attorneys, Judge Rothwax says, would answer Yes to the following questions. What do you think?

Q16. A defense attorney knows that a witness for the prosecution is telling the truth—but he tries to destroy the witness' credibility. Is this okay?

     Yes   No

Q17. A defense attorney knows that his witness will commit perjury—but still puts him on the witness stand. Is this okay?

     Yes   No

Q18. A defense attorney gives his client legal advice knowing it will tempt him to lie on the witness stand. Is this okay?

     Yes   No

Figure 3.7.
Survey questions from *Parade* magazine (July 26, 1996), survey.

QUESTIONABLE QUESTIONING

What effect do you think the preface at the beginning of the survey will have on respondent's answers? What about the question: Is that okay?

7. For each of the questions below, decide whether the background information helps the respondent make an informed choice or introduces bias and influences the respondent by suggesting the desired answer. Reword questions that bias responses toward particular answers so the reworded questions are neutral.

   a) More people have attended the movie *Gone with the Wind* than any other motion picture produced this century. Have you seen this movie?

   b) Students at Pattonville High School are required to do 50 community service hours to graduate. Do you think this is a reasonable requirement? Yes or No.

   c) Pattonville High School sells candy during lunch periods, yet they turn off the soda machines during this time because soda is unhealthy. Do you think students at Pattonville High School should be able to buy soda during lunch periods? Yes or No.

8. Create a question or sequence of questions that could increase the chances of a response in a certain direction and, thus, bias the results of the survey.

FRANK AND ERNEST reprinted by permission of Newspaper Enterprise Association, Inc.

INDIVIDUAL WORK 1

Ask So You'll Get What You Want

One means of manipulating responses to survey questions is to use emotionally-loaded terms. For example, you are more likely to get positive responses by using positively-loaded terms such as honesty, justice, and freedom. You are more likely to evoke negative responses by using negatively-loaded terms such as bureaucrats, boss, and (big) government.

1. When a survey asked if respondents supported welfare, a majority said No. However, when asked if they supported assistance to the poor, a majority said Yes. What accounts for the different response rates to these two questions?

2. Consider the questions in **Figure 3.8**. Do you think that either of these questions is designed to elicit a particular response? If so, explain how.

Q1. Do you think that smokers should have the freedom to smoke at their place of work?

     Yes   No

Q2. Given the recent reports on the dangers of second-hand smoke, do you think that companies should allow their employees to smoke in the workplace?

     Yes   No

Figure 3.8.
Survey questions related to smoking in the workplace.

3. Make up a survey question or series of questions that includes one or more emotionally-charged term designed to bias responses toward a particular viewpoint.

In addition to being influenced by charged words, if a question is objectionable, too personal, or too sensitive, respondents may refuse to answer it or may give a dishonest answer. In either case, these reactions on the part of the respondents will bias the survey results. A good way to judge whether your question is objectionable, too personal, or too sensitive is to ask yourself whether you would have responded to it honestly or not. For example, some of the students in your school may refuse to answer honestly the question: Have you ever skipped school even if you were not sick?, particularly if they think that teachers might see their answers. Instead you might ask: How do you feel about students who skip school when they aren't sick? Although this question will not provide the same information as the first question, you will still learn something about student opinions on skipping school and, more importantly, students would be more likely to answer this question more honestly than the first question.

4. Write a question you think is objectionable, too personal, or too sensitive for many students to answer honestly. Then reword your question so students would be more likely to answer honestly and you could still learn some information about student opinions on that topic.

Sometimes you can get respondents to answer sensitive questions honestly by deliberately loading the question. For example, you might load a question by adding information designed to make a respondent feel more comfortable giving an honest but socially unacceptable response.

5. Explain how the question in **Figure 3.9** has been loaded and how that might affect students' willingness to answer the question honestly.

Figure 3.9.
Loaded survey question.

> Q3. *You are not alone.* Many well-known, greatly-admired individuals have admitted that they once cheated on a school exam. In the past school year, have you ever cheated on a test or quiz?
>
>   Yes   No

6. In designing survey questions, you should take care to avoid **two-edged questions**—questions that contain two competing ideas. Look back at Item 3 in Activity 1. Q13 in Figure 3.4 is an example of a two-edged question.

   a) What are the two competing ideas contained in Q13?

   b) How do you think the inclusion of the second idea (the one near the end of the sentence) might affect the responses? Do you think the results from this survey question will provide a representative view of public attitudes toward each of these ideas? Explain.

7. In Activity 2, your class will develop a seven-question survey. Begin this process by preparing one question that might be included on the questionnaire. What would you like to know about student opinions in your school? Write a survey question that you could use to gather this information. Keep in mind what you have learned in Activity 1 and in this assignment when writing your question.

ACTIVITY

WHAT DO YOU WANT TO KNOW?

2

The 1990 wolf restoration survey of Michigan residents found the opinions of Upper Peninsula residents differed somewhat from the opinions of Lower Peninsula residents and, on some questions, hunters' responses differed significantly from farmers' responses.

Judge Orders Relocated Wolves Removed

December, 1997: Federal Judge William Downes ruled that the U.S. Interior Department's Gray Wolf Reintroduction Program is illegal and ordered the removal of the dozens of wolves that had been brought from Canada and relocated in Idaho and Yellowstone National Park since 1995. The "experimental population" designation given to the relocated wolves makes it technically easier for ranchers to shoot them if they attack livestock. The judge ruled that this actually reduces protection for other wolves native to the area; those wolves are fully protected under the Endangered Species Act. Although ranchers are happy about the decision, environmental groups and the federal government plan to appeal the decision.

Similarly, students from different schools may share certain opinions, habits, or preferences, and differ on others. Male students may have differing views from female students, or grade 10 students may disagree with grade 12 students. In this activity, your group will begin the process of designing a questionnaire to collect data about the views of students in different grade levels and, if possible, of students from another school. In later lessons, you will collect and analyze data from your class questionnaire and write a report describing your findings.

In Activity 1 and Individual Work 1, you examined some of the methods disreputable pollsters use to manipulate responses. In the survey you design, however, the aim is to gather information that is representative of the group you are surveying.

ACTIVITY

2

WHAT DO YOU WANT TO KNOW?

Checklist of Survey Items

(1) Are any words in the question difficult to understand? (When possible, use smaller, more common words.) Does the question contain a negative?

(2) Is the question ambiguous or vague?

(3) Does the question suggest how the respondent should answer? Does it include emotionally-loaded terms that might slant the responses toward a particular outcome?

(4) Is the question a two-edged question? Does it contain more than one idea?

(5) Is the question objectionable? too personal? too sensitive?

(6) Does the question assume too much knowledge?

Before you begin writing questions, here is a checklist of items to consider when evaluating survey questions.

If, in evaluating a question, you would respond yes to any of the items in the Checklist, then you should revise the question. Items 1–3 below will give you some practice applying the checklist information to a specific survey question.

1. For each of the pairs below, decide which word would be better to use in a survey question. Explain why you chose that word

   a) Help or assist?

   b) Purchase or buy?

2. Each of the survey questions in **Figure 3.10** is flawed. Discuss what is wrong with each of these questions.

> Q5. Do you agree or disagree with your governor's stand on wolf restoration?
>
> Q6. Do you agree or disagree: We should not reduce federal funding for public television.
>
> Q7. Do you favor or oppose the reduction of the U.S. military budget in order to increase spending on domestic programs such as welfare?

Figure 3.10.
Three survey questions.

3. Which question in **Figure 3.11** is less vague? Explain.

> Q3. How many older people live in your neighborhood?
>
> Q4. How many people over 65 live on this block?

Figure 3.11.
Survey questions related to age.

Now, you are ready to begin the process of designing a survey.

4. a) In your group, discuss what you would like to know about students in your school (for example, their study habits, personal tastes, opinions on some topic, and so forth).

WHAT DO YOU WANT TO KNOW?

b) Then create a set of seven questions designed to gather information on the topics you have discussed. There are three restrictions:

(1) Your questions must have Yes or No responses (or responses that can be translated into Yes or No at the time of analysis).

For example, responses to the question:

Do you favor or oppose the use of capital punishment? Favor or Oppose

can be converted to Yes-No responses by identifying Favor with Yes and Oppose with No.

(2) Since your questionnaire will have only seven questions, select questions about different topics. Do not create sequences of questions about the same topic.

(3) The wording and content of your questions must be appropriate for the school environment—that is, administrators, teachers, and parents would not object to them.

c) Remember, your goal is to gather reliable information, not to manipulate responses. So, apply what you have learned in Activity 1 about question wording and ordering. Check your questions against the Checklist of Survey Items at the beginning of this activity. If you answer yes to any of the items or there is a problem with wording, then revise your questions.

When you have completed the first draft of your questionnaire, record your questions on Handout H3.2, "Survey Questionnaire."

5. Get together with another group and exchange surveys. Each group's members should answer the other group's survey questions individually and record their answers on Handout H3.3, "Survey Response Form." After everyone has completed the Survey Response Form, examine the responses for

ACTIVITY

2

WHAT DO YOU WANT TO KNOW?

unexpected results. Check responses for indications that respondents interpreted the question the way your group had intended. Ask respondents how they interpreted each question and whether the meaning of each question was clear. Then discuss any problems related to question ordering or wording that might prejudice responses.

6. After discussing your questions with another group, revise your questions. Reword any ambiguous or leading questions, replace any questions that were too sensitive to get a response, and, if necessary, reorder your questions. Then record your questions neatly on Transparency T3.4 or a large sheet of paper so they can be shared with the class.

After your class has finalized the seven questions, either a group of students or your teacher will need to compose the questionnaire and make enough copies for the participants in the survey. The participants in your survey may answer the questions more carefully if you add a brief preface of one or two sentences describing the purpose of the project. In addition, for the purpose of gathering background information on the participants, include the following items on your questionnaire:

- Gender: Male   Female

- Grade: 9   10   11   12

If two schools are participating in your survey add:

- School Name: _____

In Lesson 4 you will decide on a sampling plan and administer your survey. In the meantime, you'll begin studying various techniques for analyzing and interpreting survey data of the type you will get from your survey.

INDIVIDUAL WORK 2

Survey Search

*I*n Lesson 5, you will write a report on the data you collect from your survey. When you come to that lesson, it will be useful to have several examples of reports, good as well as bad, from print media.

Collect five articles presenting the results of survey or public opinion polls reported in newspapers or magazines or posted on the Internet. Paste each article on a separate sheet of paper. Later, you will write your own comments critiquing each of the five articles and present your critiques at the end of the unit as evidence that you have learned the principles of reliable sample surveys.

LESSON TWO
Experience Counts

KEY CONCEPTS

Yes-No population

Variability due to sampling

Reference distributions

Simulation

Likely samples

Confidence interval

The Image Bank

PREPARATION READING

Point of Reference

There are many situations in daily life in which you make use of your past experience. For example, if a friend tells you that her cousin is 80 inches tall, you know from experience there are not many people taller than 6′ 8″ so either this must be an unusually tall person or else your friend has made an arithmetic error.

On the other hand, you might not be familiar with a different measurement scale. In Canada, you might hear the weather forecaster say that tomorrow's expected maximum temperature is 35° Celsius. Would you know immediately whether it was going to be hot or cold? If your experience of weather reports has been only with Fahrenheit readings, perhaps not. You would either have to live there for a while and experience the range of Celsius temperatures or do a quick conversion from 35° C to 95° F to realize you can expect a very hot day.

In this unit, most of the samples will be taken from **Yes-No populations**, populations of items that are connected to a response of either Yes or No (or to a response that can be transformed into Yes or No). For example, an 80%-Yes population would be a population in which 80% of the responses are Yes and 20% are No. A sample drawn from a Yes-No population will be referred to as a **Yes-No sample**. These are the kinds of samples you will obtain from your class survey. In fact, if you completed Supplemental Activity S3.1, you already have data from such a sample.

Suppose, when you complete your class questionnaire, you find 16 of 20 seniors surveyed answer Yes to your first question. That is an exact result for those 20 people, but what does it say about the rest of the senior class? Anything? Remember, the goal of sample surveys is to learn something, and probably about more than just the people who actually responded. So, do you think that 80% of *all* seniors would answer Yes to your first question? *About* 80%? How far might the actual proportion be from 80%? Do you think as few as 20% of the entire senior population might say Yes? If you have data from Supplemental Activity 3.1, do you think the difference between the two orderings is real, or is it just random luck? These are questions for which your experience probably has not prepared you well.

Your past experiences with numbers in particular situations allow you to refer to those experiences and decide whether a value is typical, or unusually high or low. But what do you do if the situation is outside of your experience? For example, to answer the questions above, you would need to acquire experience with the number of Yes answers in groups of 20 selected from different sets of people. You could make a record of the number of times you got different numbers of Yes responses in 20 people for a number of different groups of 20. Such data create a **distribution**—a list (or graph) of the values of a variable, together with the frequencies with which those variables occur. To answer questions like those in the previous paragraph, you would *refer* to your distribution, so the distribution is called a **reference distribution**. In the first few activities in this lesson, you will gather data to build your own reference distributions. Later in this lesson, you will interpret survey results by referring to those distributions.

ACTIVITY

3

A 50-50 PROPOSITION

In Lesson 1, you began drafting the questions for your seven-question survey. This lesson focuses on interpreting sample results from such surveys. The difficulty in interpreting sample results lies in the fact that samples are seldom perfect miniatures of the population from which they were taken.

CONSIDER:

Imagine that as part of a wolf restoration plan for your state, a survey was sent to a sample of state residents. Suppose exactly 80% of the respondents indicated they supported restoring the wolf population in your state.

1. Do the survey results indicate that exactly 80% of the people in your state support wolf restoration? Why or why not?

2. Based on the survey results, could you safely conclude that a majority of state residents support wolf restoration? Why or why not?

3. What other information about this survey would be useful in answering questions 1 and 2?

In the situation described above, the **population**—the entire collection of individuals, animals, or objects about which information is desired—consists of the state residents (or more likely, the adults residing in the state). Questionnaires were mailed to a portion of a population, or **sample,** of the residents. Consider question 1 provided information about a sample (80% of those surveyed supported wolf restoration) and then asked you to make an inference about the percentage of supporters in the entire population of residents. An **inference** is an analysis that reveals information about a population based on information obtained from a sample. Most likely, the percentage of supporters in the population is not exactly the same as in the sample.

A 50-50 PROPOSITION

Furthermore, if you surveyed a second sample of residents, the new sample percentage of wolf-restoration supporters might be somewhat different than 80%. So, what can you say about a population percentage based on a sample percentage?

You encountered a similar situation in the preparation reading with your hypothetical survey results. What can you say about the percentage of people in the population who would say Yes when you know that 16 in a sample of 20 did say Yes? Could the overall percentage of Yes be only 20%? This last question is actually easier to answer than some of the others posed in the preparation reading. In fact, if you had experience with a real 20%-Yes population, you could say quite quickly whether you thought getting a 16-of-20 sample might be likely from such a population.

More generally, what does an 80% sample percentage tell you about a population percentage? Reference distributions created by examining samples from various *known* populations can help you answer this question.

1. John tossed a coin 10 times and got 80% heads. A fair coin toss should result in 50% heads in the long run. John's results are not 50% heads, but, of course, 10 tosses is not much of a long run, either. This departure from perfect results could be explained in one of two ways. First, John's coin tosses are not fair. Alternatively, John's results may be due to random luck. Do you think John was tossing the coin fairly? Explain.

2. Do you have much experience in watching someone toss a coin fairly 10 times? Do you know how often such a person will have 8 of 10 tosses turn up heads? Design at least two experiments that could provide the experience on which you could base decisions on how many heads *are* likely when you toss a coin fairly 10 times. Include at least one experiment that does not involve any coins. Be sure to indicate not only what to do, but also what to record, and what everything means. How do you know the coin in your experiment really has a 50% chance of landing heads?

ACTIVITY

3

A 50-50 PROPOSITION

3. a) Select an experiment from those posed for Item 2 to obtain data on tossing 10 coins. Write the instructions for conducting the experiment clearly enough so another group could follow them. Design the instructions to produce 100 sets of 10 tosses each.

   b) Conduct your experiment. In Figure 1 of Handout H3.8, record the **frequency** or number of times that each outcome occurs. Summarize the general features of this reference distribution.

   c) Do you think the numbers in your reference distribution table will be exactly the same as those from another group? Explain why or why not. (Then check with another group to see if your answer to this question is correct.)

   d) How often in your 100 simulations did you get 8 or more heads in 10 tosses of a coin?

   e) How often in your 100 simulations did you get 2 or fewer heads in 10 tosses of a coin?

   f) What number of heads seems most likely in 10 throws of a fair coin? Based on your experiment, estimate how likely it is to get exactly that number of heads.

   g) What range of numbers of heads seem most likely in 10 fair throws of a coin? Based on your experiment, estimate how likely it is to have the number of heads fall within that range.

In Item 3, you made two separate estimates for the number of heads you would expect in 10 fair tosses of a coin. One estimate consisted of a single number for a population value; such an estimate is called a **point estimate**. In part (g), your estimate was a range, or an interval, of reasonable values. Such an estimate is called an **interval estimate**. In general, most people feel more confident when they give interval estimates; there is a better chance of being right!

A 50-50 PROPOSITION

Your simulations most likely confirmed that the mathematical probability for getting 8 or more heads in 10 tosses is roughly 5%. (You may have observed a slightly higher or lower percentage.) You might conclude from your experiment that John (from Item 1) had either been practicing or he hit the 1-in-20 chance of getting 80% or more heads in 10 throws.

4. Now, suppose John is able to get at least 80% heads out of 20 throws.

   a) Adapt your design from Item 3(a) to gather data on 100 throws of 20 coins. Carry out your design, and record your results in Figure 2 on Handout H3.8.

   b) How often did you get at least 80% heads in 20 tosses ?

   c) How often did you get 20% or fewer heads in 20 tosses?

   d) Which happened more often: getting 80% or more heads in 10 tosses, or getting 80% or more heads in 20 tosses?

   e) Assuming the coins are tossed fairly, which do you think is more likely: getting at least 16 heads out of 20, or getting at least 24 heads out of 30? Why?

   f) How many heads would you expect to get in 20 throws of a fair coin? Based on your experiment, how likely is it to get exactly the number of heads you expected?

5. Suppose 50% of the residents of a particular county support wolf restoration. A random sample of 100 residents were surveyed and asked:

   Do you support the plan for the restoration of wolves in your county? Yes or No.

   a) Design an experiment that would gather information for a reference distribution for the survey results from this population.

   b) Suppose that a group supporting endangered animals administered a survey to 100 residents of this county and

ACTIVITY

3

A 50-50 PROPOSITION

found that 80% of the respondents supported wolf restoration. Do you think they sampled the residents fairly? Explain.

6. In Lesson 1, you created (or are in the process of creating) a series of questions with Yes-No answers. Suppose you are particularly interested in how students from a large high school (1000 students) would respond to the first question on your survey. Suppose further that a random sample of 20 students completes your survey.

a) Suppose 90% of the respondents answer Yes to the first survey question. Do you think it reasonable that the sample could have been drawn randomly from a student population in which 50% of all students would respond Yes?

b) Which of the reference distributions you generated in this activity would be useful in answering (a)? How can you use this reference distribution to help you answer (a)?

c) What if 40% of the respondents answer Yes to the first survey question. Could this sample have been drawn randomly from a population in which 50% of the students would respond Yes? Explain using information from your reference distribution.

INDIVIDUAL WORK 3

Simulated Sample Examples

*I*n Activity 3, your group simulated the results from two experiments: tossing a coin 10 times and tossing a coin 20 times. Each of these experiments was repeated 100 times and the simulated data were organized into reference distributions. When you compared your reference distribution for tossing a coin 10 times with another group's, you probably found there were differences in the two reference distributions. Your sample outcomes from 100 experiments differed from the other group's.

1. Three groups of students gathered data on 100 throws of 10 coins. **Figures 3.12–3.14** present their results. Because each group only collected 100 samples, and results differ from sample to sample, the tables differed from group to group. Variations in data sets due to different samples is called **variability due to sampling**. In this question, you will examine this source of variability.

Number of heads in 10 tosses	0	1	2	3	4	5	6	7	8	9	10	Total
Frequency	0	1	2	9	21	28	16	15	7	1	0	100

Figure 3.12. Group 1's reference distribution.

Number of heads in 10 tosses	0	1	2	3	4	5	6	7	8	9	10	Total
Frequency	0	1	4	12	13	31	16	16	6	1	0	100

Figure 3.13. Group 2's reference distribution.

Number of heads in 10 tosses	0	1	2	3	4	5	6	7	8	9	10	Total
Frequency	0	1	9	10	18	23	24	10	6	0	0	100

Figure 3.14. Group 3's reference distribution.

a) Scan Figures 3.12–3.14. What features do each of these reference distributions have in common? What are some differences?

A histogram for Group 1's reference distribution is presented in **Figure 3.15**.

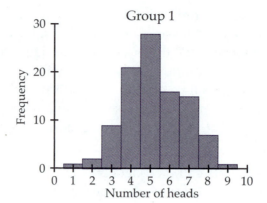

Figure 3.15.
Histogram for Group 1's reference distribution.

b) Using the same scale for the axes as was used in Figure 3.15, draw histograms for the other two reference distributions.

c) Compare the basic shapes of the histograms for the three reference distributions. Are the histograms fairly symmetric (the right-hand side appears similar to the left hand side) or quite **skewed** (lopsided)? Do the histograms tend to be **unimodal** (mound shaped with one peak) or **multi-modal** (have more than one peak)? Are there any striking differences between the three histograms?

d) Approximately where are the three histograms centered? Where are most of the data concentrated?

e) For each reference distribution, compute the average number of heads per 10 tosses observed in the 100 samples. Use this average to compute the average proportion of heads observed among all 1000 tosses. Record your results in a table similar to **Figure 3.16**.

Group number	Average number of heads per 10 tosses	Average proportion of heads in all tosses
1		
2		
3		

Figure 3.16.
Table of sample averages and proportions.

f) Which group's average proportions were closest to 0.5, the probability of getting heads when a coin is tossed fairly? Which group's average proportions were farthest away from 0.5?

2. The same three groups of students then gathered data on 100 throws of 20 coins. Their results, organized into reference distribution tables, are presented in **Figures 3.17–3.19.** (Because the outcomes 0, 1, 2, 18, 19, and 20 heads were never observed, they do not appear in these reference tables. If you find this bothersome, mentally extend the tables to include these values and set their frequencies to zero.)

Number of heads in 20 tosses	3	4	5	6	7	8	9	10	11	12	13	14	15	16	17
Frequency	0	0	1	1	4	14	15	23	22	11	7	1	1	0	0

Figure 3.17.
Reference distribution for Group 1.

Number of heads in 20 tosses	3	4	5	6	7	8	9	10	11	12	13	14	15	16	17
Frequency	0	0	1	6	6	12	16	18	16	13	7	3	2	0	0

Figure 3.18.
Reference distribution for Group 2.

Number of heads in 20 tosses	3	4	5	6	7	8	9	10	11	12	13	14	15	16	17
Frequency	1	0	1	3	5	12	15	19	17	10	9	7	1	0	0

Figure 3.19.
Reference distribution for Group 3.

a) Draw histograms for the reference distributions in Figures 3.17–3.19. Be sure to use the same scaling (on both the horizontal and vertical axes) for each of your histograms so you can compare them.

b) What features do each of these reference distributions have in common? What are some differences?

c) Approximately where are your histograms centered? Where are most of the data concentrated?

d) For each reference distribution, compute the average number of heads per 20 tosses observed in the 100 samples. Use this average to compute the average proportion of heads observed among all tosses. Record your results in a table similar to **Figure 3.20**.

Group number	Average number of heads per 20 tosses	Average proportion of heads in all tosses
1		
2		
3		

Figure 3.20.
Table of sample averages and proportions.

e) Which group's average proportion of heads is closest to 0.5? Which is farthest from 0.5?

f) Which average proportions tend to be closer to 0.5—the ones based on 10 tosses, or the ones based on 20 tosses? Which average proportions vary the least from group to group—the ones based on 10 tosses, or those based on 20 tosses?

3. Which is more likely: to observe 70% or more heads in 10 fair tosses of a coin, or 70% or more heads in 20 fair tosses of a coin? Support your answer using information from the three groups' reference distributions.

4. Suppose 50% of the voters in a county support their state's plan for wolf restoration. Approximately how likely is it that 30% of a sample of 20 voters supports the wolf restoration plan? Explain how you arrived at your answer.

5. Imagine you intended to survey a population about a question. Suppose half of this population would answer Yes to your question and the other half No. (In other words, this population is a 50%-Yes population.) Explain how you could use results from coin tossing experiments to simulate outcomes of sample surveys of this population.

6. Suppose in a Yes-No sample of size 20 you get 16 Yes responses. In other words, you get an 80%-Yes sample.

a) Do you think this sample could have come from an 80%-Yes population? What about a 90%-Yes population? Explain.

b) Could an 80%-Yes sample have come from a 50%-Yes population? A 65%-Yes population? Explain.

c) From which percentage Yes populations do you think this 16 out of 20, or 80%-Yes sample could have come?

d) Explain how you could modify your work in Activity 3 to provide information (reference distributions) on which to base a reliable answer to part (c).

7. There are many examples of Yes-No populations, populations in which people or objects fall into one of two categories, one designated Yes and the other No. Determine which of the following populations are Yes-No populations. If a population is a Yes-No population, decide which category you want to designate as Yes, and which as No.

a) Voters who plan to vote for or against the incumbent in a presidential race.

b) Parts made on an assembly line that either pass or fail inspection.

c) Residents who approve, disapprove, or have no opinion on wolf restoration.

d) M&M's candies.

e) M&M's that are red or not red.

After completing Activity 3 and this assignment, you should have a fairly good idea of what to expect in samples of 10 and 20 tosses of a coin. In particular, you should know it is very unlikely to get 80% heads in 20 tosses if the coin is being tossed fairly. Suppose, however, the coin is weighted so heads results more frequently than tails. If you got 80% heads in 20 tosses, you would most likely have no trouble believing that the probability of getting heads was 80%. But also you would be fairly likely to observe this same outcome from a coin that had a 75% or 85% probability of landing heads. The key question here is how you could use the sample percentage of 80% heads to determine likely values for the actual probability of getting heads using this coin.

REFERENCE DISTRIBUTIONS

Your experiments in Activity 3 led to the following conclusion: A sample that contains 16 or more heads in 20 fair tosses of a coin does not occur very often. In fact, samples containing 4 or fewer heads or 16 or more heads were rare. So, in terms of your class questionnaire, if you find that 16 of 20 seniors say Yes on question 1, then you can feel reasonably confident that the entire class of seniors are *not* split 50-50 on that issue.

In Item 6 of Individual Work 3, you were asked to think about a more difficult inference. Based on your 16-of-20 sample, you can be reasonably sure that the fraction of seniors who would answer Yes is not 50%. But what are the populations from which a 16-of-20 sample *could* have come? That's what you will need to know when your questionnaire results are collected.

One approach is to repeat what you did for the 50%-Yes population once for each population you think might support an 80%-Yes sample. That is, what is really needed is experience with every population. That would provide the basis for deciding whether an 80%-Yes sample would be likely from any population that ever came up. In this activity, you will carry Activity 3 further, gathering information that will permit you to do just that.

PART 1: Designing the Experiment

1 a) With your group, design and write instructions for an experiment to gather information on the likely samples from different Yes-No populations. In your data collection experiment, you will need to collect data on the number of Yes responses in 100 samples of size 20 taken from 10%, 20%, . . ., and 90%-Yes populations. You will need to write your instructions clearly enough for another group to be able to follow them and conduct your experiment. You can make use of any materials that are readily available, such as calculators, random digit tables (Handout H3.9), computer programs, or jars with colored beads.

ACTIVITY

REFERENCE DISTRIBUTIONS

4

b) After you have written your instructions, record them on a large piece of paper or on a transparency. (Your teacher will supply these materials.)

PART II: Collecting the Data

2. Your teacher will assign experiments and populations to each group. Use your assigned experiment to collect 100 size-20 samples from each of your assigned populations. Record your results on Handout H3.10, "Student Data Collection Form." After completing your form, transfer your results to a transparency or a large sheet of paper so you can share them with the class at the end of this activity.

3. Using the data from your assigned reference distributions (completed Handout H3.10), make a histogram for each distribution.

4. Study the reference distributions for the various Yes-percentage populations your group sampled. Describe any patterns or trends you see as you move from one reference distribution to another.

When all groups have completed Item 4, share your reference distributions with the class.

5. Study the tables of reference distributions for all groups' simulations. How do the reference distributions for the two sampling designs compare?

Record the pooled results on Handout H3.11. Be sure to save the completed handout for use in later activities.

6. Repeat Item 4 using the pooled results on Handout H3.11.

7. Now return to the question at the start of this activity. Based on the reference distributions you now have, from what populations would a 16-of-20 Yes sample have been likely?

INDIVIDUAL WORK 4

Population Shifts

group of students collected 100 size-20 samples from 20%, 50%, and 80% Yes populations. Their reference distribution tables appear in **Figures 3.21–3.23.**

Number of YES responses in sample	0	1	2	3	4	5	6	7	8	9	10
Number of samples	2	6	19	20	17	20	12	2	0	1	1
Number of YES responses in sample	11	12	13	14	15	16	17	18	19	20	
Number of samples	0	0	0	0	0	0	0	0	0	0	

Figure 3.21.
Reference distribution table for 20%-Yes population.

Number of YES responses in sample	0	1	2	3	4	5	6	7	8	9	10
Number of samples	0	0	0	0	1	1	5	10	11	19	22
Number of YES responses in sample	11	12	13	14	15	16	17	18	19	20	
Number of samples	10	11	5	3	0	2	0	0	0	0	

Figure 3.22.
Reference distribution tables for 50%-Yes population.

Number of YES responses in sample	0	1	2	3	4	5	6	7	8	9	10
Number of samples	0	0	0	0	0	0	0	0	0	0	0
Number of YES responses in sample	11	12	13	14	15	16	17	18	19	20	
Number of samples	0	4	7	8	22	21	19	15	3	1	

Figure 3.23.
Reference distribution table for 80%-Yes population.

1. Draw histograms for each of the reference distributions. Use the same axis scalings for each of the three histograms so that they can be compared more easily.

2. a) How does changing the population percentage of Yes responses from 20% to 50% to 80% affect the look of the histograms?

   b) Where does each of the histograms appear to be centered? What happens to this center as the population percentage of Yes responses increases?

   c) Which of the three histograms appears to be the widest? For which percentage do the data appear most concentrated?

3. For each of the three populations, calculate and record in a copy of **Figure 3.24** the average number of Yes responses per size-20 sample from the 100 samples. Use this average to compute the average proportion of Yes responses observed among all trials for that population. How close are these average proportions to the actual proportion of Yes responses in the population?

Population	Average number of Yes responses per sample	Average proportion of Yes responses per sample
20% Yes		
50% Yes		
80% Yes		

Figure 3.24.
Average number and proportion of Yes responses in size-20 samples.

4. A group of 20 students was randomly selected from a high school. They were asked the following question:

Do you think that the United States government should reinstitute drafting 18 year-olds into the armed services? Yes or No.

a) Suppose 3 of the 20 students responded Yes and the rest, No. From which of the populations—20% Yes, 50% Yes, or 80% Yes—might it be reasonably likely for these 20 students to have been selected? Explain your reasoning.

b) Based on the reference distributions you created on Handout H3.11, from which populations would a 3-of-20-Yes sample be likely to be selected?

c) Based on the 20%-Yes reference distribution in Figure 3.21, approximately what is the probability of selecting a 3-of-20-Yes sample from a 20%-Yes population?

5. A wildlife management team is assigned the task of estimating the size N of a population of turtles in their area. Initially, they capture a sample of 50 turtles, mark their shells with a notch, and then release them. Several weeks later the team captures a second sample of 20 turtles. Upon examination, 8 of these turtles have notches in their shells.

a) What makes this turtle population a Yes-No population?

b) What percentage of the turtles in the second sample were marked?

c) Estimate the size of the turtle population. Explain your reasoning and state any assumptions you made.

d) Suppose a scientist estimates there are only 62 turtles in the population altogether. If she is correct, what percentage of the turtle population has been marked? The 8 marked turtles can be thought of as an 8-of-20 Yes sample. Is an 8-of-20 Yes sample likely to be selected from a population having this percentage marked? (Base your answer on the appropriate distribution in Figures 3.21–3.23.) Do you think the scientist's estimate is correct?

e) Could your estimate for N be as low as 100? As large as 250? Base your answers on information contained in Figures 3.21, 3.22, and 3.23. Explain your reasoning.

REFERENCE REFERRAL

For this activity, your group will need a copy of the completed handout H3.11, the class reference distributions generated in Activity 4.

CONSIDER:

1. In Item 5 of Individual Work 4, 40% of a random sample of 20 turtles had marked shells. Based on the class reference distributions, from what Yes-No populations do you think it would be likely to draw such a sample?

2. Based on your answer to question 1, do you think the size of the turtle population could be as small as 75 turtles? If not, how small do you think it could be?

Did you have any trouble deciding from which populations a 40%-Yes sample was likely to be drawn?

What if, instead, the problem had involved an 80%-Yes sample? Based on your class reference distributions from Activities 3 and 4, you know that a sample of 16 or more Yes responses out of 20 (an 80% or more sample percentage) is fairly likely when you sample from an 80%-Yes population. On the other hand, a sample of 16 or more Yes responses out of 20 rarely occurs in a population containing 40% or fewer Yes responses. This does not mean that you could never observe a sample with 16 or more Yes responses from a 40%-Yes population, but only that you might have to take thousands of samples before you observed such a rare occurrence.

The key question here is, from which populations are 80%-or more Yes samples likely? You have already posed answers to this question in Activity 3 (Item 3(g)), Individual Work 3 (Item 6(c)), and Activity 4 (Item 7). Each time you have considered this question you have had a bit more experience with distributions, but

ACTIVITY

5

REFERENCE REFERRAL

you may not have set a clear criterion for deciding when 16-of-20 really belonged.

Remember, when your class questionnaire comes back, you will know the sample information exactly. What you won't have is the identity (percent Yes) of the population from which the sample came. Your goal will be to answer questions in exactly the form posed here, "From what populations would this sample be likely to have been selected?"

In order to answer such questions, you must first define your criterion. What do you mean by likely to occur? Then, for any population, its reference distribution can tell you whether your particular sample is a likely sample or not. All that's left is to choose the criterion for deciding which samples are likely and which samples are not.

Most likely, different groups used different criteria in making those decisions in the earlier activities. From now on, however, unless you are told otherwise, a population's **likely samples**—the samples (of a particular size) likely to be drawn from a specified Yes-No population—include the 90% of samples that occur most frequently. Another way of saying the same thing is that the likely samples form the middle 90% of the reference distribution for the given population.

Thus, in order to identify the likely samples in a distribution, you can start from the middle and include all categories until at least 90% is included, balancing the leftover categories so about 5% appears past each end of the likely-sample group. The *at least 90%* is important. Since the number of Yes responses in a sample of 20 can only be an integer from 0 to 20, it is almost always the case that one set of values includes less than 90%, but including just one more value puts the total over 90%.

Of course, since counting to 5% is quicker than counting to 90%, it is easier to start from the ends and eliminate values. Using that method, eliminate (classify as unlikely) values until the next one would cause the total eliminated to be larger than 5%. Do not

ACTIVITY

REFERENCE REFERRAL

5

eliminate the value that puts the total over 5%. Then repeat from the other end. An example for a 60%-Yes population is given below. First, you need the reference distribution for a 60%-Yes population. **Figure 3.25** is probably much like your 60%-Yes reference distribution.

Number of YES responses in sample	0	1	2	3	4	5	6	7	8	9	10
Number of samples	0	0	0	0	0	1	0	1	2	4	14
Number of YES responses in sample	11	12	13	14	15	16	17	18	19	20	
Number of samples	16	12	15	13	10	8	4	0	0	0	

Figure 3.25.
100 size-20 samples from a 60%-Yes population.

Remember, cut off no more than 5% of the samples from each end, leaving at least 90% of the samples for the likely-sample group. With a reference distribution table based on 100 samples (such as the one in Figure 3.25), that means you will cut off no more than 5 samples from the lower end and 5 from the upper end, leaving at least 90 samples in the middle.

1. If the reference distribution table were based on 200 samples (as is your Handout H3.11), how many samples would you cut off from each end? At least how many samples would be in the likely-sample group?

To decide which samples to cut, begin at the left end of the table at samples with 0 Yes responses, then move to samples with 1 Yes, then 2 Yes responses, and so forth. As you move from sample to sample, keep a running count of the frequencies. The last row of **Figure 3.26** records this running count for samples with 0 to 9 Yes responses in Figure 3.25.

Look at the samples with 0–8 Yes responses. The number of these

ACTIVITY

5

REFERENCE REFERRAL

Number of YES responses in sample	0	1	2	3	4	5	6	7	8	9
Number of samples	0	0	0	0	0	1	0	1	2	4
Running count	0	0	0	0	0	1	1	2	4	8

Figure 3.26.
Running count of frequencies.

samples sum to 4, $1 + 0 + 1 + 2 = 4$. So, none of the samples with 0–8 Yes responses is in the likely-sample group for the reference distribution in Figure 3.25. However, if you add the frequency associated with exactly 9 Yes responses, 4, you would have a total of 8. This would put you over the cut-off value of 5. So a sample with exactly 9 Yes responses, or a 45% Yes sample, is the first sample that is included in the likely-sample group.

Now move to the other end of the table. Start with samples containing 20 Yes responses, then move right to left to 19 Yes responses, 18 Yes responses, and so forth. (see **Figure 3.27**).

Number of YES responses in sample	16	17	18	19	20
Number of samples	8	4	0	0	0
Running count	12	4	0	0	0

Figure 3.27.
Running count of frequencies.

The sample with 16 Yes responses or the 80% Yes sample puts you over the limit, so this sample is included in the likely-sample group. Combining these results, the likely-sample group for the reference distribution in Figure 3.25 contains the samples with between 9 and 16 Yes responses, or between 45% and 80% Yes responses, inclusive.

ACTIVITY

REFERENCE REFERRAL

5

2. The likely-sample group depends on the reference distribution. Because the reference distribution in Figure 3.25 was based on only 100 samples, it probably differs slightly from your 60%-Yes reference distribution table on Handout H3.11. Use your table to find the likely-sample group for a 60%-Yes population. Compare your results to those above.

What you need from the reference distributions is a clear indication of the likely samples so you can answer the following type of questions: Is this sample likely to have come from that population? From what populations is this sample likely to have come? Histograms and numerical tables carry much more information, but that extra information does not help answer these key questions and takes up extra space.

So, in the spirit of improving your model, here's a way to modify reference distributions to be more efficient (for this decision-making process). The cells in **Figure 3.28** marked with an X correspond to the samples that belong to the likely samples in Figure 3.25. The cells marked with a hyphen indicate samples that did occur, but were not likely (using the 90% definition).

Number of YES responses	0	1	2	3	4	5	6	7	8	9	10	11	12	13	14	15	16	17	18	19	20
Number of samples						–		–	–	X	X	X	X	X	X	X	X	–			

Figure 3.28.
The likely-sample group corresponding to Figure 3.25.

Shade the cells containing X's to make the bar. Then add whiskers by drawing a line from the end of the bar through the farthest cell containing a hyphen. **Figure 3.29** shows how the likely-sample bar corresponding to the reference distribution in Figure 3.25 should look.

ACTIVITY

5

REFERENCE REFERRAL

3. Complete Figure 1 on Handout H3.13, "Likely-Sample Bars," by drawing a likely-sample bar for the 60%-Yes reference distribution on Handout H3.11 that your class created in Activity 4. Compare your likely-sample bar to the one in Figure 3.29.

Population	0	1	2	3	4	5	6	7	8	9	10	11	12	13	14	15	16	17	18	19	20
60% YES																					

Figure 3.29.
Likely-sample bar for reference distribution in Figure 3.25.

4. Next, make a likely-sample bar for each of the class reference distributions on H3.11. Begin by transferring your results from Item 3 to Figure 2 on Handout H3.13. Then use the same procedure that you used to make the 60%-likely-sample bar to make likely-sample bars for each of the your other reference distributions. The result compresses all the information from all the histograms and tables into one compact decision-making tool!

After shading, your charts should resemble a collection of horizontal bars. These bars are called **likely-sample bars**; they represent the different Yes-No populations. Your collection of bars from a set of Yes populations in tabular form will be referred to as a **likely-sample table**.

5. Look down your likely-sample table. Describe any general patterns that you observe as you move down the table from 90%-Yes populations to 10%-Yes populations. Why might you expect these patterns to exist?

6. Write an explanation of the use of the word "likely" as it is used in the following context: A sample of 16/20 Yes responses is a likely sample from a 70%-Yes population, but it is not a likely sample from a 40%-Yes population.

7. A group of 20 students were selected randomly from a high school. They were asked:

ACTIVITY

REFERENCE REFERRAL

5

Do you think the United States government should reinstitute drafting 18 year-olds into the armed services? Yes or No.

Suppose 3 of the 20 students responded Yes and the rest No.

a) Which of the populations in your likely-sample table have likely-sample bars that contain samples with exactly 3 out of 20 Yes responses? (Note: Do not include populations where the whiskers contain samples with exactly 3 out of 20 Yes responses.)

b) Use your answer to (a) to complete the following sentence. Based on this sample, we estimate that between _____% and _____% of the population would respond Yes to this question. Explain your reasoning.

c) Use your answer to (b) to complete the following sentence. Based on this sample, we estimate that approximately _____%, plus or minus _____%, of the population would respond Yes to this question.

8. a) Return to the Consider questions at the beginning of this activity. In a sample of 20 turtles, 40% had marked shells. Use your likely-sample table to estimate the possible populations from which this sample was drawn.

b) In the entire population, there are 50 turtles with marked shells. Use this information together with your populations percentages in (a) to provide a range of reasonable values for the size of this turtle population.

The method of selecting the likely-sample group in this activity used 90% as the minimum number of samples in the likely-sample group. Instead, you could have chosen a different percentage, such as 80% or 95%. To avoid confusion, from now on you will refer to your likely-sample table (Figure 2, Handout 3.13) as a 90% likely-sample table and the individual bars as 90% likely-sample bars.

INDIVIDUAL WORK 5

It's a Likely Story

You will need a copy of completed Handouts H3.11 and H3.13 for this assignment.

In Activity 5, the criterion for deciding which samples belonged to the likely-sample group was based on 90%. However, the 90% figure is arbitrary. Think about how the likely-sample bars would change if membership in the likely-sample group were based on a different percentage.

1. Suppose you decided to use 80% likely-sample groups instead of 90% likely-sample groups.

   a) Describe how you would identify in a reference distribution the likely samples, using 80% as the definition of likely.

   b) Find the size-20, 80% likely-sample group for a 60%-Yes population. (Use the class reference distribution corresponding to samples of size 20 taken from a 60%-Yes population.)

   c) Compare your 80% likely-sample group to a 90% likely-sample group for this distribution (of size-20 samples). Which is wider?

2. More generally, for any given population, would a 90% likely-sample bar be shorter or longer than a 95% likely-sample bar? Explain.

In Activity 5, you worked only with samples of size 20. However, the methods used in Activity 5 can be applied to samples of other sizes as well. Consider, for example, samples of size 10. (Refer to **Figure 3.30.**)

Number of YES responses in sample	0	1	2	3	4	5	6	7	8	9	10
Number of samples	0	0	0	9	12	21	17	26	10	4	1

Figure 3.30.
100 size-10 samples from a 60%-Yes population.

3. The reference distribution table for 100 size-10 samples from a 60%-Yes population appears in Figure 3.30.

   a) Which samples belong to the 90% likely-sample group for this distribution?

   b) Which samples belong to the 80% likely-sample group?

c) Which group is wider, the 90% likely-sample group or the 80% likely-sample group?

d) Convert your answers to (b) into sample percentages. Do the same for the 80% likely-sample group in Item 1(b). Compare the widths of the 80% likely-sample groups from the size-10 samples to the 80% likely-sample groups from size-20 samples. Which is wider (based on a comparison of the percentages)? Explain why you might have expected this result.

4. In a sample of 20 M&M's, Sharon found 6 brown M&M's.

a) What percentage of the M&M's in her sample were brown?

b) Use your 90% likely-sample table on Handout H3.13 to determine an interval of reasonable values for the population percentage of brown candies in the M&M's mixture.

5. In Florida, a student observed cars stopped at a traffic light on a hot day. He saw that 12 out of the 20 cars had their windows closed. He drew a conclusion that 60% of cars in Florida had air conditioning. Later he heard that 85% of cars in Florida had air conditioning. Is his sample consistent with the 85% figure he heard? Explain why or why not.

LESSON THREE
Say It With Confidence!

KEY CONCEPTS

Confidence
intervals

Margin of error

The Image Bank

PREPARATION READING

Driving Teenagers Crazy

Most of the samples you have collected so far have been generated from a random digits table or by some other method that generates random outcomes. In conducting a public opinion poll, however, although you can randomly select the people to be questioned, you won't be able to determine their answers with a random device. You'll have to find a way to question the people in your sample. Once you've collected your data, then the fun begins as you sift through and interpret your results. That's what this lesson is all about.

To start you thinking about interpretation, a portion of a 1996 poll commissioned by Channel 3, KDLH (Duluth, Minnesota and Superior, Wisconsin) is presented here. The questions on this survey focus on teenage driving and the testing process for drivers' licenses.

Q1. Should drivers be required to take more courses after passing their driving test?

Yes 60%

No 34%

Q2. Should new drivers be put under a 90-day probation period, requiring adult supervision to drive?

Yes 66%

No 30%

Q3. Should drivers under the age of 18 be allowed to have only one other teenager in the car with them?

Yes 22%

No 73%

Q4. Should anyone under the age of 18 be prohibited from driving between midnight and 6:00 AM?

Yes 56%

No 40%

Q5. Should anyone under the age of 18 be prohibited from driving between sunset and sunrise?

Yes 17%

No 80%

Q6. Do you think that traffic violations committed by people under the age of 18 should go on their parents' driving record?

Yes 15%

No 83%

Q7. Do you think that police should be allowed to immediately impound vehicles driven by traffic violators under the age of 18, no matter who owns the vehicle?

Yes 26%

No 67%

The poll was conducted by telephone on May 16th by Mason Dixon Political/Media Research Inc. of Washington D. C. Those interviewed were 812 registered voters, who indicated they regularly vote in Minnesota state elections. The poll has a margin of error of plus or minus 3.5 percentage points. The sample breaks down by region as follows:

Minneapolis/St. Paul 407 Interviews   Rochester/Southeast 105 Interviews

Southwest Minnesota 102 Interviews   Northwest Minnesota 98 Interviews

Duluth/Northeast 100 Interviews   Copyright: 1996, Benedek Broadcasting Corp.

CONSIDER:

1. How would your class have answered these questions?

2. Would a majority of your class be in agreement with the majority of respondents to this survey? On which questions do you think the responses from your class might differ the most from those in the Minnesota survey? Why?

ACTIVITY

6

BUILDING CONFIDENCE

1. Rosa and Jared are battling for a seat on their high school's student council. Prior to the election, the staff of the school newspaper interviewed a sample of 20 students and found that 11 were going to vote for Rosa.

   a) Clearly, this sample would be likely in a 55%-Yes population. Determine all populations for which 11 out of 20 Yes responses is a likely sample. Base your answer on your likely-sample table (Handout H3.13).

   b) Based on your answer to (a), will Rosa win the election? Explain.

Recall that 55% is a point estimate for the population percentage; it is the single "best guess" for that value. However, an interval estimate such as the one you found in 1(a) provides more confidence that your estimate is correct. Note that your answer contained the value 55%, with a little room for error on either side of 55%. Your interval estimate is called a **confidence interval**—the percentage of Yes-populations that contain a given sample percentage in their likely-sample groups. More specifically, the interval from 40% to 70% is a 90% confidence interval for the population percentage because it is based on a 90%-likely-sample table.

Using the class 90% likely-sample tables from Handout H3.13, your confidence interval is rounded to the nearest 10% since the handout only contains populations that are multiples of 10%. That can be a very rough estimate, particularly if you are trying to predict the outcome of an election. **Figure 3.31** presents a

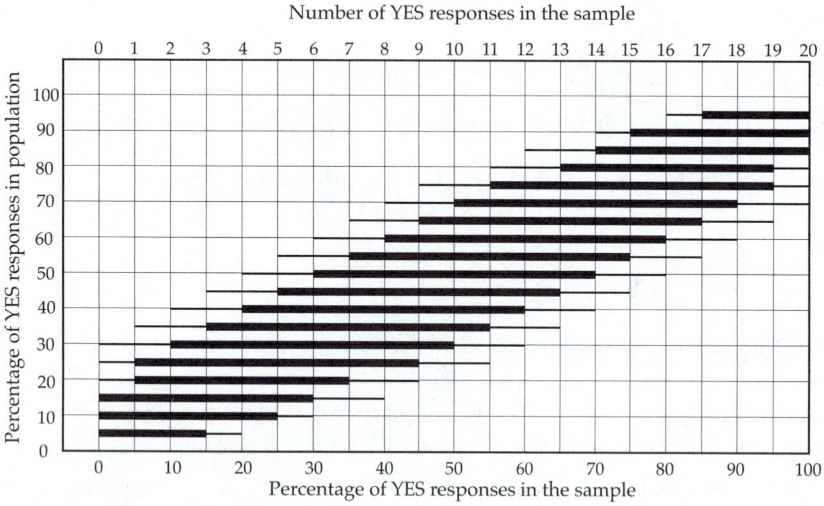

Figure 3.31.
90% likely-sample table for size-20 samples.

BUILDING CONFIDENCE

computer generated 90% likely-sample table with likely-sample bars at 5% increments in the population of percentage-Yes values, which allows a bit more precision in your estimates. Note that instead of displaying each integer value for the number of Yes responses as squares to be filled in or left blank (for example, see Figure 3.29), Figure 3.31 introduces a new format for likely-sample tables. Each integer value for the number of Yes responses is shown at the edge of a "box" in the grid.

For example, you can use Figure 3.31 to determine reasonable populations for which an 11 out of 20 or 11/20 sample is likely. Just follow the vertical line corresponding to 11 Yes responses (or 55%) in the sample and keep track of which populations' likely-sample bars it crosses. It appears that a sample with 11/20 Yes responses is in the likely-sample groups for populations having Yes-percentages between 35% and 75%. (Note that this vertical line just touches the end of the 35% likely-sample bar, so we decided to include it.) Thus, a better confidence interval would be 35% to 75%. By including more population reference distributions in the table, you could get even more precision.

2. Suppose that the sample of 20 students interviewed by the school newspaper staff found that 4, or 8, or 11, or 16 of the students planned to vote for Rosa.

   a) Make a copy of **Figure 3.32** on paper, then complete the entries in Figure 3.32 to create confidence intervals for the given size-20 samples.

Number of YES responses in the sample	Lowest population Yes percentage for which this is a likely sample	Highest population Yes percentage for which this is a likely sample
4		
8		
11		
16		

Figure 3.32.
Plausible population percentages for given sample results.

b) In which of these situations can you be fairly certain that Rosa will win? That Rosa will lose? That the election is still up for grabs?

How well do 90% confidence intervals work? Remember, there is only one correct population percentage. How frequently can you expect samples from the population to produce 90% confidence intervals that contain the actual population percentage of Yes responses?

One way to find out is to begin with a population in which the percentage of Yes responses is known. For example, in a random-digit table, 50% of the digits are even (0 is an even digit). So the percentage of Yes responses (even digits) in this population is known.

3. Explain how you could use a random-digit table to determine how often confidence intervals based on size-20 samples contain the true population percentage-Yes value of 50%. Describe your proposed experiment in detail.

4. a) From a table of random digits, obtain 15 samples of size 20. Count the number of Yes responses (even digits) in each sample and record your results in Figure 1 on Handout H3.14, "90% Confidence Intervals." Then use the likely-sample table in Figure 3.31 to determine 90% confidence intervals for the population percentage of Yes responses (even digits). Again, record your results in Figure 1.

ACTIVITY

6

BUILDING CONFIDENCE

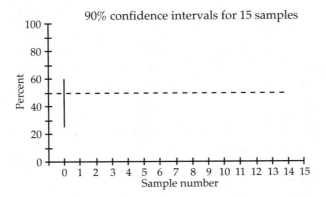

90% confidence intervals for 15 samples

Figure 3.33.
Vertical line representing a
90% confidence interval.

b) Represent the confidence interval for each of your 15 samples as a vertical line. For example, Sample 0 contained 8 even digits. The 90% confidence interval for this sample is 25% to 60%. This interval is represented by the vertical line in **Figure 3.33** drawn between percentages 25 and 60. Now, draw lines on Figure 2 of Handout H3.14 representing each of your 90% confidence intervals in Figure 1.

c) When you have completed your diagram, you may find not all of your confidence intervals contain the actual 50% population percentage. Most likely, not all of your confidence interval lines crossed the dotted line for 50%. (If all of your confidence intervals contained 50%, then check with another group.) On average (after computing numerous confidence intervals), 9 out of 10 intervals will actually cross the dotted line at 50%. Give an explanation of why this is so.

Point estimates are almost never correct. Since a point estimate is just one number, it is almost never the right one. However, your intuition should suggest that you could be correct more often if you could modify a point estimate to include a little room for error on either side. That's what a confidence interval does.

And now you can say how often such an interval estimate is correct (contains the actual population percentage Yes value). Since there *is* a correct (but unknown) population value, there is a 90%

ACTIVITY

BUILDING CONFIDENCE

6

chance that any sample will be a likely sample for that population. Since likely samples produce confidence intervals that contain the related population value, there is a 90% chance that any sample will lead to a correct confidence interval. So, the process that makes 90% confidence intervals gives right answers 90% of the time!

5. An animal rights group claims that a majority of a county's residents support wolf restoration efforts in the county.

   a) A local newspaper randomly samples 20 residents and finds that only 40% support the restoration efforts. Do the results of the newspaper's sample refute the claims of the animal rights group? Explain based on a 90% confidence interval.

   b) What if, instead, the newspaper had found that only one-quarter of those sampled supported wolf restoration? Would the results of their survey tend to refute the animal rights group's claim? Explain.

CONSIDER:

Q4 in the survey presented in the preparation reading asks:

Should anyone under the age of 18 be prohibited from driving between midnight and 6:00 AM? Yes or No.

1. The Yes and No responses fail to sum to 100%. How could that be?

2. The results from this survey were based on interviews with a sample of 812 registered voters. The sample percentage of Yes responses was 56%. Does this mean that a majority of the Minnesota voters would respond Yes?

3. Describe a simulation that could be used to determine whether a 56%-Yes sample of size 812 produces a confidence interval that lies entirely above 50%.

ACTIVITY

SIZING UP THE SITUATION

7

With the exception of the sample of 812 registered voters mentioned in the Consider questions at the end of the activity, all the samples in Activity 6 were of size 20. In fact, pretty much all your work in this unit has been with samples of size 20. It is unlikely you will want to survey only 20 students with your class questionnaire, so you need to think about how sample size affects how you interpret sample data.

You have a useful model for building confidence intervals for size-20 samples. That model is based on lots of simulations, each using samples of size 20 from a known population, in order to construct reference distributions from all possible populations. When you needed more precision than to the nearest 10%, you were able to improve your model just by simulating from more populations.

Thinking about the model you have used thus far, it should be clear that a similar approach could be used for any sample size. Of course, simulation is time-consuming. Thus, even though more simulation may be necessary, perhaps it would be wise to watch for patterns as you go along. Perhaps it is possible to describe how things behave without having to do thousands of simulations each time you use a new sample size.

CONSIDER:

1. What effect do you think the size of the sample has on the lengths of 90% likely-sample bars?

2. What effect would shorter likely-sample bars have on the widths of confidence intervals? What about longer likely-sample bars? Why?

ACTIVITY

7

SIZING UP THE SITUATION

If you had trouble answering the Consider questions, then it may be helpful to gather more data and see what happens to the length of the likely-sample bars and confidence intervals as the size of the sample increases. If you had no trouble answering the Consider questions, then this activity should confirm your answers.

If you have not already used a computer or calculator to simulate sampling from a Yes-No population, you will find that using a computer/calculator greatly speeds up the data-collection process. Your teacher will assign you one or more percentage-Yes populations.

1. Generate 500 samples each of size 20, 40, and 80 from the Yes population you were assigned. Record your results for the size-20, 40 and 80 samples in Figures 1, 2, and 3, respectively, on Handout H3.15, "Data Tables."

2. Remember the question behind the simulations: What happens to likely samples as the sample size changes? Use your simulation data from Item 1 to answer that question. (Continue to use 90% as the cut-off for likely samples; note that your data are based on 500 repetitions.)

Suggestion: In order to compare the likely-sample groups for different size samples, express your likely-sample groups in terms of percentages. For example, if likely samples were from 3 to 9 Yes responses for size-20 samples, then they are also from 15% to 45%, since 3 is 15% of 20 and 9 is 45% of 20.

3. Compare your results with those of a group who used a different population percentage. Comment on what you observe.

4. What do you think happens to confidence intervals as you increase the size of your samples? Explain your reasoning.

5. You could combine your size-40 data with that of other groups who used different populations and make at least a partial likely-sample table for size-40 samples. The same is true for your size-80 data. What would you need to do in order to have likely-sample tables good enough to find confidence intervals accurate to the nearest 5%?

INDIVIDUAL WORK 6

Color Coded

Up until 1995, packages of M&M's contained red, brown, orange, green, yellow, and tan candies. In September 1995, blue candies replaced the less flashy tan.

Before choosing the new color, M&M/Mars conducted a survey in which they asked people to select their favorite color. More than ten million voters took part in this survey. Blue M&M's got a majority of the votes. The results of this survey appear in **Figure 3.34.**

FYI   **What's In a Color?**

According to Marlene Machut, an M&M/Mars company spokesperson, ". . . tan was removed from the mix because, in our research, it was the least popular color. The company couldn't afford to add another color, but it could afford to replace one."

The Record
(7 July 1995, page B01).

Color	Percentage of voters
Blue	54
Purple	32
Pink	10
No change	4

Figure 3.34.
Results of M&M/Mars survey.

But what percentage of each color does M&M/Mars use in manufacturing M&M candies?

Up until now, the activities in this unit have focused mainly on small samples. Small samples are convenient to use in order to understand the method without requiring a lot of time to generate examples. However, as you observed in Activity 7, small samples often lead to very imprecise results because confidence intervals associated with small samples tend to be wide. For example, given a sample of M&M's containing 6 out of 20 browns, a 90% confidence interval estimates the percentage of brown M&M's to be between 15% and 50%. For a point estimate of 30%, that's a lot of room for error due to sampling variability. This interval is not very useful as an estimate for the percentage of brown M&M's in the population of candies.

To provide more precise estimates (narrower confidence intervals) for the percentages of M&M's of various colors, samples of size 50 and 100 will be used in this assignment. For your analyses, computer-generated 90% likely-sample tables are provided in **Figures 3.35** and **3.36.** You will also need Figure 3.31.

INDIVIDUAL WORK 6

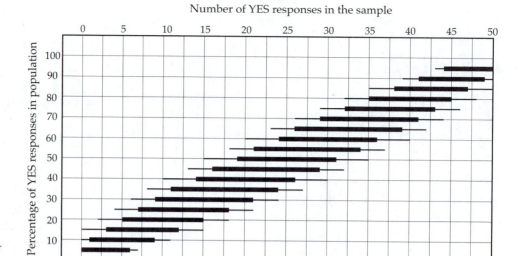

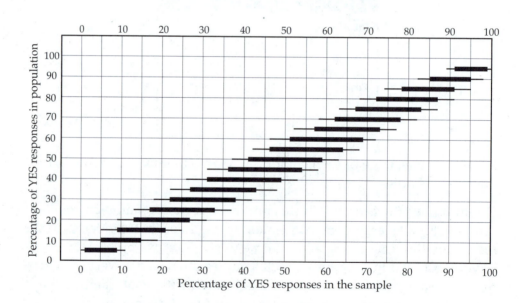

Figure 3.35.
90% likely-sample tables for size-50 samples.

Figure 3.36.
90% likely-sample table for size-100 samples.

Although the population of M&M's contains more than two colors, you can treat M&M's as a Yes-No population on a color-by-color basis. For example, when asking questions about brown M&M's, let Yes represent Brown and No, Not Brown.

1. Suppose a sample of 50 M&M's contained 12 brown, 16 yellow, 13 red, 3 orange, 4 green, and 2 blue.

   a) Complete a copy of **Figure 3.37.**

   b) Repeat part (a) for size-20 samples, keeping the sample percentages the same.

   c) Based only on parts (a) and (b), does it seem your answer to Item 4 of Activity 7 is correct?

2. Suppose that a second sample of size 50 contained 17 browns, 12 yellow, 9 red, 5 orange, 3 green, and 4 blue. Complete a copy of **Figure 3.38.**

3. Since each sample from a particular population is just a sample, you should not expect all samples to be identical. That's sampling variability. The samples in Items 1 and 2 actually did come from the same population. Discuss their similarities and differences.

4. Combine the data from Items 1 and 2 to make a single sample of size 100. Use this larger sample to determine 90% confidence intervals for the percentages of each of the 6 M&M's colors. Then complete a copy of **Figure 3.39.**

5. Next, compare the widths of the confidence intervals based on size-20 samples, size-50 samples, and size-100 samples. Comment on your observations.

6. Prior to the introduction of blue M&M's, the population of plain M&M's contained 40% brown candies. The data in this assignment were taken after the introduction of blue candies. Based on your analysis here, do you think that the percentage of brown candies is still 40%? Explain.

7. Suppose that students captured 80 grasshoppers from a field behind their school. The grasshoppers were marked (a drop of nail polish was placed on the thorax) and then released. A day

Color	Sample Percentage	90% Confidence interval
Brown		
Yellow		
Red		
Orange		
Green		
Blue		

Figure 3.37.
Color distribution from a size-50 sample of M&M's.

Color	Sample Percentage	90% Confidence interval
Brown		
Yellow		
Red		
Orange		
Green		
Blue		

Figure 3.38.
Color distribution from second size-50 sample of M&M's.

Color	Sample Percentage	90% Confidence interval
Brown		
Yellow		
Red		
Orange		
Green		
Blue		

Figure 3.39.
Color distribution from size 100 sample of M&M's.

later students, assigned to random plots in the field, captured 50 grasshoppers and noted that 6 were marked.

a) What is the sample percentage of marked grasshoppers?

b) Determine a confidence interval for the percentage of grasshoppers in the population that were marked.

c) Based on your confidence interval in (b), determine an interval estimate for the number of grasshoppers in the field.

8. Suppose a random sample of 100 high school students were asked:

Which do you prefer: Coca-Cola® or Pepsi®?

(Even if the respondent doesn't like either Coke or Pepsi, this question forces a choice of one over the other.) The results of the poll indicated that 56% of the high school students polled preferred Coke, and 44% Pepsi.

a) What is the Yes-No population in this situation?

b) Use your $n = 100$ table to determine a 90% confidence interval for high school students who prefer Coke over Pepsi.

9. Suppose a sample of 100 high school students were asked:

Which do you prefer to attend: school football games or school dances?

The results of the poll indicated that 80% of the high school students preferred attending school football games, and 20% preferred attending school dances.

a) What is the Yes-No population in this situation?

b) Determine a 90% confidence interval for high school students who prefer attending school football games.

c) Suppose you discovered the sample of 100 students was taken at an after-school football pep rally. Do you think the confidence interval in (b) is a valid estimate of the percentage of high school students who prefer attending football games to attending school dances? Explain why or why not.

MARGIN OF ERROR

The public opinion poll discussed in the preparation reading was based on a sample of 812 registered voters. Public opinion polls generally deal with much larger samples than size-50, or even size-100, samples. You have begun the investigation of how sample size influences confidence intervals, but more work is still needed there. In addition, most published polls use 95% confidence intervals rather than the 90% confidence intervals that you have used up to this point, so you will need to see how to adjust your model for that change, too.

Remember, the 90% confidence level you have been using is based on the probability that a particular set of samples will occur within a given population. Since likely samples make up 90% of all possible samples from the actual population, then 90% of all confidence intervals created from your likely-sample tables will contain the actual population percentage. Of course, whether a particular sample does contain the population percentage depends on your luck in sampling.

CONSIDER:

1. a) For a given sample, is it more likely that its 95% confidence interval will contain the actual population percentage or that its 90% confidence interval will contain the actual population percentage?

    b) Which should be wider: a 90% confidence interval or a 95% confidence interval? How do you know?

2. For a given sample percentage, which is wider: a 90% confidence interval based on a size-20 sample or a 90% confidence interval based on a size-100 sample. How do you know?

3. Why do you think that reputable polls would prefer to use a 95% confidence interval instead of a 90% confidence interval? (You may find it helpful to base your argument on the simulation experiments conducted in Activities 6 and 7.)

4. Why do you think 90% confidence intervals have been used up to this point instead of 95% confidence intervals?

ACTIVITY

8

MARGIN OF ERROR

The survey results in the preparation reading reported a margin of error of 3.5 percentage points. Remember, a confidence interval is based on a point estimate (the sample percentage) with some additional room for error due to sampling variability. That additional room is the margin of error.

You can convert this margin of error into a 95% confidence interval of the form, *from lower value* to *upper value* by subtracting 3.5% from the sample percentage to get the lower value and by adding 3.5% to the sample percentage to get the upper value. For example, 60% of those surveyed thought drivers should be required to take more courses after passing their driving test. Thus, 60% is the point estimate for the population percentage. Based on these sample results, a 95% confidence interval for registered voters who would respond Yes to this question is between 56.5% and 63.5%, (i.e. between 60% − 3.5% and 60% + 3.5%). Note the margin of error, therefore, is just half the total width of the 95% confidence interval.

If you look back at confidence intervals and reference distributions you have made in earlier work, you will notice that they are not always symmetric. That is, they are not always centered exactly on the point estimate. Here again is a modeling decision: Is the extra precision you get by computing confidence intervals exactly from their underlying reference distributions worth more than the ease and understandability of stating a margin of error instead?

For large samples, symmetric margins of error turn out to be very good approximations, so that's what is used in reality. For that reason, and since most published polls report 95% confidence intervals instead of 90% intervals, the remainder of this unit will use 95% as the basis for all confidence intervals and margins of error unless otherwise noted.

ACTIVITY

MARGIN OF ERROR

8

1. The survey in the preparation reading reported that 56% of those polled supported prohibiting anyone under the age of 18 from driving between midnight and 6 a.m.

   a) Recall that the stated margin of error was 3.5%. Look at **Figures 3.40–3.45** and explain how you can use them to verify the stated margin of error is approximately correct. Why can you not be exact?

   b) Use the stated margin of error to determine a 95% confidence interval for the percentage of registered voters who support prohibiting anyone under the age of 18 from driving between midnight and 6 AM.

   c) Based on (b), would a majority of the registered voters agree with the majority opinion of those sampled? Why or why not?

2. A poll conducted June 18–19, 1996, reported that voters preferred President Clinton 57% to 38% over Dole. A later poll taken June 27–30, 1996, reported that Clinton was preferred over Dole 54% to 39%. Both of these polls had margins of error of ± 4%.

   a) If the elections had been held June 30, 1996, estimate, using a 95% confidence interval, the percentage of voters who would have voted for Clinton. Based on your estimate, would Clinton have won the election? (That is, is the sample on which this report was based likely to have come from a population having less than 50% support for Clinton?)

   b) Shortly after these polls were taken, Reuter released a statement claiming bad publicity had hurt Clinton's standings in the polls. Do the results from the two polls (June 18–19 and June 27–30) support this statement? Explain why or why not.

ACTIVITY

8

MARGIN OF ERROR

3. A Gallup poll conducted prior to the 1996 presidential election reported that voters preferred President Clinton 57% to Bob Dole 40%. These results were based on 1,010 adults with a margin of error ± 3%.

a) If instead, the Gallup poll sampled 3,000 adults do you think the margin of error would be higher or lower? Why?

b) What if the Gallup poll had sampled only 500 adults? Then what could you say about the margin of error?

You might wonder how the Gallup Organization determined the margin of error. Some of your investigations in Activity 7 and in Individual Work 6 focused attention on how sample size affects margin of error (even though those words were not used there). From a modeling perspective, the idea is to examine known situations so patterns may be discovered.

One option, with which you have some experience, is to do lots of simulations. In order to focus more on the patterns and less on the work, computer-generated 95% likely-sample tables for various sample sizes, ranging from $n = 100$ to $n = 2000$, are provided in Figures 3.40–3.45. Think of these as sources of data for investigating the relationship between margin of error and sample size.

Figure 3.40.
95% likely-sample table for size-100 sample.

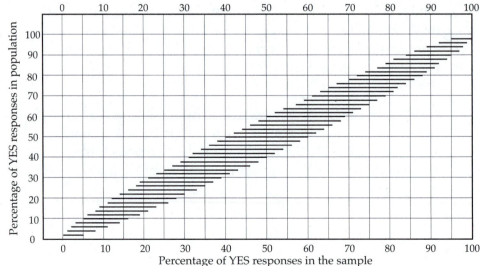

MARGIN OF ERROR

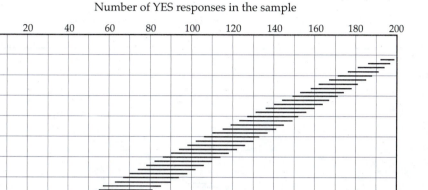

Number of YES responses in the sample

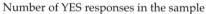

Figure 3.41.
95% likely-sample table for
size-200 sample.

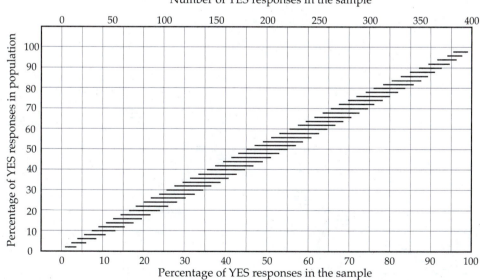

Figure 3.42.
95% likely-sample table for
size-400 sample

ACTIVITY

8

MARGIN OF ERROR

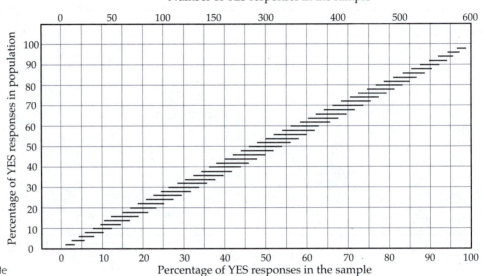

Figure 3.43.
95% likely-sample table
for size-600 sample.

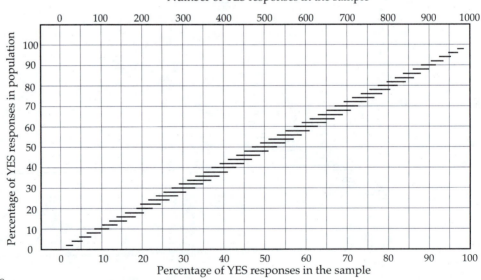

Figure 3.44.
95% likely-sample table
for size-1000 sample.

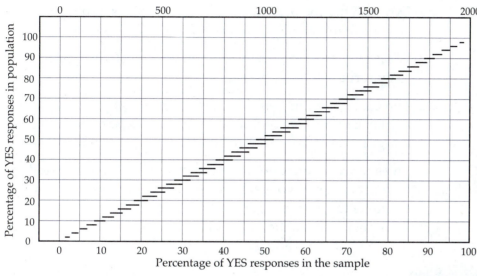

ACTIVITY

MARGIN OF ERROR

8

Number of YES responses in the sample

Figure 3.45.
95% likely-sample table for size-2000 sample.

4. Suppose that 50% of a sample responded Yes to a survey question. Investigate how the corresponding 95% margin of error depends on *n* as *n* varies. You may wish to go back to your earlier reference distributions from smaller samples and include the 95% margins of error for 50%-Yes samples from them, too. Begin by completing a table similar to that shown in **Figure 3.46,** then find an equation that fits those data reasonably well. Describe your methods.

5. Pollsters frequently use the following rule of thumb for calculating the margin of error: $100\% / \sqrt{n}$ where *n* is the size of the sample. This rule works reasonably well as long as the sample size is over 100 and the sample percentage is not too close to 0% or 100%. Graph this function together with the data from Item 4. Does this rule of thumb describe the pattern of your data?

Sample size	Margin of error
100	
200	
400	
600	
1000	
2000	

Figure 3.46.
95% margins of error.

ACTIVITY

MARGIN OF ERROR

6. Use the rule of thumb for approximating the margin of error to answer the items that follow.

a) Explain why the margin of error for a larger sample is smaller than the margin of error for a smaller sample.

b) What would happen to the margin of error if you decided to quadruple the sample size?

7. a) The Gallup poll in Item 3 was based on a sample of 1010 adults. Use the rule of thumb formula to determine the margin of error for this size sample.

b) The survey reported in the preparation reading was based on 812 registered voters. Use the rule of thumb formula to calculate the margin of error for this survey. How does your answer compare to the margin of error reported in the preparation reading?

8. How large a sample would you need in order to have a margin of error of 1%?

INDIVIDUAL WORK 7

Polling Results

1. Suppose two candidates, a Republican and a Democrat, are running for the Senate. Both candidates have strong personalities, causing few voters to be undecided in their choice of candidate. On the eve of the election, a news story reports that in an independent poll based on a random sample of 400 voters in the state, the Republican candidate has an 8-point lead over the Democratic candidate.

   a) What is the population of interest? Assuming that no one is undecided, how can this population be viewed as a Yes-No population?

   b) Assuming none of the people polled are undecided, what percentage of those polled were for the Republican candidate?

   c) What is the margin of error for this survey?

   d) Determine a 95% confidence interval for the percentage of voters in the state preferring the Republican candidate.

   e) Based on your confidence interval, should the news media report that the Republican candidate has a clear lead over the Democratic candidate? Explain.

2. Refer to the preparation reading, "Driving Teenagers Crazy".

   a) What is the population for this survey?

   b) Sixty-six percent of those surveyed felt new drivers should be put under a 90-day adult supervision period, requiring adult supervision to drive. Would you support this position?

   c) Use a 95% confidence interval to estimate the percentage of voters who would support the 90-day adult supervision period. Can you offer any explanation of why the respondents answered this question the way they did?

   d) Compute 95% confidence intervals for the percentage of Yes responses to survey Q4 and Q5. Based on your confidence intervals, would a majority of voters respond Yes to either of the questions? Both questions focus on limiting drivers under 18 from driving at night. Can you offer an explanation of why the percentage of Yes responses to these two questions were so different?

3. Suppose that students captured 425 grasshoppers from a field behind their school. Each of the grasshoppers was marked (a drop of nail polish was placed on the thorax) and released. Suppose that two days later a second sample was captured from randomly selected plots in the field. Twenty-five of the 250 grasshoppers from the second sample were marked.

a) What percentage of the second sample of grasshoppers were marked?

b) Use the rule of thumb for margins of error to determine a 95% confidence interval for the percentage of the population of grasshoppers that were marked.

c) Based on your confidence interval in (b), determine an interval of plausible values for the size of the grasshopper population in the field.

Selective Service

KEY CONCEPTS

Methods of sampling

Bias

The Image Bank

PREPARATION READING

Who Are You Going to Call?

National opinion polls, such as Gallup polls, Harris polls, and major television network polls, take great care in designing how their samples are selected. Here is an excerpt from the CBS News website outlining the selection of respondents for CBS News surveys.

FREQUENTLY ASKED QUESTIONS ABOUT THE CBS NEWS POLL

Who Does CBS News Talk To?
Most CBS News surveys are done by telephone. Anyone 18 years or older living in the continental United States is eligible to participate in our surveys.

How Does CBS News Choose The People To Interview?
In a nutshell, we choose the people we interview completely at random. We do not choose our respondents based on their age, race, political philosophy, or any other characteristic. In fact, when we reach people at home, we have no idea who they are or what categories they fall into. We only know one thing about them—their telephone number.

How Does CBS News Get Those Telephone Numbers?

A computer chooses the telephone numbers of these people for us, and it does so essentially at random. The process that the computer uses is called "random-digit dialing." We tell the computer the area code and the exchanges of every telephone in the United States. First the computer chooses a group of area codes and exchanges at random from a listing of all telephone exchanges that have at least one listed phone number. Once it selects these exchanges, it then picks the last four numbers effectively by chance.

Why Do The Telephone Numbers Have To Be Random?

CBS News goes to great lengths to make sure that the numbers are picked as randomly as possible. Why is that important? It assures that we get old and young people, rich and poor people, conservative and liberal people–and everybody in between. Let's say the computer is about to pick a telephone number from your area code and telephone exchange. There are 10,000 possible telephone numbers. So the odds are one in ten thousand that the computer would pick your telephone number if your exchange were in the sample. But here's the important part: your neighbors would also have exactly that same chance of being selected. Everyone in your neighborhood has the same chance as everyone else of being called in our survey. And the same is true of everyone with a telephone in the United States. That's why we can say that our surveys generally represent the opinions of the whole country.

Do People With Unlisted Telephone Numbers Get Called Too?

Yes, and so do people who have moved recently but whose numbers are not in the telephone book. By picking telephone numbers at random, we don't have to rely on telephone books to choose our respondents. Anyone with a telephone in his or her home has an equal chance of being called by our interviewers. That only leaves out the few people in the United States who do not have telephones. Those people make up a small portion of the public, and their numbers get smaller and smaller every year.

Who Does CBS News Talk To In Each Household?

Once we pick a telephone number and call it, our random selection procedure is not finished. The last step is to decide which individual in the household we want to talk to. Once again, we want to make sure that everyone has an equal chance of being interviewed. We don't necessarily want to talk to the first person who answers the phone. Few families randomly pick who will answer the phone each time it rings. People answer the phone because they always do, or because they were sitting closer to it, or because they were waiting for a call. So when we call, not everyone at home has the same chance of answering the telephone. We ask questions about the people in the household: how many live there, how many are men and how many are women. Then we pick who we want to interview by using a formula which changes every time we make a new call. Until we hear the answers to those two questions, we don't know who we will want to speak with. We may even want to interview someone not at home at the time we call, and we will make an appointment to speak to that person. That extra little bit of chance makes sure that we contact everyone in the country—even long-suffering parents whose children always rush to the phone when it rings.

Do CBS News Respondents Look Like The American Public?

At the end of our surveys, we find sometimes that we have questioned too many people from one group or another. Older people, for example, tend to be at home more than younger people, so there is often a greater percentage of older people in our surveys than exists in the American public. We take great pains to adjust our data so that it accurately reflects the whole population. That process is called "weighting." We make sure that our final figures match U.S. Census Bureau breakdowns on age, sex, race, education, and region of the country.

How Many People Does CBS News Call?

CBS News generally talks to about a thousand people in each of its surveys, although that number varies from a low of 600 to a high of 2,000. We will always report the number of people we have called in our news releases. How can so few people represent millions of Americans? The answer is that we draw a random "sample" of the whole public. Basic math tells us that if we follow the procedure outlined above, our "sample" will be an almost perfect replica of the whole country.

What Is The "Margin Of Error"?

Notice that our sample is an almost perfect replica. There is a catch: we must make a trade-off when we choose to interview a thousand people instead of 200 million.

That trade-off is the "margin of error." Since we are talking to relatively few people, we can only say that our results are correct 95% of the time, give or take a few percentage points. For example, let's say that you see a CBS News story which says that 75% of the public has read a book in the past month. A graphic on the screen has a line that reads: "Margin of Error: 3 points." That means that if we asked all 200 million Americans the same question, we are 95% sure of getting a result anywhere between 72% and 78%.

Sometimes you will see a story which says that a certain election or public opinion question is "too close to call." That is due to the margin of error. Suppose Candidate A has 51% in our poll and Candidate B has 49%—but the margin of error is three percentage points. Since the difference between the two candidates is smaller than the margin of error, each is as likely to win as the other. We cannot (and will not) say that Candidate A is in the lead. You will notice that when the margin of error prevents us from saying for certain who would win, we will not do so. That's why we will always tell you the margin of error in stories about our polls on CBS News — so you can tell for yourself if our results are correct or if they are "too close to call."

ACTIVITY

9

LORD OF ALL I SURVEY

One of the most famous examples of a biased sample was taken during the 1936 Landon-Roosevelt presidential election campaign. *The Literary Digest*, which went out of business soon after, predicted a Landon landslide. In fact, Roosevelt won easily, carrying every state but two. The magazine had sent its survey to a sample of 10 million people selected from lists of owners of cars and phones. Over two million (2,376,523) people returned completed questionnaires.

CONSIDER:

1. You saw in Lesson 3 that the margin of error decreases as the sample size gets larger. In fact, with over 2 million in the sample, the margin of error computed by the formula $\frac{100\%}{\sqrt{n}}$ is almost 0! How could such a large survey have been so terribly wrong? (You may find it helpful to imagine stepping back in time to 1936.)

2. Suppose you administer your questionnaires to a sample that consisted of the football team (or field hockey team). Do you think that their responses would be representative of the responses of all high school students in your school?

3. Can you give a specific example of a question that members of a sports team might answer differently than nonmembers of the team? Why do you think the two groups of students might respond to this question differently?

LORD OF ALL I SURVEY

The Literary Digest based their erroneous predictions on a very large sample. So, obviously, sample size alone does not guarantee a good sample. A good sample is one whose respondents have viewpoints representative of the entire population. In that same year as *The Literary Digest* poll, George Gallup bragged that by using mathematical probability he could predict the outcome of the national election by interviewing a sample of only 1000 people. He predicted a majority for Roosevelt.

YOUR OWN POLL

By this time, your class should have completed the survey questionnaire. Now it's time to start planning how and to whom you will administer your survey. Your sample should include at least 100 students. However, the quality of the information you get from your sample survey will depend on the **survey design**, the method you use to choose your sample. There are three basic steps in planning a sample survey. They are listed below.

Step 1: Identify the **target population**; this is the population you intend to sample.

Step 2: Create a **frame**, a complete listing of the members of the target population.

Step 3: Select a **sample design**. This is the method you plan to use to select your sample. There are many methods for selecting a sample. Six typical sample designs are listed below. Remember, though, the goal of sampling is to get information about the population, so the sample must be representative of its population, not a **biased sample**—one which over- or under-represents one or more groups from the population.

ACTIVITY

9

LORD OF ALL I SURVEY

SIMPLE RANDOM SAMPLE (SRS)

In a **simple random sample** of size n, every subset (of size n) of the target population has an equal chance of being selected. Members of the target population are chosen one at a time and independently. This method relies on random mixing to assure the sample represents its population fairly; this is what you did when you constructed your reference distributions in Lessons 2 and 3.

SYSTEMATIC SAMPLE

A **systematic sample** is a sampling design in which a starting point is selected from a list and then the sample is chosen by taking every kth name after the starting one. Start with your frame. Select a name near the beginning of the list and then sample every tenth (or fifteenth) name on the list until you have the size sample that you need. To avoid bias, you may want to select the starting point and the value of the increment randomly (rather than using 10 or 15 as suggested). Note that each name depends on the one before it, so the "independently" part of simple random sampling is violated in systematic sampling. This sampling method assumes that names with special properties are randomly mixed within your ordered list.

CLUSTER SAMPLE

A **cluster sample** is a sampling design in which a simple random sample of groups is selected and then all individuals within the selected group are surveyed. This method is often used in a door-to-door survey. The basic idea is to take a random sample of clusters and then administer the survey to all the people in the selected clusters. For example, a city may be broken into blocks. Randomly select a sample of blocks from the city. Then canvas each household living on these blocks.

ACTIVITY

LORD OF ALL I SURVEY

9

STRATIFIED SAMPLE

A **stratified sample** is a sampling design used when you want to include representation from several different nonoverlapping groups in a population. Decide what nonoverlapping groups, called strata, you want represented in your sample. (For example, your strata might be males and females; or Democrats and Republicans; or even male Democrats, male Republicans, female Democrats and female Republicans.) Then, take simple random samples from each of the strata. Your design can call for samples of equal size from each stratum or sample sizes proportional to the sizes of the strata within the population. This method replaces some of the randomization with careful identification of special characteristics.

SELF-SELECTING SAMPLE

A **self-selecting sample** is a sampling design in which the sample consists of people who respond to a request for participants in the survey. Rather than selecting a sample, you advertise and let volunteers decide whether they want to be part of your sample.

CONVENIENCE SAMPLE

The **convenience sample** is a sampling design in which you select any sample that is easy to obtain. This is by far the easiest sampling design to administer, because it uses any method that is convenient. It is often used in schools (and sometimes in marketing) to provide quick access to data. For example, your class is a convenience sample.

ACTIVITY

9

LORD OF ALL I SURVEY

Now it's time to begin planning your sampling method.

1. Identify your target population.

2. Make the frame, a listing of the members of the target population. Where can you get this listing? If such a list is not readily available, how could you put such a list together?

3. For each of the sample designs described above, describe how you could collect a sample of 100 students (or slightly more than 100 students) in your school using that method. Then, for each method, write a set of instructions that a team of students could follow to collect the data according to that method.

4. Decide as a class (with input from your teacher) which design to use for administering the sample survey. For your records, write a list of instructions for this design. Describe in precise detail exactly how the sample will be selected and the survey administered; who will do what, and when? If possible, you may want to plan to sample more than 100 students; then if some students don't return their questionnaires, you will still have a sufficiently large number of responses.

5. Go out and collect your data!

INDIVIDUAL WORK 8

Poll Vaulting

For Individual Work 2, you were asked to collect at least five newspaper or magazine articles or reports posted on the Internet. (You may have collected even more articles since then.) But how good are the reports you have collected? What should you look for in a good survey report?

Here is a list of questions you should ask about every survey report you read. If the answer to any of these questions is No, the results of the survey may be questionable.

KEY QUESTIONS ABOUT A SURVEY REPORT

Did the survey report publish

1. the questions asked?
2. the number of people polled?
3. the method used to obtain the sample?
4. the source of the sample (population from which the sample was taken)?
5. the date(s) when the poll was administered?
6. the margin of error?

---

1. Reread each of your articles. Determine whether each of the six items above is present in the report. Take brief notes on the items that are present. For example, if the margin of error is stated in your article, write its value in your notes or highlight it on your article. Then, comment on the reliability of any conclusions drawn from each of these surveys.

2. Read the report: "Americans Brace Themselves Against More Terrorism" by David W. Moore, reprinted below. Then answer items (a-d) referring back to the report as needed.

   a) Make a note of how each of the 6 Key Questions About a Survey Report was handled in this report. Comment on the reliability of the survey results.

b) During April 21–24 (1995), 51% of the sample responded that they approved of the way Bill Clinton was handling his job. Does that mean a majority of Americans approved? Is the sample that produced this point estimate a likely sample from a population having less than 50% Yes responses? Explain.

c) The poll dealing with the presidential approval rating was conducted on Friday–Monday, April 21–24. Why do you think the poll was conducted over several days and not on a single day? Comment on whether or not this was a good choice of days, or whether it would have been better to conduct the poll from Tuesday to Friday.

d) There are two numbers in this article (54% and 3%) followed by [sic]. This means there is an error in the original article immediately preceding the notation [sic]. What should the correct numbers be? Explain your reasoning. Do you think these errors were deliberate (in order to misguide the reader) or accidental?

REPORT:

"Americans Brace Themselves Against More Terrorism"

By   David W. Moore
From: *The Gallup Poll Newsletter* Archive
The Gallup Organization April 95 Newsletter Archive
Volume 59, No. 48a. Saturday, April 29, 1995

Most Believe It Will Happen Again

Princeton, NJ—In the aftermath of the bombing in Oklahoma City, the public seems resigned to the expectation that other parts of the country will also experience terrorist acts in the near future. According to the latest Gallup poll, almost nine of ten Americans (86%) say it is likely that bombings or similar acts of violence will occur somewhere else in the United States —with 50% saying it is "very" likely to happen in the near future, and another 36% saying it is "somewhat" likely.

People are less pessimistic about terrorist acts occurring in their own community: overall, only 28% think such acts are likely to occur, less than one-third the number who believe they will occur somewhere else in the country. Just 9% say they are "very" likely to occur in their own community, and 19% "somewhat" likely.

The Oklahoma City bombing has not produced widespread alarm, but a small group of people are quite concerned about their own safety. About one in seven Americans (14%) say they are "very" worried that they or someone in their family will become victims of a terrorist attack, while another 28% say they are "somewhat" worried. Among those who say they are not worried about becoming victims, (54%) [sic] almost half still think there is some danger, but believe there isn't anything they can do about it.

Women More Worried Than Men

Considerably more women than men express concern about becoming victims and about future terrorist attacks. Over half (54%) of women say they are worried about becoming victims, compared with 30% of men. Also, 33% of women, compared with 22% of men, say that terrorist acts are likely to occur in their own communities; and 91% of women, compared with 82% of men, expect terrorist acts to happen elsewhere in the country.

Small "Rally Effect" for Clinton

As often happens during a period of heightened interest concerning a threat to national security, the President has experienced a surge in public support. His performance rating shortly before the bombing incident was 46% approval, 45% disapproval. The latest poll shows a 51% to 39% rating.

There is some evidence, however, that the rally effect may have already dissipated. Daily tracking figures for the four day period of the poll shows an increase over three days— 47% approval on Friday, 51% on Saturday, and 58% on Sunday—but a drop back to 48% on Monday. This trend has to be viewed with caution, however, as each day's results are based on about only 250 respondents, with a margin of error of about 7 percentage points.

Methodology

The results dealing with public attitudes about the bombing in Oklahoma City are based on telephone interviews with a randomly selected national sample of 758 adults, conducted April 21-23, 1995. For results based on a sample of this size, one can say with 95 percent confidence that the error attributable to sampling and other random effects could be plus or minus four percentage points. The results dealing with the presidential approval rating are based on a national sample of 1008 adults, conducted April 21-24, 1995, with a margin of error of plus or minus three percentage points. In addition to sampling error, question wording and practical difficulties in conducting surveys can introduce error or bias into the findings of public opinion polls.

More Violence in U.S.?— Trend
Sample size: 601 April 20
767 April 21–23

[Question 1]
How likely do you think it is that bombings or similar acts of violence will occur elsewhere in the United States in the near future—very likely, somewhat likely, somewhat unlikely, or very unlikely?

	April 20	April 21–23		
	Total	**Total**	**Men**	**Women**
Very likely	47%	50%	48%	53%
Somewhat likely	42%	36%	34%	3%[sic]
Somewhat unlikely	5%	9%	12%	6%
Very unlikely	3%	3%	4%	2%
No opinion	3%	2%	2%	1%
	100%	100%	100%	100%

In Your Community?

[Question 2]
How likely do you think it is that bombings or similar acts of violence will occur in your community in the near future—very likely, somewhat likely, somewhat unlikely, or very unlikely?

	April 21–23		
	Total	Men	Women
Very likely	9%	8%	10%
Somewhat likely	19%	14%	23%
Somewhat unlikely	27%	24%	30%
Very unlikely	44%	53%	35%
No opinion	1%	1%	2%
	100%	100%	100%

In Your Family?

[Question 3]
How worried are you that you or someone in your family will become a victim of a terrorist attack similar to the bombing in Oklahoma City—very worried, somewhat worried, not too worried, or not worried at all?

*less than 0.5%

	April 21–23		
	Total	Men	Women
Very worried	14%	11%	17%
Somewhat	28%	19%	37%
Not too	33%	36%	30%
Not at all	24%	33%	16%
No opinion	1%	1%	*
	100%	100%	100%

Why Not Worried?
April 21–24

[Question 4]
(Asked of those not too/not at all worried, 433 respondents, ±5%) Which of the following statements better describes why you are not worried about a terrorist attack— You are not worried because the chance that something like that will happen to you or your family is small, or, you are not worried because even though there is some chance that something like that will happen, there is nothing you can do to prevent it?

	April 21–24
Chances small	45%
Nothing can do	45%
Both equally (vol.)	6%
Other (vol.)	3%
No opinion	1%
	100%

Clinton's Handling of Bombing

[Question 5]
Do you approve or disapprove of the way Bill Clinton is handling the events surrounding the bombing in Oklahoma City?

	April 21–24
Approve	84%
Disapprove	7%
No opinion	9%
	100%

Clinton Job Approval— Recent Trend

[Question 6]
Do you approve or disapprove of the way Bill Clinton is handling his job as President?

	Approve	Disapprove	No opinion
1995 April 21-24	51%	39%	10%
1995 April 17-19	46%	45%	9%
1995 April 5-6	47%	45%	8%
1995 March 27-29	44%	47%	9%
1995 March 17-19	46%	45%	9%
April 21–24: Daily Totals			
Friday (278)	47%	41%	12%
Saturday (232)	51%	40%	9%
Sunday (257)	58%	34%	8%
Monday (241)	48%	44%	8%

ACTIVITY

10

CROSS-TABULATION

Sometimes the most interesting information is contained in how responses to two or more questions are linked. For example, David W. Moore's article (reprinted in Individual Work 9) contains the following comment.

> About one in seven Americans (14%) say they are "very" worried that they or someone in their family will become victims of a terrorist attack, while another 28% say they are "somewhat" worried. Among those who say they are not worried about becoming victims, (57%)* almost half still think there is some danger, but believe there isn't anything they can do about it.
>
> *The percent in the original article, 54%, was in error and has been corrected for the purposes of this discussion.

This analysis looks at the responses to the third and fourth questions on the survey. (Refer to Moore's report for the actual wording of the questions.) In particular, it looks among those people who indicated they were not worried about becoming victims of terrorist attacks (see tables under In Your Family?), Moore finds that these 57% do not dismiss the possibility of the reality of this danger but, instead, feel there is nothing they can do about it (see tables under Why Not Worried?). So, their lack of worry about being a victim is predicated on their belief that being a victim is out of their control and not on a belief that no danger is present.

Now it's your turn to try your hand at this type of cross-tabulation analysis. The last four survey questions from Lesson 3's preparation reading are restated (and renumbered) in **Figure 3.47**.

ACTIVITY

CROSS-TABULATION

10

> Q1. Should anyone under the age of 18 be prohibited from driving between midnight and 6:00 AM?
>
> Q2. Should anyone under the age of 18 be prohibited from driving between sunset and sunrise?
>
> Q3. Do you think traffic violations committed by people under the age of 18 should go on their parents' driving record?
>
> Q4. Do you think police should be allowed to immediately impound vehicles driven by traffic violators under the age of 18, no matter who owns the vehicle?

Figure 3.47.
Survey questions on driving.

Suppose these questions were repeated on another survey and then given to 1000 voters in another state. Their (fictitious) responses are presented in **Figures 3.48 and 3.49.** (Assume that No Opinion was not a response choice.)

Q1 and Q2 relate to restricting teenagers from driving at night and Q3 and Q4 relate to traffic violations. Since these pairs of questions appear to be linked, analysis of how Yes respondents to the first question in each pair answered the second question may prove interesting. In order to facilitate this analysis, the data have been organized into cross-tabulation tables, one table for each pair of questions. **Cross-tabulation tables** are tables that break down responses by two or more questions (or two or more variables).

1. Check to see that the responses of all 1000 people surveyed are accounted for in each of the tables.

   Because No Opinion was not one of the responses and the interviewers administering the survey were able to get responses to all questions from everyone surveyed, the percentage of Yes and No responses for each question will sum to 100%.

2. What percentage of those surveyed responded Yes to Q1? Responded No?

3. What percentage of those surveyed responded Yes to Q2? Responded No?

4. How many people responded Yes to Q2? What percentage of these people also responded Yes to Q1? Do you find this result surprising? Explain why or why not.

		Question 2	
		Yes	No
Question 1	Yes	180	390
	No	0	430

Figure 3.48.
Data from Q1 and Q2.

		Question 4	
		Yes	No
Question 3	Yes	130	20
	No	150	700

Figure 3.49.
Data from Q3 and Q4.

ACTIVITY

CROSS-TABULATION

10

5. What percentage of the people who responded Yes to Q1 also responded Yes to Q2? What percentage of the people who responded Yes to Q1 responded No to Q2?

6. Why do you think that a majority of those who responded Yes to Q1 responded No to Q2?

7. a) What percentage of the respondents who answered Yes to Q3 also answered Yes to Q4?

   b) What percentage of the respondents who answered Yes to Q4 also answered Yes to Q3?

   c) What percentage of the respondents answered Yes to both Q3 and Q4?

8. The results in Items 7(a-c) all deal with answering Yes to Q3 and Q4. The answers to Items 7(a and b), however, are considerably larger than the answer to Item 7(c).

   a) Could you change the data in Figure 3.49 in such a way that, based on the altered data, the answer to Item 7(c) would be larger than the answers to both Items 7(a and b)? If so, complete a table similar to Figure 3.49 showing how you would alter the data. If not, explain why not.

   b) How would the data in the cross-tabulation table have to look in order for the answers to Items 7(a, b, and c) to be equal?

   c) Could you change the data in Figure 3.49 in such a way that the answer to Item 7(b) is larger than the answer to Item 7(a)? If so, complete a table similar to Figure 3.49 showing how you would alter the data. If not, explain why not.

9. Return to the original data in Figures 3.48 and 3.49. Write one or two paragraphs reporting some results of interest from this survey. Include at least one comment that shows how the responses to two questions are linked. (In other words, those who answered Yes to the first question are more likely—or less likely—to answer Yes to the second question also.)

A Different Slant

As you know, confidence intervals depend on the confidence level (for example, 90% or 95%) and on sample size. For large sample sizes, you know a formula for approximating the margin of error for 95% confidence intervals. For small samples, though, you still need likely-sample tables. **Figures 3.52-3.60,** at the end of this lesson, are 90% likely-sample tables for a variety of sample sizes. Refer to them for this assignment and, as needed, in later activities.

	Yes	No
Male	7	43
Female	33	17

Figure 3.50.
Results of a survey.

The headmaster at a large private school wanted to institute a new school regulation, but first he wanted the approval of the student body. Instead of giving a questionnaire to the entire student body, he decided to design a survey and administer the questionnaire to a sample of 100 students. He selected a stratified sampling design and gave the questionnaire to 50 randomly selected female students and 50 randomly selected male students. The results for support of the proposed regulation are given in **Figure 3.50.** (A response of Yes indicates approval of the regulation.)

1. Do the male and female populations hold similar views on the issue of the proposed school regulation? Support your answer using sample percentages and 90% confidence intervals for the subpopulation percentages.

2. What percentage of students in the entire sample approved of the regulation? Determine a 90% confidence interval estimating the percentage of all students in the school who would approve this proposed regulation.

3. What percentage of the students surveyed disapproved of the regulation? Determine a 90% confidence interval estimating the percentage of all students in the school who would not approve this regulation..

4. The headmaster said he would go along with the will of the majority of the students. Based on the results of his survey, will he implement the regulation?

5. The breakdown of the student body by gender is 20% male and 80% female. Are the results of this survey reliable? Explain your reasoning.

6. Suppose the headmaster had used a stratified sampling design with male and female students sampled proportionately to their percentages in the school.

   a) How many male students would be in this hypothetical sample of size 100? How many female students?

   b) Complete a copy of **Figure 3.51** for the hypothetical sample assuming the sample percentages of the male and female students responding Yes or No stay the same as in the first survey. (You will need to round to the nearest whole number.)

	Yes	No
Male		
Female		

Figure 3.51.
Hypothetical survey results.

   c) Suppose the survey results had been the ones in your answer to (b). Estimate, using a 90% confidence interval, the percentage of the entire school that would support this regulation. Should the headmaster implement the proposed regulation in this situation?

Number of YES responses in the sample

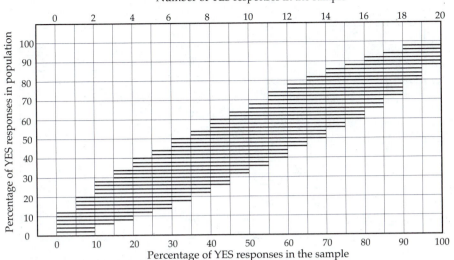

Figure 3.52.
90% likely-sample table for size-20 samples.

Number of YES responses in the sample

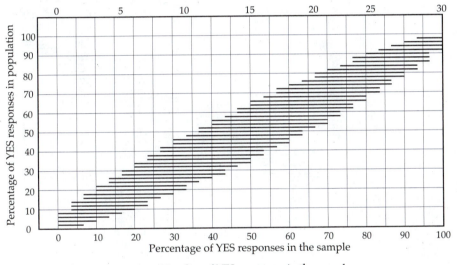

Figure 3.53.
90% likely-sample table for size-30 samples.

Number of YES responses in the sample

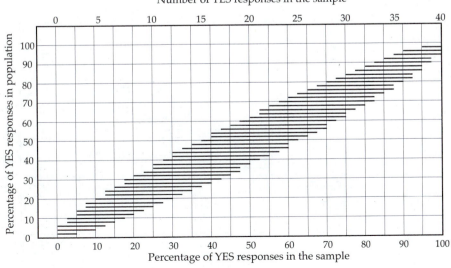

Figure 3.54.
90% likely-sample table for size-40 samples.

INDIVIDUAL WORK 9

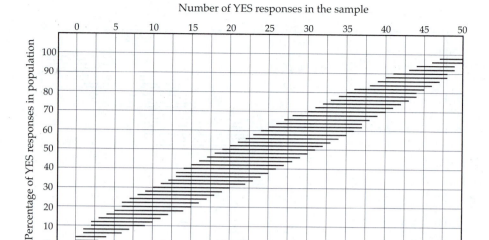

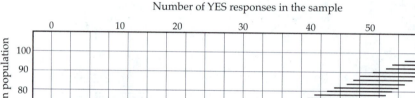

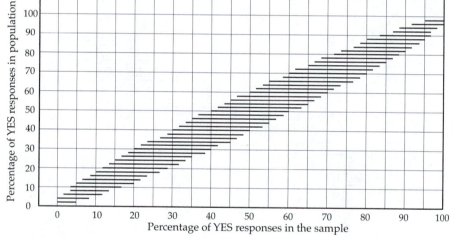

Figure 3.55.
90% likely-sample table for size-50 samples.

Figure 3.56.
90% likely-sample table for size-60 samples.

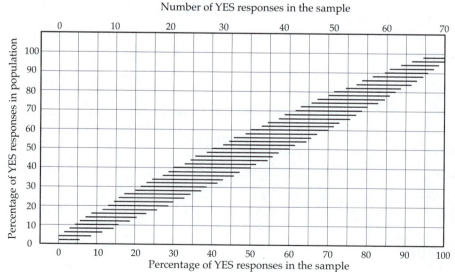

Figure 3.57.
90% likely-sample table for size-70 samples.

Number of YES responses in the sample

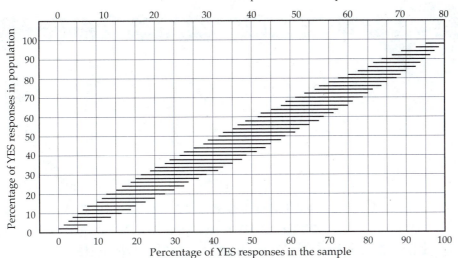

Figure 3.58.
90%- likely-sample table for size-80 samples.

Number of YES responses in the sample

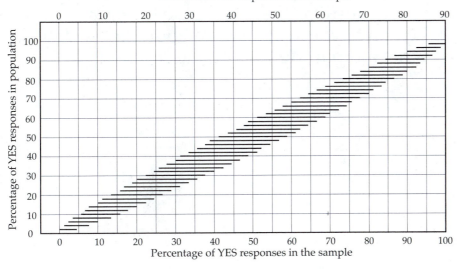

Figure 3.59.
90% likely-sample table for size-90 samples.

Number of YES responses in the sample

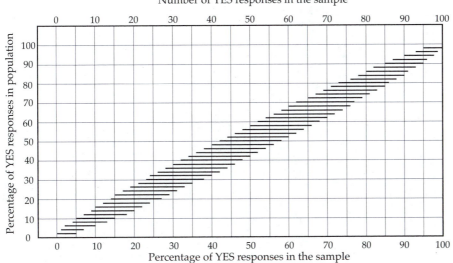

Figure 3.60.
90% likely-sample table for size-100 samples.

ACTIVITY

11

ORGANIZING YOUR DATA

After you have administered your survey, record your results in Figures 1 and 2 on Handout H3.19, "School Survey Results." Divide among groups the work of compiling the survey results. Then, combine group results. In Lesson 5, you will analyze your survey data and write a report describing the results.

The Results Are In!

KEY CONCEPTS

Confidence intervals

Inference

Statistical significance

The Image Bank

PREPARATION READING

East Meets West

Y ou either have, or soon will have, data from your class questionnaire. **Figures 3.61 and 3.62**, on the next page, present data collected from a survey given to students at two schools, one in Washington state and the other on the east coast. In this lesson, the Washington-state/east-coast schools' survey will provide an example of how other students analyzed their data. This example may give you some ideas about how you might explore the data from your own survey.

Questions	25 Grade 11 Girls		25 Grade 11 Boys		25 Grade 12 Girls		25 Grade 12 Boys	
	Yes	No	Yes	No	Yes	No	Yes	No
Q1.Did you drive a car to school at least three times this week?	5	20	4	21	5	20	6	19
Q2. Have you lived for more than two years in the same house?	15	10	18	7	17	8	19	6
Q3. During this year, have you participated in an organized sport (at least once per week in the season)?	10	15	8	17	7	18	6	19
Q4. In the past 2 weeks, have you spent more than $25 on a date?	4	21	15	10	6	19	11	14
Q5. During the past year, have you been involved in a motor vehicle accident?	6	19	8	17	3	22	4	21
Q6. During the past year, have you attended a live concert more than 4 times?	12	13	14	11	15	10	15	10
Q7. Is English your first language?	8	17	9	16	9	16	7	18

Figure 3.61.
Survey results from a school in Washington state.

Questions	25 Grade 11 Girls		25 Grade 11 Boys		25 Grade 12 Girls		25 Grade 12 Boys	
	Yes	No	Yes	No	Yes	No	Yes	No
Q1. Did you drive a car to school at least three times this week?	2	23	3	22	3	22	2	23
Q2. Have you lived for more than two years in the same house?	20	5	15	10	21	4	17	8
Q3. During this year, have you participated in an organized sport (at least once per week in the season)?	10	15	11	14	6	19	7	18
Q4. In the past 2 weeks, have you spent more than $25 on a date?	3	22	5	20	8	17	9	16
Q5. During the past year, have you been involved in a motor vehicle accident?	2	23	5	20	5	20	7	18
Q6. During the past year, have you attended a live concert more than 4 times?	3	22	4	21	5	20	6	19
Q7. Is English your first language?	17	8	19	6	20	5	19	6

Figure 3.62.
Survey results from a school on the east coast.

As you can see, data gathered from even a relatively modest survey (even with only seven questions) can be mind-boggling! Take a few moments to scan through the data in Figures 3.61 and 3.62.

CONSIDER:

1. What was the target population for this survey?

2. What type of survey design was used for this survey? Why do you think students decided on this design?

3. What specific instructions do you think guided the sample selection process?

4. Would this type of survey design be reasonable to implement in your school?

5. What can you say about these two schools just from looking at the numbers? Do any startling differences between the two schools jump out at you?

You expect differences among sample percents, even when samples are taken from identical populations. There is always sampling variability. But is the difference real? The question: Is the difference between samples from two groups large enough to believe that the populations are different? involves the concept of statistical significance. That's the focus of this lesson.

WHAT'S THE DIFFERENCE?

All of the items in this activity are based on the East-meets-West survey presented in the preparation reading. (See Figures 3.61 and 3.62). Were you surprised at the amount of data collected from a seven-question questionnaire? Where do you begin your analysis?

You could start methodically with each question and go down the list one by one. However, sometimes, a good place to start is with a single question you find interesting. For example, what percentage of the students at your school regularly drive to school? (Interpret regularly to mean a student drives to school at least three times per week.) How would your school's percentage compare to the percentages for the Washington-state or the east-coast schools? Which of these two schools has a higher percentage of students who regularly drive to school?

Notice that all the questions in the previous paragraph involve percentages. The data, however, in Figures 3.61 and 3.62 present numbers of students. So, the first step in the analysis is to convert raw numbers to relevant sample percentages.

Because of the sample design of the Washington-state/east-coast surveys, you use the 90% likely-sample tables in Figures 3.52–3.60 at the end of Lesson 4 for much of the analysis of these data.

1. a) Determine the sample percentage of students who respond Yes to survey Q1 for each of the two schools. Then, as appropriate, use likely-sample tables or a margin of error formula to determine confidence intervals for the Yes percentage for each school's total population. State the confidence level (90% or 95%) for your intervals and the method you used to get them.

   b) Look at your confidence intervals determined for part (a). Based on your interval estimates, can you say the percentage of students who regularly drive to school is definitely different for the two schools? Explain why you can or why

WHAT'S THE DIFFERENCE?

you can't. (Is there any single Yes-No population for which both these sample percentages are likely? Is the difference in the sample percentages large enough that it cannot be attributable to chance?)

Your interval estimates for the percentage of students from each school who regularly drive to school were based on sample percentages. A 90% likely-sample table provides a link between the sample results and the estimate of the population percentage. As you read in Lesson 2, this type of analysis in which sample results and probability join forces to provide information about the population is called inference. Finding confidence intervals, then, is a kind of inference.

For this survey, the target population is juniors and seniors enrolled in either of the two schools. Within this target population, there are many subpopulations that share particular characteristics. For example, in Item 1 you analyzed the results from the Washington-state students and the east-coast students as separate subpopulations. There are many other possible subpopulations that may be of interest. For example, the Washington-state juniors, Washington-state seniors, east-coast juniors, and east-coast seniors form four non-overlapping subpopulations.

Frequently, researchers want to compare the viewpoints of different subpopulations and make inferences about differences between the subpopulations. That is the kind of information sought in Item 1(b). No doubt you will be interested in such questions with your class questionnaire, too. In general, before you claim a real difference exists, the difference between sample values needs to be large enough that both values could not reasonably have come from any single population.

2. How many of the Washington-state students would need to switch their answers to Q1 from No to Yes in order for the confidence intervals in Item 1(a) not to overlap? Explain how you arrived at your answer.

ACTIVITY

WHAT'S THE DIFFERENCE?

12

3. Next, look at the data about attendance at concerts (survey Q6). In the Washington-state school, 56/100 of the juniors and seniors attended at least four live concerts in the past year. At the east-coast school, only 18/100 students attended at least four live concerts in the past year.

   a) Is there a real difference (rather than a chance difference due to sampling variability) between the two schools' *populations* on Q6? Is there any Yes-No population that contains both a 56/100 or 56%-Yes sample and an 18/100 or 18%-Yes sample as likely samples? Explain your reasoning.

   b) How many of the east-coast students in the sample would have to change their answers to Q6 from No to Yes in order for at least one Yes-No population to contain both this changed sample percentage and the 56%-Yes sample in their likely-sample groups?

Remember, that for each population there really is some percentage-Yes; it just happens that the actual percentage-Yes value for the population is unknown. A confidence interval names all populations for which a particular sample is likely. Likely means that, among all possible samples from the given population (Remember all your simulations!), the sample is among the 90% (or 95%) most frequent. If two samples from two groups lead to two confidence intervals that overlap, then there is at least one population (in the overlap) for which *both* samples are likely. That is, it is reasonable to think that both samples are related to the *same* population percentage-Yes.

In Item 3, you saw it was not possible for a single population to contain both 56/100 or 56%- and 18/100 or 18%-Yes samples in its 90% likely-sample group. However, in Item 1, there were populations that contained both 20/100 or 20%- and 10/100 or 10%-Yes samples in their likely-sample groups. In the case illustrated by Item 3, you can say there is a statistically significant difference at the 90% level between the two schools on Q6. Note that **statistically significant difference** *only* means the confidence intervals

ACTIVITY

WHAT'S THE DIFFERENCE?

12

do not overlap; no claim is made about the practical significance—how *important* is the difference. In the case illustrated by
Item 1, there is not a statistically significant difference between
the two schools on Q1.

4. a) What happens to the widths of confidence intervals as the
sample sizes decrease? How will that affect the chances
that differences in sample percentages of two subpopulations will be found to be statistically significant?

b) Verify your answer to part (a) by constructing 90% confidence intervals to complete the following sentences about
(sub)population percentages. Identify the likely-sample
table from Figures 3.52–3.60 or Handout H3.20 that you
use for each statement.

• We estimate that between ____% and _____% of juniors
and seniors in the east-coast school have lived in the same
house for more than two years.

• We estimate that between ____% and _____% of junior and
senior girls at the east-coast school have lived in the same
house for more than two years.

• We estimate that between _____% and _____% of the
senior girls at the east-coast school have lived in the same
house for more than two years.

5. Refer to Q5 in the survey: During the past year, have you
been involved in a motor vehicle accident?

a) The percentage of seniors at Washington-state involved in
motor vehicle accidents was half that of the juniors (7/50
for seniors to 14/50 for juniors). Is the difference in the
sample percentages sufficiently large to conclude that the
population of seniors at Washington-state who would
respond Yes to this question is lower than the population
of Washington-state juniors who would respond Yes?
Explain your reasoning.

ACTIVITY

WHAT'S THE DIFFERENCE?

12

b) Suppose that 20% of all seniors at the Washington-state school had actually been involved in motor vehicle accidents during the past year. Are the sample data from the survey consistent with this fact? Explain how you decide.

Your answers above were based on 90% confidence intervals. Thus you decided whether a difference in sample percentages between two groups was significant based on a 90% level of confidence. Statisticians, however, are slightly more particular about use of the word *significant* than are people in general. Unless otherwise indicated, they use the word significant to mean statistically significant at the 95% (or higher) level. This means that in order to determine whether the difference between two sample percentages is significant, you must work with 95% likely-sample tables rather than 90% likely-sample tables. Statisticians reserve the phrase *highly significant* to mean significant at the 99% (or higher) level.

How can you determine significance at the 95% level without access to 95% likely-sample tables? Recall that you developed a formula to approximate margins of error in Activity 8, Lesson 3. It applies whenever the sample size is at least 100.

6. Q7 in the survey asked: Is English your first language?

   a) What percentage of all students surveyed in the Washington-state school answered Yes to this question?

   b) Use the appropriate 90% likely-sample table to determine a 90% confidence interval for the percentage of all students at the Washington-state school who would answer Yes to this question.

   c) Since the sample size is large ($n \geq 100$), your formula (rule of thumb) from Activity 8, Lesson 3 for approximate 95% confidence intervals applies. Recall that the formula says that the 95% confidence interval has endpoints:
   sample percent $\pm \frac{100\%}{\sqrt{n}}$, where n is the sample size.

ACTIVITY

WHAT'S THE DIFFERENCE?

12

Use this formula to determine a 95% confidence interval for the percentage of all students at the Washington-state school who would answer Yes to this question. Compare this 95% confidence interval to the 90% confidence interval from (b). Did the rule of thumb method for determining 95% confidence intervals give a reasonable result? Explain.

d) Use the rule of thumb to determine a 95% confidence interval for the percentage of all students at the east-coast school who would answer Yes to the same question.

e) Is the difference between the percentage of students claiming English as their first language at these two schools significant? Explain your reasoning and interpret your results.

INDIVIDUAL WORK 10

Significant Differences

For Items 1 and 2, refer to Figures 3.52–3.60 at the end of Lesson 4, to Handout H3.20, and to the East-Meets-West survey from the preparation reading.

1. Look at the data about the amount spent on a date (see survey Q4). In the Washington-state school, 36/100 of the juniors and seniors had spent more than $25 on a date, but at the east-coast school only 25/100 students had spent more than $25 on a date. Is there a Yes-No population that contains both of these samples in their 90% likely-sample groups? Is the difference in the sample percentages large enough that it cannot be attributable only to chance? In other words, is the difference significant at the 90% level?

2. For each of the survey questions and paired groups listed in **Figure 3.63**, decide whether the difference between the two groups is statistically significant at the 90% level. Justify your answers.

Figure 3.63.
Comparisons between subpopulations.

Questions	Grade A	Grade B	Significant difference yes/no
a) Have you lived for more than two years in the same house? (Q2)	Juniors	Seniors	
b) Have you lived for more than two years in the same house? (Q2)	Washington junior boys	Washington senior boys	
c) During this year, have you participated in an organized sport (at least once per week in the season)? (Q3)	Grade 11	Grade 12	
d) In the past 2 weeks, have you spent more than $25 on a date? (Q4)	Junior girls	Senior girls	
e) In the past 2 weeks, have you spent more than $25 on a date? (Q4)	East coast senior boys	Washington senior boys	
f) During the past year, have you attended a live concert more than 4 times? (Q6)	East coast boys	Washington girls	

INDIVIDUAL WORK 10

3. Now, examine your own school survey questions and identify sub-populations who might respond differently to them. If you have joined with another school, then you also may be interested in looking at differences between the responses of the students at the two schools. Make a list of four question comparisons for your survey, similar to those listed above, that are of interest to you.

4. For each of your comparisons identified in Item 3, determine whether the difference in the sample percentages is sufficiently large to be statistically significant at the 90% or the 95% level (select whichever level you want). Explain your reasoning.

5. The pie charts in **Figure 3.64** display results from nationwide surveys of adults conducted in the 1990s by the National Opinion Research Center at the University of Chicago.

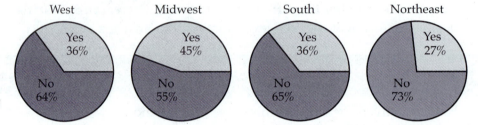

Figure 3.64.
Hunting and fishing in four regions.

a) Can you conclude, without any further information, that there is a significant difference between the hunting and fishing pastimes of adults in the four regions of the United States? Explain your answer.

b) Assume that random samples of size n (same n for each sample) were selected from each of the four regions. How large must n be for the difference between the West and Midwest sample percentages to be significant?

c) How large must the sample size, n, be for the difference in the West and Northeast sample percentages to be significant?

6. You know that a sample difference may be significant for large samples when the same difference is not significant for smaller samples, since confidence intervals for small samples are larger. What is the corresponding comparison between 90% and 95% levels?

ACTIVITY

ANOTHER APPROXIMATION

13

You have developed two models for making inferences from samples. The first relies on direct access to reference distributions for your selected sample size. These might be provided in a book, or you might need to generate them from simulations. Using reference distributions, you can set your confidence level at 90% or 95% (or anything else you want). This method is the most exact, but only if you use many simulations for each population and include many populations. That takes a *lot* of time!

If the sample size is large, a second method is available. You can determine 95% confidence intervals using the rule of thumb for margins of error. However, it provides only 95% confidence intervals, and it only applies when the sample size is at least 100. When you analyze your own survey data, some interesting sub-population sample sizes will be less than 100. It's time for a new model!

Here is a more exact formula for approximating 95% confidence intervals.

The 95% confidence interval = sample percent $\pm\ 100\% \times 2\sqrt{p\dfrac{1-p}{n}}$,

where p is the sample proportion (i.e., $\dfrac{\text{sample percentage}}{100\%}$)

and n is the sample size.

This formula still only gives 95% intervals, but that is the usual level anyway. It also has a size restriction on its use, but the restriction is less stringent: the product of the sample size, n, and sample proportion, p, must be at least 5 ($np \geq 5$), and $n(1 - p) \geq 5$.

ACTIVITY

ANOTHER APPROXIMATION

13

To see why these restrictions might make sense, remember that margins of error create intervals centered on point estimates. But think back to your simulations in early lessons. Reference distributions are not symmetric when the percentage-Yes population is near 0% or 100%, and larger samples tend to give more symmetric reference distributions than do small samples. Basically, the condition $np \geq 5$ keeps the percentage-Yes far enough away from 0%, and $n(1 - p) \geq 5$ keeps it away from 100%.

1. Use this new formula to determine an approximate 95% confidence interval for the percentage of students at the Washington-state school who claim English as their first language. Is your 95% confidence interval using this method close to your answer to Item 6(c) of Activity 12?

2. For each of the comparisons you identified in Item 3 of Individual Work 10 that also meet the np restrictions, determine whether the difference in the sample percentages is sufficiently large to be statistically significant at the 95% level using the new formula. Explain your reasoning.

3. Recall that for large samples (sample size $n \geq 100$), pollsters determine confidence intervals using the simpler approximation $\dfrac{100\%}{\sqrt{n}}$ instead of the more exact approximation $100\% \times 2\sqrt{p\dfrac{(1-p)}{n}}$. The new formula involves p; the old one does not. (Remember, p is a number between 0 and 1.)

   a) Based on your work with reference distributions and likely-sample tables, how does the size of confidence intervals (all for the same sample size) change as the sample percentage changes? For example, what kinds of sample percentages produce the largest confidence intervals?

ACTIVITY

ANOTHER APPROXIMATION

13

b) Compare the approximations provided by the two formulas for 95% margins of error, using a fixed (large) sample size. Round all approximations to the nearest tenth of a percent. A table, similar to that shown in **Figure 3.65** for samples of size 900, may prove useful. You may wish to try the comparison for a variety of sample sizes.

Sample percentage: $(100\% \times p)$	Formula $100\%(2\sqrt{(p(1-p)/900)})$	Formula $100\%/\sqrt{900}$
10%		
20%		
30%		
40%		
50%		
60%		
70%		
80%		
90%		

Figure 3.65.
Comparing formulas for 95% margin of error.

c) Algebraically determine the value of p that makes $100\%\left(2\sqrt{p\dfrac{(1-p)}{n}}\right) = \dfrac{100\%}{\sqrt{n}}$, regardless of the sample size, n.

d) In general, which confidence intervals will be wider, the ones based on the old rule of thumb for margins of error, or the ones based on the new formula involving p? Assuming that the formula involving p is more accurate, does the old rule of thumb provide more or less confidence than 95%?

INDIVIDUAL WORK 11

Connections

1. Repeat Items 5(b) and 5(c) of Individual Work 10, this time using the new approximation formula for 95% confidence intervals.

2. Suppose an article in a school newspaper contains the following statement:

   According to our survey, 80% of the boys in a school's senior class did less than 2 hours homework per week, but only 50% of the senior girls spent less than 2 hours each week on homework.

   The article neglected to specify the sample sizes. For each of the sample sizes in (a-d), use the $100\% \times 2\sqrt{p\dfrac{(1-p)}{n}}$ formula to find 95% confidence intervals for the percentage of boys and then girls in the senior class who spent less than 2 hours each week on homework. Round your answers to the nearest 1%.

   a) Both samples were of size 25.

   b) The sample sizes were 50 boys and 50 girls.

   c) The sample sizes were 25 boys and 50 girls.

   d) The sample sizes were 50 boys and 25 girls.

   e) Decide whether the difference in the boys' 80% and girls' 50% samples is significant for each of the sample sizes in (a-d). (Remember, to a statistician, significant means statistically significant at the 95% (or greater) level.)

3. Why do the sample sizes in Item 2 affect whether the difference between the 80% and 50% sample responses is statistically significant?

The unit began with an interest in the size of a wildlife population, particularly if the species is endangered. Lesson 6 returns to the problem of estimating the size of an animal population. The next item will get you in the proper frame of mind to begin Lesson 6.

4. Suppose, in a sample of 1089 salmon, a scientist finds that 23% were marked.

   a) How can the salmon population be viewed as a Yes-No population?

b) Use the old rule of thumb formula to determine an approximate 95% confidence interval for the percentage of marked salmon in the population. (Round your answer to the nearest tenth of a percent.)

c) Use the new $100\% \times 2\sqrt{p\dfrac{(1-p)}{n}}$ formula to calculate an approximate 95% confidence interval for the percentage of marked salmon in the population. (Round your answer to the nearest tenth of a percent.)

5. A biologist examined samples of salmon caught on two different days. On the first day, 50 of the 1000 salmon had been previously tagged. No additional salmon were tagged on this day. On the second day, 140 of 1000 salmon had been tagged.

a) What percentage of the salmon in the first day's sample were tagged?

b) What percentage of the salmon in the second day's sample were tagged?

c) For each of the samples, use the rule of thumb to determine the Yes populations that contain the sample percentage in their 95% likely-sample groups.

d) Is the difference in the sample percentages for the two days significant?

e) Offer one or more plausible explanations for observing two samples from the same population that give significantly different results. (Remember to interpret the phrase *significantly different* as a statistician would.)

6. In Lesson 5, you will see that the stratified sampling design used by the Washington-state and east-coast students made the analysis of their subpopulation results easier. What would you need to know about these schools in order to determine whether the results of their survey are representative of the student populations in their schools?

ACTIVITY

THE WRITE STUFF

14

You've designed your survey questionnaire, selected your sample, administered your survey, and organized your results. All that's left is to complete the analysis of your data and write the report.

To help you think about ways to present your survey results, go back to Individual Work 8 and review the list of six elements that should be incorporated into a reputable report.

1. Read Handout H3.21, "Poll: Clinton still way ahead of Dole." This article appeared in *USA Today* on July 23, 1996, prior to the 1996 Republican and Democratic Conventions.

   Did the *USA Today* article include the six Key Questions About a Survey Report introduced in Lesson 4, Individual Work 8? Describe those included, and list those omitted.

2. What other elements in the article turned the survey results into a report suitable for publication in a newspaper?

3. Now that you have had some experience with the methods used in analyzing survey data, complete the analysis of your data. When you have finished, transform your survey results into a report that will be understandable and interesting to your reader. (Perhaps your report would be suitable for publication in the school newspaper.)

THE WRITE STUFF

Report Guidelines

- Focus on several of the issues in your survey that were of greatest interest to you, rather than giving a question-by-question analysis.

Your report should include:

- at least one comparison between two groups.

- at least one graphic display representing your results to make your report visually appealing.

- all the information needed to assess the reliability of the sample survey (margin of error for the entire survey and confidence intervals or the margins of error on questions dealing with a subsample of your survey).

- a title (or headline) and the authors' names.

- an introduction, a presentation of results, and a conclusion.

Remember, your report should be written in a way that is accurate, attracts attention, and is clear to the reader.

LESSON SIX

Tag, You're It!

KEY CONCEPTS

Mark-recapture methods

Petersen estimate

Proportional reasoning

The Image Bank

PREPARATION READING

Balancing Act

How many wolves are there in Michigan? Are their numbers increasing, decreasing, or remaining relatively constant? How large is the moose population in Maine, New Hampshire, and Vermont? How many black bear are in Oregon? How many sea turtles (in particular, the endangered Kemp's ridley) are there in the Gulf of Mexico? What is the population of desert tortoises in the Mojave Desert?

Why would anyone care about these questions?

Humans have, at times, upset the balance of ecosystems. For example, in Scotland, wolves and bears were hunted to extinction. Recall that wolves were also nearly hunted to extinction in the United States. This has left the red deer with no nonhuman natural predators, which in turn has led to large increases in the deer population. In many areas, the native vegetation has been unable to sustain the increased deer population. Today, wildlife managers must decrease the deer population to avoid widescale degradation of habitat and widespread starvation of deer.

How do scientists estimate the abundance of animal populations? There are several main techniques, which include distance sampling, mark-recapture methods, and catch data methods. You may want to do some independent research on the other methods. This lesson will focus on mark-recapture methods because the methods used earlier to analyze sample-survey data can be applied directly to mark-recapture data. The **mark-recapture method** is a method for estimating the size of an animal population based on at least two sampling episodes. An initial sample of animals is captured, marked, and then released. Later, a second sample is caught, and the fraction of marked animals in that group is recorded.

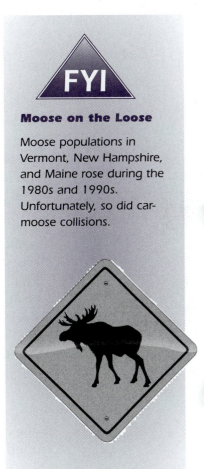

FYI

Moose on the Loose

Moose populations in Vermont, New Hampshire, and Maine rose during the 1980s and 1990s. Unfortunately, so did car-moose collisions.

CONSIDER:

What animals (including insects) in your state do you think wildlife managers routinely monitor?

ACTIVITY

RATS AND BEANIE BEARS

15

Rats!

Rat infestations in populated areas can bring disease and other problems into homes. Poisons are one means of controlling the spread of disease-carrying rats; however, some rats develop resistance to certain poisons. For example, initial enthusiasm over poison as a means of controlling the brown rat was tempered around 1960 by the discovery of resistant populations. In response to this new development, scientists initiated studies to gain a better understanding of the brown rats' population size and factors contributing to its growth.

One such study, conducted by ecologists J. A. Bishop and D. J. Hartley sought to estimate the size and degree of movement within and between populations of brown rats near Welshpool, Wales. They used a mark-recapture experiment to collect data. They chose an area of about 1 km^2 that was partially enclosed by two rivers. However, their original sampling design, to capture and then release rats among the farmhouses, hedgerows, and woodlands, had to be altered because farmers vehemently opposed releasing rats around their farmhouses. Instead, the team decided to focus on rats in the hedgerows and woodlands, leaving the rats in the areas around farmhouses out of their study.

They set up 122 permanent trapping stations in the sample area, concentrating the stations in regions where the rat infestation was thought to be the heaviest. The traps—steel-mesh cages baited with wheat, maize, and meal—had a spring-loaded door with a release treadle near the bait tray. Sprung traps were emptied into a cloth bag. Captured rats were weighed with a spring balance, and their gender and general physical condition were recorded. After marking (two toes were clipped), the rats were released. The trapping took place over a period of two years. The results of their study were published in 1976 in the *Journal of Animal Ecology*.

RATS AND BEANIE BEARS

This reading tells about ecologists who conducted a mark-recapture study to gather information about populations of poison-resistant rats. In fact, mark-recapture methods have been used to track the sizes of all types of animal populations, from fish to rat, human to insect, large mammal to reptile.

The techniques you have learned for analyzing sample surveys can be applied to mark-recapture data. So, you, too, have the tools to solve the kinds of problems faced by scientists when they want to estimate the size of an animal population.

Beanie Bears

Imagine yourself as a wildlife manager in Oregon monitoring the black bear population.

As part of your research you will need to answer the following questions:

- How many bears are there?

- Are their numbers increasing or decreasing?

Because bears are solitary and not easily detected by sighting surveys, mark-recapture methods (or some combination of methods that include mark-recapture techniques) have been used to estimate the size of the bear population.

In this activity, you will simulate the results of a mark-recapture study using beans to represent the bears. You will use your simulated data to estimate the size of the beanie-bear population and then assess how well the mark-recapture method did in estimating the number of beans.

The Experiment

Your teacher will give you a paper lunch bag (or some other container) that contains the beans. Imagine the beans in your bag represent the present population of bears in Oregon.

ACTIVITY

15

RATS AND BEANIE BEARS

PHASE 1:

Marking the first sample

Grab two handfuls of beans from the bag. (These represent the captured bears.) Count and record in a table similar to **Figure 3.66** the number of captured beans. Clearly mark each bean in the sample with a magic marker, then return each of the beans to the bag.

PHASE 2:

Selecting the second sample

Carefully shake the bag until the marked and unmarked beans are mixed thoroughly. (Remember the importance of representative samples, so mix well.) Select a second sample by grabbing several handfuls of beans without replacement. Count and record in your table the number (total) of beans in this sample, as well as the number of recaptured beans (beans already marked).

Phase 1: First sample	
Number captured and marked	
Population size	N (unknown)
Phase 2	
Number captured	
Number marked (marked beans)	

Figure 3.66.
Data table.

1. For answers to (a-c), do not round.

   a) Compute the sample percentage of marked beans as an estimate of the population percentage of marked beans.

ACTIVITY

RATS AND BEANIE BEARS

15

b) Determine a 95% confidence interval for the percentage of marked animals in the population. Clearly indicate your method, and verify that the conditions for using your method are satisfied.

c) Interpret the meaning of a 95% confidence interval for the percentage of marked animals in the population.

d) Complete the following sentences based on your answers to (a) and (b). (Round your answers to the nearest whole number.)

Point estimate: We estimate there are _____ animals in the population.

Interval estimate: Based on a 95% confidence interval, we estimate the size of the population is between ____ and ____ animals.

e) The confidence interval in (b) is symmetric about the sample percentage of marked animals. (In other words, when computing the confidence interval, you added the same amount to the sample percentage that you subtracted from the sample percentage.) Is your interval estimate in (d) symmetric about the point estimate for the population size?

2. How good is your estimate of the number of beans in your bag? To find out, estimate the population size using a second method. (This estimate could be based on weight, volume, or some other method.) Compare this estimate with the one based on your mark-recapture study.

In Activity 15, you invented a method of applying your knowledge of confidence intervals for population percentage-Yes data to the task of determining an interval estimate for wildlife populations. You are a modeler. But did you remember to write out all your assumptions carefully, so others could check the validity of your model? Did you generalize your work into a formula that others could use in similar situations, but with their own data? Did you test your model's behavior under a variety of conditions? If not, this activity is for you!

C.G.J. Petersen

In 1896, Danish fisheries biologist C.G.J Petersen carried out the first ecological use of mark-and-recapture. Tagging of fish was first used to study movements and migration of individuals, but Petersen realized that tagging could also be used to estimate population size and to measure mortality rates.

The **Petersen method** is the simplest mark-recapture method because it is based on a single sample of marked, released animals and a subsequent sample of recaptured and first-time-captured animals. It is probably the one you came up with on your own. The validity of the Petersen estimate is based on the following assumptions.

Assumptions for Petersen Method

(1) The population is closed; in other words, its size is constant.

(2) All marks are permanent (at least for the duration of the experiment) and are noted correctly upon recapture.

(3) Marking the animals does not affect their chances of subsequently being recaptured.

(4) All animals, marked or unmarked, have an equal chance of being captured. (Often, this means there must be enough time between the two samples for marked and unmarked animals to mix.)

ACTIVITY

THE PETERSEN METHOD

16

1. Describe how each of these assumptions was satisfied in your simulation experiment of Activity 15.

2. Petersen's method for estimating the size of a wildlife population involves the following quantities:

   M = the number of marked animals released into the population.

   C = the sample size of the second sample.

   R = the number of marked objects in the second sample.

   N = the size of the population (unknown).

   a) Use the method of generalization and your work in Activity 15 to get a formula for a point estimate of N, the size of the population. This formula is called the Petersen estimate of population size.

   b) Suppose none of the animals in your second sample are marked. What value would you get from the Petersen estimate? Provided none of assumptions (1)-(4) have been violated, what do you think this really says about the size of your population?

   c) Suppose a very high percentage of animals in your second sample are marked. Provided none of assumptions (1)-(4) have been violated, what can you conclude about the sample size?

3. The Goodwin Conservation Center in North Windham, Connecticut, has been the site of several small-mammal studies. During the summer of 1996, one such study focused on the population of white-footed mice. Mice were trapped one night and marked by trimming fur on the sides of their bodies. (When the weather is warm, trimming the fur on a mouse does not harm the mouse. Since the experiment was planned for a two- to three-week period, the trimmed area on the marked mice would remain visible for the duration of the experiment.) The marked mice were released. Traps were set again on another night.

ACTIVITY

16

THE PETERSEN METHOD

a) Suppose 35 mice were captured on the first night, marked, and then released. On the second night, of the 28 mice captured, 6 of them were found to be marked. Determine the value of Petersen's estimate for the size of the population of white-footed mice. (Round your answer to the nearest whole number.)

b) Suppose, after their first capture experience, some of the marked mice became trap-happy. They enjoyed the food in the trap and did not mind the marking process. When traps were set out a second time, these mice headed straight for a trap. Which of Petersen's assumptions would this violate? In this situation, would you expect the estimate in (a) to underestimate or overestimate the actual size of the mouse population? Explain.

c) Suppose, instead, some of the marked mice became trap-shy after their first capture experience. They became afraid of being caught again and avoided the traps on the second night. Which assumption would this violate? In this situation, would you expect the estimate in (a) to underestimate or overestimate the actual size of the mouse population? Explain.

d) Suppose because of bad weather the second trapping was delayed. Because of this delay, the trimmed fur on some of the marked mice was not visible. Which assumption would this violate? In this situation, would you expect the estimate in (a) to underestimate or overestimate the actual size of the mouse population? Explain.

ACTIVITY

THE PETERSEN METHOD

16

Wolves are natural predators of deer. In areas where the natural predators have been killed by humans, deer populations can increase to numbers that are unsupportable by their habitat. In many areas of the country, deer populations are monitored so they can be properly managed.

4. Suppose roe deer were captured and marked with brightly colored leather collars. Later a second sample of deer were taken by binocular sightings. The recaptured deer were those deer sighted wearing the distinctive collars. The data are given below.

Number of deer marked and released: 175

Number of sightings of deer after release: 220

Number of sightings of marked deer: 78

a) What percentage of the sighted deer were marked? Determine a 95% confidence interval for the percentage of marked deer in the population. (Retain at least two decimal places in the lower value and upper value of your confidence interval. Wait until (b) to round your answers any further.)

b) Complete the following sentences. (Round your answers to the nearest whole number.)

We estimate the population consists of _____ deer.

We estimate the size of the deer population to be between _____ and _____ deer.

c) Suppose you unknowingly sight two (uncollared) deer twice, thus overcounting the sighted deer by two. How much would this overcount affect your point estimate for the size of the deer population? Your interval estimate of the deer population?

ACTIVITY

16

THE PETERSEN METHOD

d) Suppose the marked collars made deer easier for illegal hunters to see and therefore kill. How would a loss of marked deer affect your estimate for the population size at the time of the second sample? If possible, write a formula for the size of the error in the point estimate.

e) Suppose forest rangers discovered that 15 marked deer (none of the unmarked deer) had been killed by hunters. Based on this knowledge, estimate the size of the population at the time of the second capture. Use this result to check part (d).

Phase 1: First sample	
Number captured and marked	155
Population size	N (unknown)
Phase 2	
Number captured	78
Number of recaptured (marked)	8

Figure 3.67.
Results of grasshopper study.

Phase 1: First sample	
Number captured and marked	46
Population size	N (unknown)
Phase 2	
Number captured	60
Number of recaptured (marked)	28

Figure 3.68.
Results of grasshopper study.

5. As part of a class experiment, students captured a sample of grasshoppers from randomly selected plots in a large field behind their school. They carefully marked the captured grasshoppers with a dot of nail polish and released them in the middle of the field. The next day students returned to the field and captured a second sample of grasshoppers. Their data are presented in **Figure 3.67**.

a) Estimate the number of grasshoppers in the field.

b) Another class at the same school also decided to conduct this experiment. They had little time and captured the second sample approximately 15 minutes after releasing the first sample in the middle of the field. **Figure 3.68** presents their data. Based on these data, what is your estimate for the number of grasshoppers in the field?

c) The two class experiments were conducted in the same field during the same week. Offer an explanation for the large discrepancy in the two estimates. Which of the two estimates do you think is more reliable? Why?

M A T H   A T   W O R K

Diane-Heger Boyd is one of a unique group of wildlife researchers. She works long hours under harsh conditions in the field because she dedicates much of her time to gathering and interpreting data about wolves. Diane sets a target number of wolves that she wants to capture as her sample from each wolf pack, then she moves on to another area to do the same. Some of her work involves trapping wolves found in the northwest corner of Glacier National Park and injecting them with a tranquilizer. Once that is done, she draws blood samples and examines the animals to check their physical condition. She also fits wolves with radio collars, allowing radio tracking of their movement and behaviors. The data Diane gathers from her samples helps to provide information about the larger wolf population.

INDIVIDUAL WORK 12

Hare Today, Gone Tomorrow?

1. As the wolf population in states such as Minnesota increases, scientists are interested in how the sizes of the populations upon which wolves prey might be affected. Wolves will prey on deer, moose, and even snowshoe hare. Data from a mark-recapture study conducted near Lake Alexander, Minnesota, are presented in **Figure 3.69.**

Phase 1: First sample	
Number captured and marked	948
Population size	N (unknown)
Phase 2	
Number captured	421
Number of recaptured (marked)	167

Figure 3.69.
Results of snowshoe hare study.

a) What is the Petersen estimate for the snowshoe hare population near Lake Alexander?

b) Determine an interval estimate based on a 95% confidence interval for the percentage of marked snowshoe hare in the population.

c) Suppose scientists, concerned that the growing wolf population might be adversely affecting the snowshoe hare population around Lake Alexander, returned several years later to complete a follow-up study. Hypothetical results from this study are presented in **Figure 3.70.**

Phase 1: First sample	
Number captured and marked	820
Population size	N (unknown)
Phase 2	
Number captured	408
Number of recaptured (marked)	162

Figure 3.70.
Results from follow-up snowshoe hare study.

d) Based on the data in Figure 3.70, determine a point estimate for the number of showshoe hare in the Lake Alexander area.

e) Determine an interval estimate for the size of the snowshoe hare population at the time of the follow-up study. Based on your interval estimate, does it appear that the size of the snowshoe hare population has changed significantly from the time of the first study to the time of the follow-up study? Is there evidence that the increased number of wolves may have adversely affected the showshoe hare population?

2. A class of 30 physics students went to the fairground to collect data on applications of physics to amusement rides. One student noticed that out of 100 students on the ferris wheel ride, there were only 6 students from her class.

a) Determine a confidence interval for the percentage of students at the fair who were from the physics class.

b) Based on your confidence interval for (a), determine an interval estimate for the number of students at the fair.

c) Discuss why the interval in (b) is so wide.

3. During her summer vacations, Naomi volunteers at the Reifel Bird Sanctuary in British Columbia. Each year she helps with collecting data during the annual winter Snow Goose migration. One day, in a sample of 1000 geese, she observed 85 that had been banded at the Alaskan breeding grounds the same year. She discovered that 950 newly-hatched geese had been banded that year. Use Naomi's experiences to write a paragraph that could be used as an extra credit science report. Include in this report a discussion of the reliability of your population estimate. What factors might make the estimate less reliable?

THE DYE IS CAST

Petersen's model does a great job of estimating wildlife populations when there is only one cycle of capture-mark-release-recapture. Larger samples give more reliable and precise estimates. It might be difficult to increase the number of recaptures in a single cycle, but it is possible to repeat the release and recapture cycle more than once. That's the idea behind one possible refinement of your mark-recapture model.

In an experiment in England in the 1960's, a biologist was given the task of estimating the size of the squirrel population in a forest. His experimental design consisted of capturing and releasing six samples of squirrels. Squirrels from the first two samples were marked with a harmless dye. On the first day of the experiment, he caught 15 squirrels. He marked the squirrels and released them. The next day, he caught 20 squirrels, three of which were already marked. Then he marked the 17 squirrels that were first-time captures and released all the squirrels. On each of the next four days, he captured another sample of squirrels. After he recorded the size of the sample and the number of marked squirrels in a sample, he released the squirrels. (He did not mark any additional squirrels during these four days.) His data were similar to the data in **Figure 3.71.**

Figure 3.71.
Squirrel data.

Sample	Sample Size	Number of marked animals in sample	Number of First-time captures marked
1	15	No animals have been marked	15
2	20	3	17
3	24	6	0
4	30	11	0
5	19	8	0
6	31	9	0

ACTIVITY

THE DYE IS CAST

17

1. a) What is the Petersen estimate of the size of the squirrel population based on the results of the second sample and the number of marked squirrels at the time the second sample was taken?

   b) What is the Petersen estimate of the size of the squirrel population based on the information from sample 3 and the number of marked squirrels at the time the third sample was taken?

   c) How would you combine your estimates from parts (a) and (b) into a single estimate for the size of the squirrel population? What is your combined estimate?

2. Hypothetical results from another study are presented in **Figure 3.72.**

Sample	Sample Size	Number of marked animals in sample	Number of First-time captures marked
1	15	No animals have been marked	15
2	7	2	5
3	40	6	0

Figure 3.72.
Results from hypothetical study.

   a) What is the Petersen estimate of the population size based on the results from the second sample and the number of marked squirrels at the time the second sample was taken?

   b) What is the Petersen estimate of the population size based on the results of the third sample and the number of marked squirrels at the time the third sample was taken?

   c) Which do you think is more reliable, your estimate from (a) or your estimate from (b)? Explain.

d) Taken together, samples 2 and 3 contained 47 squirrels. What proportion of those squirrels came from sample 2? What proportion from sample 3?

e) When determining a combined estimate from your answers to (a) and (b), the estimate (either (a) or (b)) you feel is most reliable should be given more weight. Form a combined estimate by using your proportions from (d) to weight your estimates from (a) and (b). What is your combined estimate for the population? Does this answer seem reasonable given your estimates in (a) and (b)?

3. Return to your combined estimate in Item 1(c). Did you use a weighted average of your estimates from 1(a) and 1(b)? If not, adjust your combined estimate so 1(a) and 1(b) are weighted by their respective proportions 20/44 and 24/44. What is your combined estimate?

Note that individual estimates from larger samples are given more weight in the combined estimate than individual estimates from smaller samples.

Items 4 and 5 refer to the data from Figure 3.71.

4. a) What is Petersen's estimate for the size of the squirrel population based on the information from the fourth sample and the number of marked squirrels at the time that the fourth sample was taken?

b) Explain how you would combine your estimates from Items 1(a), 1(b), and 4(a) into a single estimate for the size of the squirrel population. Note that sample 4 is the largest sample among the first four samples, so your estimate from 4(a) should carry the most weight. Explain how you determined your estimate.

5. Estimate the size of the squirrel population using all the data in Figure 3.71. Justify your choice of estimate.

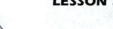

ACTIVITY

THE DYE IS CAST

17

Petersen's estimate for population size is widely used because it is intuitively clear and easy to apply. However, it has a tendency to over-estimate the size of the population when the number of recaptured animals is small, in particular if $R < 10$. **Bailey's modification** of Petersen's estimate is used when the number of recaptures is less than 10; it is given below.

$N = [M(C + 1)/(R + 1)]$ where,

N = the size of the population,

C = the sample size of the second sample,

R = the number of marked animals in the second sample,

N = the size of the population.

6. Suppose a mark-recapture study was completed on a wild dog population in Bucklin, Montana. The data from the study resulted in $M = 45$, $C = 16$, and $R = 8$.

   a) Estimate the wild dog population using Petersen's estimate.

   b) Estimate the wild dog population using the Bailey's modification.

   c) Which estimate is larger, Petersen's or Bailey's?

7. a) Investigate whether Bailey's modification always produces a number less than Petersen's estimate. It may be helpful to determine first the conditions under which the two estimates are equal.

   b) As the number of marked animals in the second sample increases, what happens to the difference between Petersen's estimate and Bailey's modification?

8. Now return to the data in Figure 3.71. Rework Item 1 using Bailey's estimate instead of Petersen's. Compare the two estimates.

There are many other modifications to Petersen's estimate. Some modifications work better under some conditions than others. The perfect means of estimating wildlife populations has not yet been found, and scientists continually search for better estimation methods.

Wrapping Up Unit Three

1. The following article appeared in the *Worcester* (Massachusetts) *Telegram and Gazette.*

Survey says taxpayers support science-related costs.

CAMBRIDGE—Americans' enthusiasm for inventions and inventiveness appears alive and well and headed into outer space.

One-sixth of adults surveyed would pay more taxes to fund a search for extraterrestrial life, according to a survey by an MIT-affiliated group that promotes innovation.

Closer to home, more than 80 percent were willing to pay higher taxes to search for cures for AIDS and cancer.

"Americans are still adventurers at heart and understand that science is the endless frontier where there are always new explorations to be made," said Lester Thurow, a professor of management at the Massachusetts Institute of Technology and chairman of the Lemelson-MIT Awards, which conducted the survey.

a) Comment on the reliability of the results in this article. In particular, what information is contained in this article that would make you believe the survey information is reliable? What might lead you to believe the survey results are not reliable?

b) Only one-sixth of those surveyed would pay more taxes to fund a search for extraterrestrial life, but 80% would be willing to pay higher taxes to search for cures for AIDS and cancer. Are these differences in sample percentages statistically significant? Why or why not?

2. The two questions in **Figure 3.73** appeared on a survey questionnaire designed by students.

Q1. In the past, school has always started after Labor Day. Do you think it is a good idea to begin school before Labor Day in years when Labor Day falls late?

Yes   No

Q2. Don't you think that parents should be involved in decisions made by the principal that affect students?

Yes   No

Figure 3.73.
Two questions from a student questionnaire.

a) Critique each of these questions. If you think a question is biased or confusing, explain the source of the bias or confusion. Then, explain how you would reword the question to clarify it or to remove bias.

Suppose the survey questions were given to students in a particular school. This school has roughly the same number of male students as female students and approximately the same number of students in grade 10 as in grade 11. The results are presented in **Figure 3.74.**

	Grade 10				Grade 11			
	Male		Female		Male		Female	
Response	Yes	No	Yes	No	Yes	No	Yes	No
Q1	28	30	22	20	40	30	12	18
Q2	18	40	30	12	50	20	10	20

Figure 3.74.
Survey results.

b) What was the target population? What kind of a sampling design did the students use? Do you think this was a good design? Why or why not?

c) Would a majority of all the students at this school respond Yes to Q1? Base your answer on a 95% confidence interval.

d) Is the difference between the boys' and girls' responses to Q2 statistically significant? Explain.

3. **Figure 3.75** presents mark-recapture data for a hypothetical series of three samples from a field vole population in the southwestern Yukon. Each sample was captured over a period of two days and samples were taken two weeks apart.

Sample	Sample Size	Number of marked animals in sample	Number of first-time captures marked
1	32	No animals have been marked	32
2	44	4	40
3	30	5	

Figure 3.75.
Results of mark-recapture study.

a) Using the data from the first two samples only, give a point estimate for the size of the population of voles.

b) When the math teacher asked for a confidence interval for the percentage of marked voles in the population, Takashi used the rule of thumb for the 95% margin of error. What was his confidence interval? Was this a reasonable thing to do? Explain why or why not.

c) Wanda used the following rule to compute her 95% confidence interval:

$$9\% \pm 100\% \left(2\sqrt{\frac{(0.09)(0.91)}{44}} \right).$$ Was this a reasonable thing to do? Why or why not?

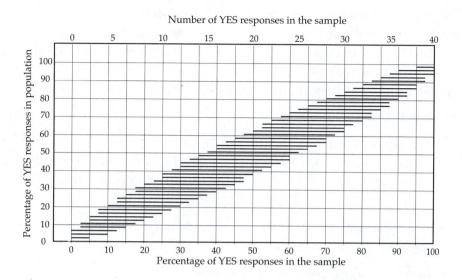

Figure 3.76.
90% likely-sample table for samples of size 40.

d) Carmen decided to use the 90% likely-sample table shown in **Figure 3.76**. What was her confidence interval? Was this a reasonable thing to do? Why or why not?

e) Use the confidence interval from (d) to determine an interval of plausible values for the size of the vole population.

f) Your interval in (e) is based on a 90% likely-sample table for size-40 samples. However, the sample size was 44. If you could find a 90% likely-sample table for size-44 samples, would your results for an interval estimate be wider or narrower than (e)?

g) Determine a point estimate for the size of the vole population based on all three samples. Explain how you determined your estimate.

Mathematical Summary

Two major uses of sampling are explored in this unit: sample surveys and mark-recapture studies. One major goal of this unit is to give you experience conducting your own opinion poll. This means writing the questionnaire, selecting a sampling design, administering the survey, analyzing the results, and writing a report.

QUESTIONNAIRES

Questionnaires are intended to gather reliable information from the target population. To reach this goal, questions must be worded and ordered carefully to avoid bias in the results. When critiquing a survey question, it can be helpful to ask the following:

- Are the words in the question difficult to understand or does the question contain a negative?

- Is the question ambiguous or vague?

- Does the question suggest how the respondent should answer or try to sway the respondent with emotionally-loaded terms?

- Does the question contain more than a single idea?

- Is the question objectionable? too personal? too sensitive?

- Does the question assume too much knowledge?

If the answer to any of these questions is Yes, then the survey question should be rewritten.

SAMPLING DESIGNS

Reputable pollsters take great care in selecting the sample to be surveyed. There are many sampling designs to choose from, but all sampling designs are not created equal. Some designs avoid bias by producing samples that are likely to be representative of the population as a whole. For example, simple random samples and systematic samples generally accomplish this goal. Other designs produce samples that are likely to over- or under-represent some group in the population. Self-selecting samples and convenience samples frequently fall into this category.

SURVEY DATA ORGANIZATION

Data needs to be organized before they are analyzed. Cross-tabulation tables provide an excellent means of organizing data. For example, the data in **Figure 3.77** were collected using a stratified sampling design. The six strata (grade 10 males, grade 10 females, grade 11 males, grade 11 females, grade 12 males, grade 12 females) were sampled in proportion to the size of the strata within the population. Approximately half the students were male and half female; 30% of the students were seniors, 33% juniors, and 37% sophomores. Check to see if you can see these percentages reflected in the numbers in the table.

	Grade 10				Grade 11				Grade 12			
	Male		Female		Male		Female		Male		Female	
Response	Yes	No	Yes	No	Yes	No	Yes	No	Yes	No	Yes	No
Q1	10	27	24	13	13	20	17	16	15	15	19	11
Q2	12	25	24	13	15	18	21	14	14	16	10	20

Figure 3.77.
Sample data from a sample survey organized into a table.

DATA ANALYSIS

There are two basic types of questions relevant to Yes-No survey data: likely-sample questions and likely-population questions. Likely-sample tables such as the one in **Figure 3.78** can be used to answer both likely-sample and likely-population questions.

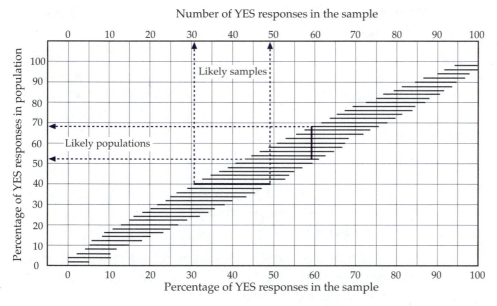

Figure 3.78.
90% likely-sample table for samples of size 100.

Consider this likely-sample question. Suppose that 40% of the students at Tantasqua are going to vote for Kim for student government. If the student newspaper randomly selects 100 students, what percentage of those surveyed are likely to be supporters of Kim? You can answer this question by finding the samples that correspond to a 40%-Yes population's likely-sample bar. (See the likely-samples between the vertically-pointing arrows originating from the ends of the horizontal 40% bar in Figure 3.78.) You should get sample-percentages between 31% and 49%.

More common are the likely-population questions. For example, in the data from Figure 3.77, 100 girls were surveyed and 60% responded Yes to Q1. Does this mean a majority of the girls in this school would respond Yes to Q1? The populations that contain a 60%-Yes sample are those with between 52% and 68% Yes responses. (See the likely populations between the horizontally-pointing arrows originating from the ends of the vertical 60% mark in Figure 3.77.) So, based on a 90% confidence interval for the population percentage, you can conclude that a majority of the girls in this school would respond Yes to Q1.

Here's an important point to remember. You expect 90% confidence intervals to contain the actual population percentage, on average, 90% of the time. However, this means that your conclusions based on 90% confidence intervals will be incorrect, on average, 10% of the time. In a given situation, you'll never know if you are right or wrong. You just know that when you base your decisions on 90% confidence intervals, after numerous decisions, you'll have a track record of being correct roughly 90% of the time.

The 90% confidence interval for the percentage of girls who would answer Yes to Q1 was determined by a 90% likely-sample table for samples of size 100. When the sample size is large ($n \geq 100$), you can approximate 95% confidence intervals based on this rule of thumb for margin of error:

$$\text{margin of error} \approx \frac{100\%}{\sqrt{n}}, \text{ where } n \text{ is the sample size.}$$

The margin of error is one-half the width of a 95% confidence interval centered about the sample percentage. (Note the change from 90% to 95% confidence.)

When the product of the sample proportion, p, and the sample size, n, is at least five ($np \geq 5$) and $n(1-p) \geq 5$, you can approximate 95% confidence intervals using a better rule:

$$\text{sample percentage} \pm \ 100\% \times 2\sqrt{p\frac{(1-p)}{n}},$$

where n is the sample size and

$$p = \text{sample proportion} \ \left(\frac{\text{sample percent}}{100\%}\right).$$

These two rules can be helpful in situations where likely-sample tables are not available.

If 95% confidence intervals for two population percentages do not overlap, then the difference in the sample percentages from the two populations are said to be statistically significant. In this case, you can conclude that the percentage of Yes responses in the two populations are different and that the difference in the sample percentages was not due to chance. (Of course, this procedure will only be correct, on average, for 95% of all samples.)

MARK-RECAPTURE ANALYSIS

Mark-recapture techniques provide one method for estimating the size of a mobile animal population. The basic idea is to capture at least two samples from the wildlife species being studied. After recording the number of animals in the first sample, mark and release them. After allowing enough time for the marked animals to mix with the unmarked animals, capture a second sample and record the number of animals captured, as well as the number of recaptured (marked) animals. By using the percentage of marked animals in the second sample as an estimate of the percentage of marked animals in the population, proportional reasoning produces a point estimate of the population size. This estimate is called the Peterson estimate.

The validity of Peterson estimates depends on four assumptions:

- The size of the population is constant.

- All marks are permanent and will be noted correctly upon recapture.

- Marking the animals does not affect their chances of subsequently being recaptured.

- All animals in the population have an equal chance of being captured.

Violation of any of these assumptions can produce estimates that grossly over- or underestimate the population size.

Confidence intervals may also be used to estimate the population percentage of marked animals. This, in turn, provides a lower and an upper value for the population size.

Glossary

BAILEY'S MODIFICATION:
A modification to Peterson's estimate that is used when the number of recaptures is less than 10.

BIAS:
Not representative of the population.

BIASED SAMPLE:
A sample that over-represents (or under-represents) one or more groups from the population.

CLUSTER SAMPLE:
A sampling design in which a simple random sample of groups is selected and then all individuals within the selected groups are surveyed.

CONFIDENCE INTERVAL:
A confidence interval consists of the percentage-Yes populations that contain a given sample percentage in their likely-sample groups.

CONVENIENCE SAMPLE:
A sampling design in which you select any sample that is easy to obtain.

CROSS-TABULATION TABLES:
Tables that break down responses by two or more questions (or two or more variables).

DISTRIBUTION:
A list (or graph) of the values of a variable, together with the frequencies with which those values occur.

FRAME:
A complete listing of the members of the target population.

FREQUENCY:
The number of times an outcome occurs.

INFERENCE:
Analysis that reveals information about a population based on information obtained from a sample.

INTERVAL ESTIMATE:
An estimate for a population value, reported as an interval of reasonable values.

LIKELY SAMPLE:
The samples (of a particular size) likely to be drawn from a specified Yes-No population. For example, the specified population's 90% likely-sample group consists of the samples (of a particular size) from that population that are observed at least 90% of the time.

LIKELY-SAMPLE BAR:
A bar that represents the likely-sample group. For example, a 90% likely-sample bar represents the samples in a Yes-No population's 90% likely-sample group.

LIKELY-SAMPLE TABLE:
A collection of likely-sample bars from a set of Yes-populations. A 90% likely-sample table is based on 90% likely-sample bars.

MARGIN OF ERROR:
One-half the width of a confidence interval (centered about the sample percentage).

MARK-RECAPTURE METHOD:
A method for estimating the size of an animal population based on at least two sampling episodes. An initial sample of animals is captured, marked, and then released. Later, a second sample is caught, and the fraction of marked animals recorded.

MULTIMODAL HISTOGRAM:
A histogram that appears to have more than one peak.

POINT ESTIMATE:
A single-number estimate for a population value.

POPULATION:
The entire collection of individuals, animals, or objects about which information is desired.

PETERSEN METHOD:
The simplest mark-recapture method; it is based on a single sample of marked, released animals and a subsequent sample of recaptured and first-time captured animals.

SAMPLE:
A portion of a population from which data is collected.

SAMPLE DESIGN:
Method for selecting the sample to be surveyed.

SELF-SELECTING SAMPLE:
A sampling design in which the sample consists of people who respond to a request for participants in the survey.

SIMPLE RANDOM SAMPLE (SRS):
A sampling design in which every subset (of the proper size) of the population is equally likely to be chosen for the sample.

SKEWED HISTOGRAM:
A lopsided unimodal histogram (as opposed to a symmetrical one).

STATISTICALLY SIGNIFICANT DIFFERENCE:
The difference between two sample percentages is statistically significant when confidence intervals corresponding to these samples do not overlap. Statisticians use the term significant to mean statistically significant at the 95% (or higher) level. The phrase, "highly significant" is reserved for differences that are statistically significant at the 99% (or higher) level.

STRATIFIED SAMPLE:
A sampling design in which nonoverlapping groups, called strata, are specified and simple random samples are selected from within each of the strata.

SUBPOPULATION:
A group within a population that shares a particular characteristic. Frequently, subpopulations are referred to as populations when they are the subject of an analysis.

SURVEY DESIGN:
The method you use to choose your sample.

SYSTEMATIC SAMPLE
A sampling design in which a starting point is selected from a list and then the sample is chosen by taking every kth name after the starting name. (For best results, you should randomly select an integer between 1 and k for the starting name. The value of the increment k can also be chosen randomly.)

TARGET POPULATION:
Population you intend to sample.

TWO-EDGED QUESTION:
A question that contains two competing ideas.

UNIMODAL HISTOGRAM:
A histogram that is mound-shaped or looks as if it has a single peak.

VARIABILITY DUE TO SAMPLING:
Variations in data sets due to different samples.

YES-NO POPULATION:
Populations containing items that are connected to a response of either Yes and No (or to a response that can be transformed into Yes or No).

YES-NO SAMPLE:
A sample that is drawn from a Yes-No population.

UNIT

Mind Your Own Business

Running a business, even a small business, is a challenge because there are many variables that contribute to its success or failure. For example, if a business sets the price of its product too low, it will not recover its costs of production. If the price of the product is set too high, customers will buy from a competitor. The price a business sets for its product, therefore, is one of the variables that affects the profits (or losses) that the business realizes.

Most of the mathematical models you have developed in the *Mathematics: Modeling Our World* program have involved functions of a single variable. A business's profits depend on many variables. In this unit, you will create models that involve functions of more than one variable and develop techniques for analyzing such models.

SMALL BUSINESS: NO SMALL MATTER

Small business is a vital part of the American economy. For example, according to the United States Small Business Administration, in 1996 there were about 22.1 million small businesses in the country and about 75% of the 2.5 million new jobs created in 1995 were in small-business-dominated industries. Small businesses provide most Americans with their first jobs and, therefore, with much of the on-the-job training that develops marketable skills. No doubt someone you know is employed by a small business; perhaps someday you will operate one of your own.

Because small business affects the lives of so many people, you are likely to find knowledge of related matters useful at some time in your life. In this unit, you will see how mathematical models can help small businesses develop strategies to ensure their growth and prosperity.

LESSON ONE

So, You Want to Be in Business

KEY CONCEPTS

Simulation

Optimization

Functions of more than one variable

Linear functions

Quadratic functions

The Image Bank

PREPARATION READING

Getting Started

Mathematical models always involve simplification; some factors that affect a situation are ignored, at least temporarily, so that the problem is manageable. The trick is to identify the important factors and develop a model based only on those factors.

Your task in this lesson is to research the operation of a small business in order to identify factors to incorporate in a model. You will also try your hand at a simulation of a small business. The simulation will enable you to collect data in a particular situation to help you understand relationships among some of the important factors affecting the success of a small business.

There are many kinds of small businesses. The business that you will study in this lesson is a small manufacturing operation. Manufacturing has certain factors in common with other kinds of businesses, but other factors are unique to manufacturing. What does success mean in a manufacturing business? What are some factors that determine the success or failure of such a business?

ACTIVITY

1

MODEL RESEARCH

In order to create a mathematical model, the modeler must know something about the real-world situation that is being modeled.

Therefore, your task in this first activity is to develop a basic familiarity with a small business, specifically a small manufacturing business.

There are many resources you can consult. For example, most libraries have books and magazines about running a small business. The Internet has many small business sites, such as the one operated by the United States Small Business Administration. However, perhaps the best resource is the owner of a small manufacturing business in your own community.

In your research, try to develop answers to the following two questions.

1. How is the success of a small business measured? (Keep in mind that a quantitative definition is desirable when developing a mathematical model.)

2. What factors affect the success of a small business? Since there are many factors, try to separate your factors into two groups: those over which the business has quite a bit of control and those over which it does not. (Since in this unit you will be analyzing the operation of a business over a period of a few months, think of control as meaning control during a relatively short period of time.) In addition, try to rank the items in each list according to their importance. The division and ranking will help you decide which factors to include and which to ignore.

When you have finished your research, prepare a report that summarizes your answers to these two questions.

INDIVIDUAL WORK 1

Towards a Model

1. The following is a list of definitions of the successful operation of a small business. Tell why you feel each is or is not a workable definition for developing a mathematical model that will help operate a business successfully.

   a) A successful business is one that makes its customers happy.

   b) A successful business is one that maximizes its sales.

   c) A successful manufacturing business is one that minimizes the cost of producing its product.

   d) A successful business is one that maximizes its **profits**, defined as the difference between a business's revenues (money it takes in) and its costs (money it pays out).

   e) A successful business is one that avoids paying taxes.

2. The following is a list of factors that might affect the success of the operation of a small manufacturing business. In each case, state whether you think the factor is one the business can control over a relatively short period of time (a few months to a year or two). Explain your answers.

   a) The cost of the materials the business uses to make its product.

   b) The amount of raw material (the material used to make the finished product) that the business has on hand.

   c) The monthly payment on a loan.

   d) Payments on utilities such as water, gas, and electricity.

   e) The price the business charges for its product.

   f) The amount the business pays in salaries.

   g) The interest the business receives on money it has in the bank.

   h) The quantity of its product that the business manufactures.

3. Write a summary of what you feel is an appropriate definition of the successful operation of a small manufacturing business, including factors that affect that operation. Identify and discuss the factors that you feel are important enough to be considered in a mathematical model and those that might be ignored, at least temporarily.

ACTIVITY

YOU'RE THE BOSS

2

This activity is a simulation of a small manufacturing business. Your task is to make monthly decisions and enter them into either the computer or calculator version of the simulation. Keep a record of your decisions and the corresponding results on a copy of Handout H4.2.

Read the following information about the simulation before running it the first time.

ABOUT THE SIMULATION:

Both the spreadsheet and the calculator version of the simulation are titled BIZ1, and they produce identical results. However, the spreadsheet version maintains a column for each of twelve months; the calculator version maintains only two columns: one for the current month and one for the next month. The spreadsheet displays negative numbers by enclosing them in parentheses; the calculator uses the standard negative sign.

The line numbers on Handout H4.2 match the line numbers in both the spreadsheet and calculator versions. The spreadsheet version includes labels that match those on the handout, but the calculator version does not. (Note that the spreadsheet's first three rows are blank. You can use these cells to type a title, the names of your group members, or other information.)

ABOUT THE BUSINESS:

Your business currently has $55,043 in the bank.

You have an outstanding loan balance of $604,380. The bank charges 8% interest compounded monthly. The monthly loan payment of $10,596.74 is reflected in the BIZ1 simulation.

The company's assets include manufacturing and warehouse facilities that are in good repair. Working at full capacity, you

YOU'RE THE BOSS

can produce 2000 units of your product each month, but you can decide to produce fewer than 2000 units a month.

To simplify this simulation, the raw materials used to make your product are called raw material units (RMUs). One raw material unit makes one unit of product.

Your warehouse facilities can hold up to 10,000 raw material units and up to 5000 units of finished product. The simulation begins with 3000 RMUs and 2600 units of finished product in storage. A simplifying assumption made in this simulation is that both raw materials and finished product have an indefinite storage life, so spoilage is not a concern.

You have some costs over which you have little control. These include the expenses associated with owning the property (such as depreciation, upkeep, taxes, insurance, and utilities) and the payroll for your employees. The simulation assumes these costs are fixed; that is, they are unaffected by how much product you make or sell. Expect these costs to run about $37,000 monthly.

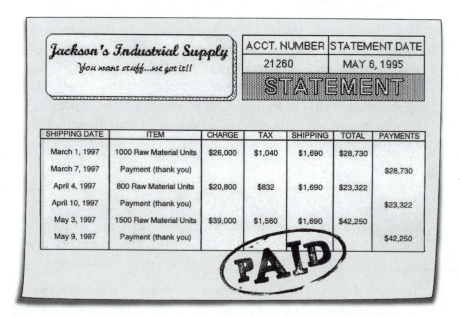

SHIPPING DATE	ITEM	CHARGE	TAX	SHIPPING	TOTAL	PAYMENTS
March 1, 1997	1000 Raw Material Units	$26,000	$1,040	$1,690	$28,730	
March 7, 1997	Payment (thank you)					$28,730
April 4, 1997	800 Raw Material Units	$20,800	$832	$1,690	$23,322	
April 10, 1997	Payment (thank you)					$23,322
May 3, 1997	1500 Raw Material Units	$39,000	$1,560	$1,690	$42,250	
May 9, 1997	Payment (thank you)					$42,250

Jackson's Industrial Supply
You want stuff...we got it!!

ACCT. NUMBER	STATEMENT DATE
21260	MAY 6, 1995

STATEMENT

PAID

Figure 4.1.
Statement from supplier.

YOU'RE THE BOSS

Other expenses will vary depending on how much product you make or the number of RMUs you order. The cost of RMUs varies with the number you order. A statement from your current supplier is shown in **Figure 4.1.**

Because of your state-of-the-art equipment, it costs only $5.15 per unit to manufacture your finished product. This is the most significant competitive advantage your company has because it gives you some flexibility in setting the price of your product. Pricing is an important consideration for your company because the demand for your product varies with the price you charge.

Handout H4.2 is divided into several sections. The first is the Inventory Statement **(Figure 4.2)**, which keeps track of the RMUs and finished product on hand. There is a one-month lag between the time you order RMUs and their availability for manufacturing. Similarly, there is a one-month lag between the time you decide to order the manufacture of finished product and its availability for sale.

Inventory statement	
RMU's on hand	3000
Finished Product on hand	2600

Figure 4.2.
The inventory statement.

ACTIVITY

2

YOU'RE THE BOSS

Profit/loss statement	
RMU Order	
RMU Costs	
Manufacturing Order	
Manufacturing (actual)	
Manufacturing Costs	
Depreciation	($5,036.50)
Salaries, rent, insurance, etc.	($32,000.00)
Total costs	
Price	
Sales	
Sales Revenue	
Total Revenue	

Figure 4.3.
The Profit/Loss Statement.

The Profit/Loss Statement (**Figure 4.3**) includes all costs of producing a finished product. These costs include the cost of the RMUs, the costs associated with the manufacturing process, costs of the business itself (salaries, rent, insurance, etc.), and depreciation (wear and tear on your equipment). This statement also shows the price you charge for your product, the number of sales that result, and the total amount of revenue obtained from the sales.

YOU'RE THE BOSS

Cash flow statement	
Beginning Balance	$55,043.00)
RMU Costs	
Manufacturing costs	
Salaries, rent, insurance, etc.	($32,000.00)
Loan Payment	($10,596.74)
Revenue	
Net Cash Flow	

Figure 4.4.
The Cash Flow Statement.

The Cash Flow Statement (**Figure 4.4**) shows your bank account balance at the beginning of the month. The remainder of this statement shows the money flowing out of the company each month and the revenue–the money flowing in. The net cash flow is determined by subtracting the money flowing out from the money flowing in. The net cash flow is added to the beginning bank balance to obtain the beginning balance for the next month.

Your goal in running the simulation is to achieve a successful operation of the business. Think about the definition you developed in Activity 1 and apply it here. If you feel your definition is inadequate, then revise it so it seems reasonable for the business in this simulation.

YOU'RE THE BOSS

The simulation permits you to control three important variables each month: The number of RMUs ordered, the manufacturing order (the number of finished product units produced that month), and the price you charge for your finished product (see **Figure 4.5**).

Profit/loss statement	
RMU Order	Decision #1
RMU Costs	
Manufacturing Order	Decision #2
Manufacturing (actual)	
Manufacturing Costs	
Depreciation	
Interest on loan	
Salaries, rent, insurance, etc.	
Total Costs	
Price	Decision #3
Sales	
Sales Revenue	
Interest Income	
Total Revenue	

Figure 4.5.
Three monthly decisions.

DECISION #1: RMU Order

Based on the number of units you order, the simulation calculates the cost of ordering the raw materials and enters the result in the row labeled RMU Costs. This value is also used to update the number of RMUs on hand for next month.

YOU'RE THE BOSS

DECISION #2: Manufacturing Order

Based on the number of finished product units you decide to manufacture, the simulation determines the actual amount manufactured and the manufacturing costs. If you forget that your company has limited capacities, the simulation makes the necessary adjustment.

DECISION #3: The Price You Charge for Your Product

This value should be somewhere between $20 and $80. Based on the value you enter, the simulation determines the number of units sold and the associated revenue, which is calculated by multiplying the price per unit by the number of units sold.

Finally, here are the items you should do in this activity:

1. Run the simulation for 12 months and keep a record on Handout H4.2. Do the best you can, but your main goal is to become familiar with the simulation.

2. Analyze the results of Item 1 and develop a strategy you think might result in a successful 12-month operation of the business. Run the simulation again to test your strategy. Keep a record of the results on another copy of Handout H4.2. Prepare a report describing your strategy and the results (see Item 3, below).

3. If time permits, repeat Item 2 with a new strategy, particularly if you are not satisfied with the results your first strategy produced. If you have trouble developing a strategy that works, keep in mind that you have control over three variables and it can be difficult to see the effects of each variable if you are changing all three of them at once. You may want to do a few trial runs in which you hold two of the variables constant and allow only one to vary. If you have time to try more than one strategy, your report in Item 2 should summarize all of them.

CONSIDER:

1. Does it make the most sense to measure the success of a business in terms of the revenues the business receives, in terms of the costs it incurs, or in terms of the profits it realizes? Explain.

2. Does the price a manufacturing business charges for its product have an important effect on the success of the business? Explain.

M A T H   A T   W O R K

Marilyn Hamilton is an inspiring example of someone who has made a success of her own small manufacturing business, and much more. A year after a hang gliding accident left her a paraplegic, Marilyn Hamilton came up with the concept of manufacturing a more mobile, maneuverable, lightweight wheelchair using materials like those used in making hang gliders. In 1986, six years after she and two associates began manufacturing their high-performance chairs in a backyard garage, Marilyn's company, Motion Designs, had sales figures of about $21 million. At that point, her company was purchased by Sunrise Medical Inc. where she retains a position as Vice President of Consumer Development.

Among her many achievements outside the business world, Marilyn has won three titles in the National Wheelchair Tennis Championships and is a six-time National Disabled Ski Champion. She is also the founder of Winners on Wheels, which provides young people in wheelchairs with challenging experiences and leadership training.

INDIVIDUAL WORK 2

Some Strategies

In this individual work, you will use some of the data you gathered in Activity 2 to develop strategies you can use to improve your success with the BIZ1 simulation.

1. The price you charge for a unit of finished product determines sales: if you charge too much, you sell less because some of your customers take their business elsewhere; if you charge less, you attract more customers and, therefore, sales increase. For now, ignore the effect of production costs and concentrate only on the relationship between the price you charge and the sales that result.

   a) Explain the mathematical relationship between revenue and the other two variables listed in the table shown in **Figure 4.6.**

   b) Copy the table in Figure 4.6 onto your paper and enter at least five sets of sample values from your records of the simulation.

Price					
Sales					
Revenue					

   Figure 4.6.

   c) Explore the relationship between sales and price. If possible, write an equation relating these quantities. Explain any techniques you use and discuss what your result tells you about the relationship between sales and price.

   d) Explore the relationship between revenue and price. Explain any techniques you use.

   e) Based on the model you found in (d) relating revenue and price over a reasonable range, what recommendations can you make to the company if it measures its success by maximizing revenue? Do you think revenue maximization is a realistic way to measure success?

2. The costs incurred in the operation of a business are an important factor in the success or failure of the business. In the BIZ1 simulation, your manufacturing costs and your RMU costs are variable costs controlled by the number of units you manufacture and by the number of RMUs you order, respectively. These costs are called variable costs since they vary with the number of items produced.

a) Use data that you collected in Activity 2 or the statement from your supplier in Figure 4.1 to explore the relationship between the number of RMUs you order and the cost. That is, if rmu(x) represents the cost of ordering x RMUs, find a symbolic expression for rmu(x). Discuss what your result tells you about the relationship between RMU cost and the number ordered. (Interpret the control numbers in your equation.)

b) If m(x) represents the cost of manufacturing x units of finished product, find a symbolic expression for m(x).

c) Although the number of RMUs you order is not required to be the same as the number of units of finished product you manufacture, it seems reasonable to keep them the same since it takes one RMU to make one unit of finished product. If the number of RMUs ordered and the number of finished product units manufactured are equal, what is an expression for the total variable costs associated with ordering x RMUs and manufacturing x units of finished product? (Remember, variable costs are the cost of raw materials and the cost of manufacturing.)

d) The total costs to your business are the combined total of the variable costs and the fixed costs. Use your answer to (c) and information about the fixed costs from Activity 2 to develop a model for the total costs your business incurs when x RMUs are ordered and x units of finished product are manufactured.

e) Sketch a graph of your model from part (d). Be sure to label your axes clearly.

3. When you ran the BIZ1 simulation in Activity 2, you may have tried to find a strategy that kept the business operating relatively smoothly. One such strategy is to check the sales that result from the price you set, then order exactly the same number of RMUs and manufactured product as the sales. That way you are sure you will not run out of product or RMUs and that you will not order too many of either and exceed your storage capacity.

If you adopt the practice of matching RMU and manufacturing orders to sales, then not only are sales determined by the price you set, but so are the RMU costs and the manufacturing costs. Therefore, the costs in Item 2 can be re-expressed in terms of price.

Re-expression is something you have done before. For example, in Course 1, Unit 5, *Animation*, the location of a pixel on a graphing calculator screen can be described by a pair of parametric equations like

$x = 2t + 1$, $y = 3t + 2$. The variable t represents time, and since time is an important variable that controls the speed of a motion, expressing vertical and horizontal position in terms of time is crucial to successful animation. In addition, vertical position can be re-expressed in terms of horizontal position. Rewrite the first parametric equation as $t = \dfrac{x-1}{2}$ and replace t in the second equation with $\dfrac{x-1}{2}$ to obtain

$y = 3\left(\dfrac{x-1}{2}\right)$. Now y, the vertical position, is expressed in terms of x, the horizontal position. If you want to study the path of the motion and are not concerned about location at a particular time, you may feel this form is more useful. If time is an important factor in your work, then the parametric equations are more useful.

a) Use your results in Items 1 and 2 of this individual work to develop a model for the company's total profits in terms of p, the price charged. Assume that the number of RMUs ordered and the number of finished product manufactured are the same as the sales. (Hint: You will have to re-express the cost model you found in Item 2 in terms of price, which you can do by using the sales model you found in Item 1. Remember that profit is what is left after costs are subtracted from revenue.)

b) Use the profit model you developed in (a) to develop a recommendation for successful operation of the company. Support your recommendation.

c) Graph revenue in terms of price, and cost in terms of price on the same grid. Interpret the features of the graph in the context of this manufacturing business.

4. When a quantity is calculated from at least two variables, mathematicians say that the quantity is a **function of more than one variable**. The BIZ1 simulation contains several examples of quantities that are functions of more than one variable. For example, because the revenue for a given month is found by multiplying the sales for that month by the price, revenue is a function of price and sales. The symbolic statement $R(p, s) = p \times s$ means that the revenue from price p and sales s is found by multiplying p and s.

a) Another quantity in BIZ1 that depends on more than one variable is the number of RMUs on hand for a given month. On what other variables does this quantity depend?

b) Another quantity in BIZ1 that depends on more than one variable is the bank balance for a given month. On what variables does this quantity depend?

c) When an amount of money is deposited in a savings account, on what variables does the current amount in the account depend?

d) A teacher uses the function $G(Q_1, Q_2, P, H, E) = 0.15Q_1 + 0.15Q_2 + 0.25P + 0.15H + 0.3E$ to compute the final grade in a course in which there are two quizzes, a project, homework, and an exam. Two students have identical grades on their quizzes and the exam; one earns 90% on the project and 70% on homework, while the other earns 70% on the project and 90% on homework. Which student has the higher grade? Explain.

e) The volume of a cylinder is found by multiplying the height by the radius squared, then by the constant π. In other words, the volume is a function of the height and the radius. Express this mathematical fact in symbolic form.

5. Business people use the term **marginal cost** to describe the cost of producing one additional unit of product. Marginal cost can be thought of as the rate at which costs are changing with respect to increased production.

   a) In the BIZ1 simulation, what is the marginal cost's value?

   b) What role does the marginal cost's value play in the models you developed in Items 1-3? Can you see it in your models?

   c) Business people also use the term marginal revenue, which has a definition similar to that of marginal cost. **Marginal revenue** is the additional revenue obtained by producing and selling one additional unit of product. In order to determine marginal revenue, revenue must be expressed in terms of the number of items produced (and sold), not in terms of the price charged. Use your work in Item 3 to express revenue in terms of the number of items produced. Then compare the behavior of marginal revenue to that of marginal cost.

6. Business people use the term **profit margin**—the ratio of profit to revenue—to describe the percent of your revenue that you get to keep as profit.

   a) **Figure 4.7** shows the results of the BIZ1 simulation after a student entered a price, manufacturing order, and RMU order for the months of May and June. Find the profit margins for May and June. Show how you obtained your answers.

	May	June	July
Inventory Statement			
RMU's on hand	3000	3000	3000
Finished Product on hand	2600	2600	2200
Profit/Loss Statement			
RMU Order	1600	1000	
RMU Costs	($44,954.00)	($28,730.00)	xxxxxxxx
Manufacturing Order	1600	1000	1600
Manufacturing (actual)	1600	1000	xxxxxxxx
Manufacturing Costs	($8,240.00)	($5,150.00)	xxxxxxxx
Depreciation	($5,036.50)	($5,036.50)	($5,036.50)
Salaries, rent, insurance, etc.	($32,000.00)	($32,000.00)	($32,000.00)
Total Costs	($90,230.50)	($70,916.50)	xxxxxxxx
Price	60	65	
Sales	1600	1400	xxxxxxxx
Sales Revenue	$96,000.00	$91,000.00	xxxxxxxx
Total Revenue	$96,000.00	$91,000.00	xxxxxxxx
Cash Flow Statement			
Beginning Balance	$55,043.00	$55,252.26	$69,775.52
RMU Costs	($44,954.00)	($28,730.00)	xxxxxxxx
Manufacturing Costs	($8,240.00)	($5,150.00)	xxxxxxxx
Salaries, rent, insurance, etc.	($32,000.00)	($32,000.00)	($32,000.00)
Loan Payment	($10,596.74)	($10,596.74)	($10,596.74)
Revenue	$96,000.00	$91,000.00	xxxxxxxx
Net Cash Flow	$209.26	$14,523.26	xxxxxxxx

Figure 4.7. Student results of the BIZ1 simulation.

b) Compare the profit margins you found in (a). Explain any differences.

c) Profit margin can also be thought of as the ratio of profit to profit + costs. Explain.

d) Suppose that by shrewd management, you are able to increase your profit margin over time. Explain why you can never achieve a profit margin of 100%.

e) If your profits remain constant over time, but your costs become arbitrarily large, what happens to your profit margin? Explain.

f) What happens to profit margin if costs are larger than revenues? Explain.

7. Business people use the term **average unit cost** to describe the cost associated with one unit of product. For example, if the business spends $13,000 to produce 1000 units of product, the average unit cost is $13,000 ÷ 1000 = $13. Average cost models are sometimes useful in determining strategies for operating a business successfully, which you will do later in this unit.

a) Use the cost model you developed in Item 2(a) to write an expression for the average RMU costs associated with x units of product.

b) Use the cost model you developed in Item 2(c) to write an expression for the average raw material and manufacturing costs associated with x units of product.

c) Use the cost model you developed in Item 2(d) to write an expression for the average total costs associated with x units of product.

d) Use the average cost model you found in part (c) to find the average cost per unit if the company manufactures 1000 units.

e) Find the slope of the line segment connecting (0, 0) to the point on the total cost model in Item 2(e) that represents the total cost of 1000 units. Make a sketch and interpret the slope in this context.

f) Write an equation for the slope of the segment joining (0, 0) to (x, Total Cost of x). Comment on your result.

8. A company's sales are modeled by the linear function
   $s(p) = 2850 - 34p$, where p is the price the company charges for each unit it sells.

   a) Write a function for the company's revenue in terms of the price it charges for each item it sells.

   b) The company's costs are modeled by $20000 + 27x$, where x is the number of units manufactured. Assuming the company manufactures the same number of units that it sells, re-express the costs as a function of the price the company charges for each unit it sells.

   c) Write a function that models the company's profits based on the price it charges for each unit sold. What type of function is your model?

   d) Develop a pricing recommendation that you think will ensure the company's profitability over time. Discuss mathematical procedures that can be applied to the profit model to produce your recommendation.

9. One of the modeling assumptions of this lesson is that the company sets its manufacturing and its raw material order to match its sales. Explain why this may be an unrealistic assumption for a manufacturing business.

LESSON TWO

Who's Minding the Store(room)?

KEY CONCEPTS

Average cost function

Asymptote

Hyperbola

Rational function

The Image Bank

PREPARATION READING

Gaining Interest

The mathematical models for costs, revenues, and profit that you developed in Lesson 1 have produced a recommendation for the small manufacturing business in the BIZ1 simulation. By strategically setting its price, the business can achieve success by maximizing its profits.

However, the model you used in Lesson 1 made several simplifying assumptions. For example, you assumed that both the amount of raw materials ordered and the amount of product manufactured each month were equal to that month's sales.

Your model also ignored some factors that might affect a business, primarily because those factors did not seem as important as those that were included. An example of a factor not included in Lesson 1 is interest. Since the company has a loan, part of the payment it makes each month is interest. Since the company has a bank account, the monthly balance probably earns interest.

In this lesson, you will question assumptions you made in Lesson 1 and consider factors you ignored. Will their inclusion improve the recommendations you have already made?

THE COST OF MONEY

Money, like many things, costs money. When you take out a loan, you are charged interest, which is the cost of borrowing the money.

Similarly, if you spend money that you have in a savings account, part of the price you pay is the interest you lose by not leaving the money in the account.

Your task in this activity is to analyze a suggestion that one of the employees of the company in the BIZ1 simulation has brought to the company's management. The suggestion is to make better use of the company's storage facilities by ordering RMUs three months at a time. That is, instead of making separate orders in May, June, and July, make one order in May for all three months. The employee's argument is that ordering in larger quantities saves money since the shipping charge is paid only once.

Although it seems clear the employee is correct, the company needs a model it can use to predict the cost of ordering in larger quantities. Since you will be developing an average-cost model, you may want to look back at the RMU cost model you developed in Item 2 of Individual Work 2 before going further.

Then begin by looking at the three-month strategy. Assume the company sets the price you recommended in Lesson 1.

1. Determine the total cost and the average cost per RMU if the company orders each month separately.

2. Determine the total cost and the average cost per RMU if the company orders just once for all three months. Be sure to consider the lost interest on the money paid for the June and July supply of RMUs. Assume the company's bank account pays 4% annual interest paid monthly. You will need to consider the interest lost on the June supply and the July supply separately since the June supply is ordered one month in advance and the July supply two months in advance. (For simplicity, assume the lost interest does not itself earn interest.)

THE COST OF MONEY

3. The total amount of interest lost over a period of t months can be described in terms of the series $1 + 2 + 3 + ... + (t - 1)$. Explain why this is the case, and express the sum without including the series (that is, in closed form).

4. Finally, develop an average-cost model for the strategy of ordering a several-months' supply of RMUs. Express the model in terms of t, the number of months for which a supply is ordered, and be sure to include lost interest in your model. What conclusions can you draw from your model? What recommendations can you make to the company?

INDIVIDUAL WORK 3

Average Cost Functions

*I*n this individual work, you will take a closer look at some of the mathematics that occurs when average-cost models are used to optimize the performance of a business.

1. The total cost of ordering raw materials is often a multiple of the cost of a single unit plus a fixed charge for shipping. For example, if materials cost $10 per unit plus a fixed delivery charge of $150, then the total cost of x units is $10x + 150$. The average cost of x units is $\dfrac{10x + 150}{x}$. A graph of the average-cost function is shown in **Figure 4.8(a)**. **Figure 4.8(b)** shows the same graph being traced in a larger window.

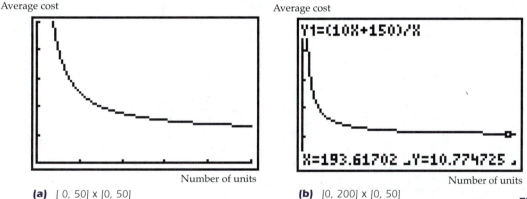

Average cost

(a) [0, 50] x [0, 50]

Average cost

Y1=(10X+150)/X

X=193.61702 .Y=10.774725 .

Number of units

(b) [0, 200] x [0, 50]

Figure 4.8.
The graph of an average cost function.

a) What does the trace readout in Figure 4.8(b) tell you about costs of ordering raw materials?

b) What does the shape of the graph tell you about the average raw-material costs?

c) The graph in Figure 4.8 has a horizontal **asymptote**. An asymptote is a line that a graph approaches. What horizontal line is the asymptote in Figure 4.8? (If you are not sure, try graphing and tracing the function $y = \dfrac{10x + 150}{x}$ in a larger window.)

d) Interpret the asymptote in the context of ordering raw materials.

e) Use a graph or a table to conduct a similar analysis of the average RMU cost function you found in Lesson 1. (See, for example, Item 7(a) of Individual Work 2.)

f) What general conclusion can you draw about average cost functions of the type $y = \dfrac{Ax + B}{x}$? (If necessary, make up a few functions of your own and explore their behavior with graphs or tables.)

2. The graphs of average cost functions are often hyperbolas. A **hyperbola** is a curve characterized by two sections or branches, each of which is a symmetric curve. (The curvature of each branch differs from the curvature of a parabola; a hyperbola is *not* just a tilted parabola.) One branch is a 180° rotation of the other. The simplest symbolic equation that produces a hyperbola is $y = 1/x$. The graph of $y = \dfrac{1}{x}$ is shown in **Figure 4.9.**

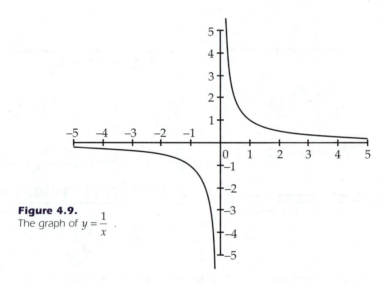

Figure 4.9.
The graph of $y = \dfrac{1}{x}$.

a) Describe the behavior of the graph when x is close to 0. Also describe the behavior when x is fairly large.

b) The functions $y = \dfrac{10}{x}$, $y = \dfrac{1}{x + 2}$, and $y = \dfrac{1}{x} + 2$ have graphs that are transformations of the graph of $y = \dfrac{1}{x}$. Describe each transformation.

The circle, ellipse, parabola, and hyperbola are the subjects of *Conic Sections*, written by the Greek mathematician Apollonius of Perga around 200 B.C. Apollonius showed that the four curves are formed when a plane intersects a "double" cone at varying angles. When the plane is perpendicular to the cone's axis, the intersection is a circle. As the plane is gradually tilted, the intersection first becomes an ellipse, then a parabola, then a hyperbola. Thus, a **conic section** is a curve produced by intersecting a plane and a cone.

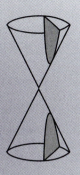

c) A fraction in which the numerator has more than one term can be written as separate fractions: $\dfrac{1+2}{5} = \dfrac{1}{5} + \dfrac{2}{5}$. Use this fact to write

the average cost model $\dfrac{10x + 150}{x}$

from Item 1 as two separate fractions. Simplify each of the fractions as much as possible. Use your result to discuss the relationship between the graph of the average cost function and the graph of $y = \dfrac{1}{x}$.

3. The average cost functions you have seen in this unit are examples of **rational functions**. A rational function is formed by writing the ratio of two polynomials. Linear functions like $2x + 3$ and quadratics like $3x^2 - 7x + 2$ are examples of polynomials. A **polynomial** is an expression composed of one or more terms in which the variable is raised to a positive integer power. (One of the terms can be a constant.)

Suppose the cost function is not a linear function, but a quadratic. For example, suppose the total cost of x RMUs is given by $x^2 - x + 52$.

a) What is the average cost function?

b) The graph of the average cost function is a hyperbola. Explore its behavior. Interpret your findings in this context.

c) Write the average cost model as three separate fractions and simplify any of the three fractions that can be expressed in a simpler form.

d) Create a new function by dropping any fractions that cannot be simplified in your answer to (c). Graph this new function along with the function you graphed in (b). What do you notice?

e) Fractions that have a constant in the numerator and a variable in the denominator, such as $\frac{10}{x}$, produce very small values when the variable is replaced with a large value. Use this fact about fractions to explain the graph you drew in (d).

f) Describe a procedure for determining an asymptote for functions of the form $y = \frac{p(x)}{x}$, where $p(x)$ is a linear function or a quadratic.

4. When a company orders and pays for materials several months in advance, the cost of doing so includes lost interest on money that would have stayed in the company's bank account. Incorporating lost interest into an average cost model is tricky because the amount of lost interest is different for each month and because the interest itself earns interest (compounding). A reasonably accurate model for lost interest can be developed by assuming that one month's lost interest is a constant, thus ignoring the effect of compounding.

There is no lost interest on the cost of the current month's supply because it is needed now. There is one month's lost interest on next month's supply since you could wait one month before ordering. Likewise, there is two month's lost interest on the following month's supply, three month's lost interest on the supply for the month after that, etc. Thus, the number of months of lost interest when a supply for t months is ordered and paid for all at one time is $1 + 2 + 3 + ... + (t - 1)$.

There are several ways to develop a formula for $1 + 2 + 3 + ... + (t - 1)$. You may recall one or more methods from Course 1, Unit 6, *Growth*. In case you don't, here are two possibilities:

Use a particular value of t, say 8. Find the sum $1 + 2 + 3 + 4 + 5 + 6 + 7 + 8$ by adding the first and last terms, the second and the next to last, etc. and observing how many such sums there are. Generalize this pattern.

Use several specific values of t to gather data on the sum. Apply data analysis techniques.

Use a method of your own choosing to develop a formula for
$1 + 2 + 3 + \ldots + (t - 1)$.

5. A company pays $32 per unit of raw materials plus $700 shipping.

a) Find a model for the average cost per raw material unit.

b) Demand for the company's product requires that it produce 1100 units of finished product monthly. Re-express the average cost model in terms of t, the number of months for which a supply is ordered.

c) If the company loses about $115 in interest when raw materials are ordered one month in advance, incorporate lost interest into your average cost model.

d) Use your average cost model to develop a recommendation for the company.

6. A children's summer camp has fixed expenses of $67,000, which includes rent, equipment, and insurance. It costs the camp about $487 per child to provide food, supervision, and transportation.

a) Develop a model for the average cost per child.

b) Analyze the average cost function. What recommendation can you make to the camp about the amount it should charge each camper?

7. **Figure 4.10(a)** shows monthly sales data gathered by a company. **Figure 4.10(b)** is data on the company's monthly costs.

a) Use these data to develop a profit model for the company, then use the model to recommend a pricing strategy.

b) What are the sales, revenue, profit, and total costs associated with your recommendation in (a)?

c) The company's supplier charges $12 per raw material unit plus a delivery charge of $900. The company loses about $55 in interest for each month in advance it orders a month's supply of raw materials. Develop an average cost model for the company's raw materials and use the model to recommend an optimal raw material ordering strategy.

d) Give one or more reasons the company might not be able to implement the recommendations you made in (b).

Price charged	Units sold
50	1800
60	1560
70	1320
80	1080

Figure 4.10(a).
Monthly sales data.

Units produced	Total cost
1000	$55,500
1200	$59,300
1500	$65,000
1600	$66,900

Figure 4.10(b).
Monthly costs data.

8. Determine the marginal cost and the marginal revenue associated with the strategy you recommended in part (a) of Item 7. What do you notice? (If necessary, review the definitions of marginal cost and marginal revenue in Item 5 of Individual Work 2. Before you can find the marginal revenue, you will need to express revenue in terms of the number of items produced.)

9. The average cost functions you have studied in this lesson are a type of rational function. There are many other kinds of rational functions. For example, $y = \dfrac{2x^3 - 3x + 5}{x^2 + 2}$ and $y = \dfrac{x + 4}{2x^2 + 3x + 5}$ are both rational functions. Some rational functions have asymptotes and some do not. One way to check for asymptotes is to graph the function in a window that uses fairly large values of x.

a) Some rational functions, such as $y = \dfrac{x + 4}{2x^2 + 3x + 5}$, have a higher power of the variable in the denominator than in the numerator. Use graphs to determine this function's asymptote. Extend and confirm your conclusion by trying one or two similar rational functions of your own.

b) In some rational functions, such as $y = \dfrac{3x^2 + 4}{2x^2 + 3x + 5}$, the highest power of the variable is the same in both numerator and denominator. Use graphs to determine this function's asymptote. Extend and confirm your conclusion by trying one or two similar rational functions of your own.

c) In some rational functions, such as $y = \dfrac{x}{x - 2}$, there are one or more values of x for which the function does not have a value. In this case, the function has no value when x is 2, which causes an unusual type of asymptote. Use a graph to determine the asymptote for this function. (You may find it helpful to use the dot graphing mode of your calculator.) What can you conclude?

d) In some rational functions, such as $y = \dfrac{2x^2 + x + 1}{3x}$, the numerator's highest power is one more than the denominator's highest power. In such cases, there is an asymptote that is neither vertical nor horizontal. Use a graph to show that this function has such an asymptote. Can you find the asymptote's equation?

e) What can you say about asymptotes of rational functions in which the numerator is more than one power higher than the denominator?

ROAD TEST

4

The recommendations obtained from a mathematical model must always be tested in the real world. Therefore, in this activity you will do a "road test" of the optimal pricing and raw material ordering strategies you recommended to the company based on your analysis of their situation.

The simulation you will use in this activity is called BIZ2. As with BIZ1, the spreadsheet and graphing calculator versions produce identical results.

The only difference between BIZ1 and BIZ2 is that two kinds of interest are included in BIZ2: the interest on the company's loan and the interest on its bank account.

The 8% interest on the loan is included in the monthly costs. However, the loan interest has no new effect on cash flow since loan interest is part of the loan payment.

The 4% interest on the company's bank account is included in the monthly revenues. This interest will improve cash flow slightly.

Use the results of your recommendations for successful operation of the company in the BIZ1 simulation to run BIZ2 for 12 months. You may need to modify your recommendations to accommodate the realities under which the company operates: limited storage capacity, a relatively small bank balance, etc. Review the BIZ1 simulation described in Activity 2 now if you have forgotten some of the details of the situation.

Keep a record of your results on Handout H4.3.

When you are finished, prepare a report describing the results of the test of your modeling recommendations.

INDIVIDUAL WORK 4

What Can You Afford?

*A*lthough mathematical models provide clear recommendations for improving the performance of the company in the BIZ1 and BIZ2 simulations, those recommendations must be tempered against realities such as the availability of cash to pay for a large RMU order. In this individual work, you will examine how a mathematical model's recommendations can be implemented.

1. A company pays $18.50 per RMU plus $950 shipping per order. If the company has $43,700 available to purchase raw materials, how many units can it buy? Explain.

2. A company has an opening bank balance of $72,400 on which it receives 4% annual interest compounded monthly. The company's fixed monthly costs total $46,300. The company expects sales of $98,000 for the current month and manufacturing costs of $15,000. If it pays $18.50 per RMU plus $950 shipping, what is the maximum number of RMUs it can order this month? (Assume that accounts are paid at the end of the month.) Explain.

3. **Figure 4.11** shows the beginning of the BIZ2 simulation. Assume the company uses the optimal pricing strategy produced by your profit model in Lesson 1.

   a) Determine the maximum number of RMUs the company can order without overdrawing its bank account if the company intends to manufacture no finished product during the month. Explain how you obtained your answer. (Be sure to consider the revenue the company receives from the price you set and the interest the company receives on its opening bank balance.)

   b) Determine the maximum RMU order if the company intends to manufacture finished product equal to the month's sales.

4. In Activity 3, you developed an average cost model that you used to recommend an ordering strategy for the company in the BIZ1 and BIZ2 simulations. Unfortunately, you may have found that the company's bank balance does not permit full implementation of your recommendation. Companies that find themselves in such situations often decide to pay for large orders of raw materials with a short-term loan or with credit from their supplier. Revisit your average

cost model and adapt it to a situation in which the company buys on credit from its supplier, which charges 15% annual interest. (Assume the company makes monthly payments that cover the cost of that month's supplies plus interest on the remaining months' supplies, and that interest is not compounded.)

5. If you are taking a chemistry course or have taken one in the past, you may have had to strengthen or weaken chemical solutions needed for experiments. For example, if you have 4 liters of a 50% acid solution, 50% is the solution's concentration, which is the percent equivalent of the ratio of pure acid in the solution to the total amount of liquid in the solution:

$$\frac{\text{amount of acid}}{\text{amount of solution}} = \frac{2}{4}.$$

a) To strengthen the solution, you add pure acid to it. If x represents the amount of acid added, then a model for the concentration is $\frac{2+x}{4+x}$. Create a graph of the model and interpret the graph in this context.

b) The solution can be weakened by adding pure water. Model the addition of pure water to the solution. Create a graph of the model and interpret the graph in this context.

c) Suppose you want to increase the concentration of the original 50% solution to 70%. Discuss ways a model can be used to determine the amount of acid required.

	May
Inventory Statement	
RMU's on hand	3000
Finished Product on hand	2600
Profit/Loss Statement	
RMU Order	
RMU Costs	xxxxxxx
Manufacturing Order	112
Manufacturing (actual)	xxxxxxx
Manufacturing Costs	xxxxxxx
Depreciation	($5,036.50)
Interest on loan	($4,029.20)
Salaries, rent, insurance, etc.	($32,000.00)
Total Costs	xxxxxxx
Price	
Sales	xxxxxxx
Sales Revenue	xxxxxxx
Interest Income	$183.48
Total Revenue	xxxxxxx
Cash Flow Statement	
Beginning Balance	$55,043.00
RMU Costs	xxxxxxx
Manufacturing Costs	xxxxxxx
Salaries, rent, insurance, etc.	($32,000.00)
Loan Payment	($10,596.74)
Revenue	xxxxxxx
Net Cash Flow	xxxxxxx
Loan Outstanding	$604,380.00

Figure 4.11

6. a) In words, describe what you know happens to an object's weight as its distance from Earth increases.

   b) NASA scientists use the model $\left(\dfrac{3950}{3950+d}\right)^2$ to predict the portion of an object's weight that remains when the object is d miles from Earth. Discuss why the model reflects your description in (a).

   c) Show how the model can be used to determine when an object has lost 90% of its Earth weight.

7. The company in the BIZ2 simulation keeps its money in a bank account that pays 4% interest. An advantage of such an account is that the money is readily available. A disadvantage is that the interest rate paid by a standard bank account is usually fairly low. By putting its money in an account that cannot be touched for six months or a year, the company could get a better interest rate. Another way the company might get a better return on its money is to invest it in the stock market. However, the stock market is quite unpredictable, especially over short periods of time, so the company could actually lose money.

   Suppose a company invests in the stock market and experiences a 4% loss the first year, but a 12% gain the second year.

   a) Compare the result to that of putting the money in a bank account paying 4% annual interest, compounded annually. Which is the better investment? Construct an example to support your conclusion.

   b) Find an interest rate that produces an account balance identical to the stock's value after two years. (Hint: Write and solve an equation in which the interest rate is the variable.)

   c) Recall from Unit 2 that the arithmetic mean of two numbers is found by adding them, then dividing by two, and that the geometric mean of two numbers is found by multiplying them, then finding the square root. Can either the arithmetic mean or the geometric mean be applied to the stock market rates to obtain the rate you found in (b)? Explain.

   d) Use your discovery to answer this question quickly. If a stock market investment pays 1% one year and 11% the next, what annual interest rate would you have to receive from a bank to match the return on the stock market investment?

8. In Unit 2 you used a symbolic method to show that the geometric mean is never larger than the arithmetic mean. In this item, you will give a geometric proof of that fact.

In **Figure 4.12(a)**, two numbers *a* and *b* are represented as the lengths of two line segments lying along the same line and separated by point P. In **Figure 4.12(b)**, the midpoint of the entire line segment is at M, which is also the center of the semi-circle. In **Figure 4.12(c)**, a perpendicular extends from P to point Q on the semi-circle.

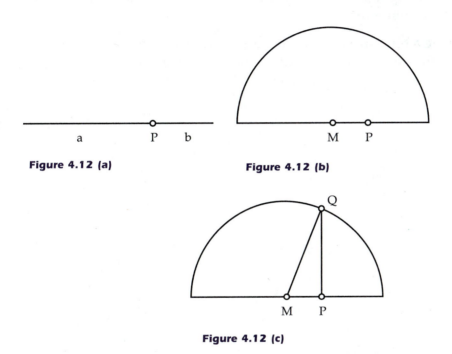

Figure 4.12 (a)

Figure 4.12 (b)

Figure 4.12 (c)

a) Which side of ΔMPQ is the longest? Explain.

b) The lengths of sides $\overline{MQ}$ and $\overline{MP}$ can be expressed in terms of *a* and *b*. Find an expression for each.

c) Use your results from (b), together with the Pythagorean formula, to write the length of side $\overline{PQ}$ in terms of the lengths *a* and *b*. Simplify your answer.

d) Identify the arithmetic mean and geometric mean of *a* and *b* as lengths in Figure 4.12. Use that identification to write an inequality describing the relative sizes of the arithmetic and geometric means. Can they ever be equal?

The inequality you developed in Item 8(d) is extremely powerful. In fact, it is so useful that it has a name. It is known as the Arithmetic Mean-Geometric Mean Inequality, or the AM-GM Inequality for short. One important consequence of the AM-GM Inequality is the fact that if two variable quantities have a constant product, then their minimum sum occurs when the two quantities are exactly equal.

For example, the two quantities $2x$ and $18/x$ have a constant product of 36 (check it). Thus, their sum should be lowest when $2x = 18/x$, or when $x = 3$. You might like to try using a spreadsheet or function grapher to verify this minimum.

9. Write a brief summary of the results you have obtained from modeling the operation of a small business. Include any modeling assumptions you feel are questionable.

LESSON THREE

Changing Assumptions

KEY CONCEPTS

Rate

Profit margin

Piecewise-defined function

Greatest integer function

Ceiling function

Step function

The Image Bank

PREPARATION READING

The Price Is Fixed

Your analysis of the small business in the BIZ1 and BIZ2 simulations enabled you to recommend a price that maximized profits. By developing an average cost model, you were able to recommend an optimal ordering strategy that decreased costs. The mathematical models for profits and average costs were based on several assumptions. One of these assumptions is that the company's monthly sales total is a linear function of the price it sets for its product.

Your research on small businesses may have shown this assumption is not always valid. Not all businesses can control the prices of their products. For example, when a business is one of many producing the same product, the business may find that an increase in price over the current market price drives most customers away, and that a decrease in price goes unnoticed and produces little increase in sales. The company must set a price very close to the price other companies are charging. In other words, the price is fixed, or very nearly so.

In this lesson, you will consider whether models you created for a situation in which a business has considerable control over price can be adapted to a situation in which it does not. What strategies can such businesses use to improve their performance?

ACTIVITY

5

RATING YOUR BUSINESS

The company in the BIZ1 and BIZ2 simulations controlled the price it received for its product. In this activity, you will re-examine the models you developed and the recommendations you made, but you will do so for a company that does not control the price of its product.

The company in this activity charges $65 per unit of finished product because $65 is the current market price. All other circumstances of this company are the same as those in BIZ1 and BIZ2, including:

Raw material units (RMUs) cost $27.04 each, and there is a shipping charge of $1690 per order. RMUs are ordered monthly.

Each unit of finished product costs $5.15 to manufacture.

Monthly fixed costs, which include depreciation, salaries, rent, and insurance, total $37,036.50.

Warehouse facilities can hold up to 10,000 RMUs and up to 5000 units of finished product.

Maximum monthly manufacturing capacity is 2000 units of finished product.

---

1. Review the model you used in recommending an optimal pricing strategy for the company in BIZ1/BIZ2. Discuss changes in the model for this new situation and the implications of those changes.

2. Review the average cost model you developed for the company in BIZ1/BIZ2 (see Item 7(d) of Individual Work 2) and adapt it to this situation. Use your model to recommend a strategy that will produce a profit for the company. Explain your recommendation.

RATING YOUR BUSINESS

3. Recall that a company's profit margin is the portion (or percentage) of revenues that it keeps after paying all costs. (See Item 6 of Individual Work 2.) Develop a model for the profit margin of this business. What advice can you give the company based on your knowledge of this type of mathematical model and the company's circumstances?

4. Since profit margin is the ratio of profits to revenues, it is a rate. More specifically, it is the rate of return on revenues. You have seen that rates are often more useful than totals, and that is true in business. For example, economists feel that a company's profit margin is a more useful indicator of the company's success than total profits. Why do you think economists feel this way?

5. Review the average RMU cost model you developed in Activity 3 and adapt it to this situation. Use your model to recommend an optimal ordering strategy for this company.

CONSIDER:

1. What circumstances might prevent a business that has little control over the price it gets for its product from implementing modeling recommendations?

2. How might a company overcome those circumstances?

INDIVIDUAL WORK 5

Adaptations

1. Use the models you developed in Activity 5 to discuss the company's outlook if it has a monthly demand for 1400 units of finished product. Consider monthly profit and profit margin, and both monthly and optimal RMU ordering policies.

2. Two companies that manufacture similar products had annual revenues of $8,000,000 and $2,000,000 and costs of $7,000,000 and $1,500,000, respectively.

   a) By what measure could the first company be considered to have had a better year than the second? Explain.

   b) By what measure could the second company be considered to have had a better year than the first? Explain.

3. **Figure 4.13** contains data for a company in two consecutive years.

Figure 4.13.
Company data.

Year	Revenues	Costs
1997	$750,000	$550,000
1998	$1,300,000	$1,050,000

   a) Although revenue has increased, a member of the company's board of directors could view these figures as reason for concern. Explain.

   b) A closer inspection of the company's increased costs reveals a one-time expenditure of $150,000 for a new piece of equipment and $35,000 in salaries for new employees to run the equipment. Based on this information and the information in Figure 4.13, project what might happen in 1999.

4. **Figure 4.14** shows soy-bean production data for the United States in several recent years.

Figure 4.14.
Soy bean production data.
(Source: U.S. Dept. of Agriculture)

Year	Harvest (million bushels)	Price (per bushel)
1997-97	2,382	$7.38
1995-96	2,177	$6.77
1994-95	2,731	$5.48
1993-94	2,239	$6.40

a) Consider a farmer who normally harvests about 35,000 bushels of soybeans. Is the farmer likely to have much control over the price the 35,000 bushels will bring? Explain.

b) The farmer has fixed production costs of $20,000 and per bushel costs of $5.32. The projected price for the current season is $6.90 per bushel. Develop an average cost model and use the model to determine the production level for which the farmer will break even.

c) If the farmer produces 35,000 bushels, what is the total profit and what is the profit margin? Explain how you obtained your answers.

d) Can the farmer increase the profit margin under these conditions? Explain.

5. Among the products produced by a small bakery are dinner rolls that sell for $0.18 each. The costs associated with production of the rolls include $600 in office expenses, $2500 for machinery and salaries, $2100 for a delivery truck and driver capable of delivering 36,000 rolls monthly, and $60 per 1000 rolls in manufacturing expenses. The bakery's capacity is 100,000 rolls per month.

a) Develop average cost and profit margin models for the dinner roll operation. Discuss the implications of these models for the company.

b) How might the company improve its current situation? Would implementation of your suggestion(s) require revision of the models you developed in (a)?

6. A company pays $9.40 per unit of raw materials and a delivery charge of $650 regardless of the size of the raw material order. The company currently produces 8000 units of finished product monthly. Each unit of finished product requires one unit of raw materials. For each month in advance that the company orders a month's supply of raw materials, it loses about $250 in interest. Develop an average RMU cost model and use it to recommend an optimal ordering strategy for the company.

7. Your solution to the RMU ordering problem in Item 6 was probably obtained with the aid of a calculator. Such a solution is quite acceptable in a modeling situation provided you are careful to obtain the precision the application requires. It is also possible to obtain an exact solution, which you will do in this item.

a) Begin by using symbolic procedures to simplify the model you developed in Item 6. Express your answer as separate fractions. (Since it is common to make mistakes when applying symbolic procedures, you might compare graphs of the original and your answer to see if they appear to be equivalent.)

b) Average RMU cost functions are often of the form $\frac{a}{t} + bt + c$, where a, b, and c are constants, although they are not often whole numbers. Find the arithmetic mean and the geometric mean of the terms $\frac{a}{t}$ and bt.

c) Does one, both, or neither of these means vary as t changes? Explain.

d) Apply the AM-GM inequality to this situation to write an inequality involving the Average-RMU-cost function and constants. (Look back to the discussion following Item 8 of Individual Work 4 for ideas.)

e) Under what conditions is the inequality an equation? What can you conclude about minimizing Average-RMU-cost functions such as those described here?

f) Apply your conclusion for the general case in (e) to the average RMU cost function you found in (a). Give an exact value for the optimal monthly ordering interval.

g) How sensitive is the optimal ordering interval to changes in the price of RMUs? For example, suppose the price of RMUs increases by 10%. Is there a similar change in the optimal ordering interval?

h) Repeat part (g) for the shipping charge on the RMU order.

8. Mathematicians sometimes use the AM-GM inequality to quickly determine the minimum for functions of the form $\frac{a}{x} + bx + c$. Determine the minimum of each of the following.

a) $\frac{8}{x} + 2x - 3$

b) $5x + \frac{10}{x}$

THE BUSINESS GROWS

Most companies consider an increase in business a good thing. However, even a business that prefers to maintain its size may find growth a necessity. For example, consider a business with a declining profit margin: in order to avoid an eventual loss, the business may find it necessary to increase its capacity and take steps to increase sales. Such steps usually have new costs associated with them and, therefore, are not undertaken without risk.

In Activity 5, you adapted your models for the company in the BIZ1/BIZ2 simulations to a situation in which the company has little control over the price of its product. In this activity, you will adapt your model again, this time to include a plan for growth of the company.

The company in the BIZ1/BIZ2 simulations is considering expansion and has hired a consultant to develop a plan. The consultant recommends that the company rent equipment and hire new employees to increase its manufacturing capacity and undertake an advertising campaign to increase sales. The consultant estimates that the increase in costs will be $25,000 monthly, and that manufacturing capacity will increase to 4000 units of finished product per month.

Since the fixed costs depend on whether manufacturing capacity is above or below 2000 units, you will find piecewise-defined functions helpful in developing new models.

Recall that a piecewise-defined function is one that is described by more than one equation. For example, consider the piecewise-defined function $y = \begin{cases} x-1, & x < 2 \\ 2x+1, & x \geq 2 \end{cases}$.

ACTIVITY

6

THE BUSINESS GROWS

The graph of this function also occurs in two distinct pieces that reflect the two parts of the function's definition **(Figure 4.15).**

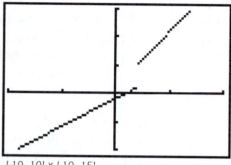

Figure 4.15.

[-10, 10] x [-10, 15]

Recall that to graph this function on a graphing calculator, the function is entered as $(x-1)(x<2) + (2x+1)(x \geq 2)$. The graph should be plotted in dot mode to avoid an incorrect connection between the two parts.

1. Review the models for total profit, average cost (per unit of finished product), and profit margin from Activity 5. Revise the models to reflect this new situation. Graph the models and interpret the graphs in this context.

2. Unless the company sells enough units after expansion, profits will not be as high as they were when the company was making and selling its capacity of 2000 units. The company's pre-expansion profits and the new profit model can be used to determine the level of sales necessary. Show how to do this by writing and solving an equation.

3. Use a method similar to the one you used in Item 2 to analyze average cost and profit margin after expansion. What advice can you give the company?

ACTIVITY

THE BUSINESS GROWS

6

Another way to model a situation in which costs increase abruptly at some point is with a mathematical function called the **greatest integer function.** Most graphing calculators use the symbol int(x) for this function. The greatest integer of any number is the greatest integer not larger than the given value. Thus, this function's value is the whole number part of any non-negative number. For example, if x is 2 or any number between 2 and 3, and $y = $ int(x), then y is assigned the value 2.

Mathematicians sometimes use $[\ ]$ or $\lfloor\ \rfloor$ to represent the greatest integer function. Since this function moves all non-integer numbers down, it is sometimes called the floor function, a name suggested by the notation $\lfloor\ \rfloor$. For example,
int(2.1) = $[2.1] = \lfloor 2.1 \rfloor = 2$.

A graphing calculator graph (dot mode) of $y = $ int(x) is shown in **Figure 4.16.** Note that the portion of the graph between 0 and 1 is not visible since it is on the x-axis. Also, though your calculator graph will probably not be able to show it, the definition above shows that each step is closed on the left and open on the right. That is, each step includes the integer at its left-hand end. For example, $x = 2$ produces the left-hand point on the second visible step in Figure 4.16, not the right-hand point on the first step.

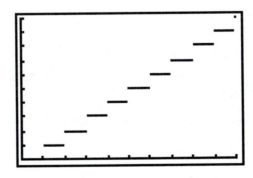

Figure 4.16.

[0, 10] x [0, 10]

ACTIVITY

THE BUSINESS GROWS

6

This graph shown below resembles a set of stairs or steps. Therefore, functions that are transformations of $y = \text{int}(x)$ are often called **step functions**. For example, the function $y = \text{int}(x/2) + 1$ is a step function. It stretches the graph in Figure 4.16 horizontally by a factor of 2 and shifts it vertically one unit. The resulting graph is shown in **Figure 4.17.**

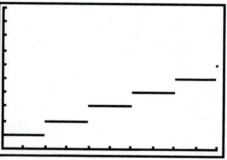

Figure 4.17.

[0, 10] x [0, 10]

4. Use the greatest integer function to model average costs, total profit, and profit margins if the company can increase its manufacturing capacity by 2000 units for every $25,000 of increased costs. Comment on how well it helps describe the quantities you are modeling.

CONSIDER:

1. Do you prefer a piecewise-defined function or the greatest integer function to model the growth of a business? Explain your preference.

2. Which type of model offers the greatest flexibility?

INDIVIDUAL WORK 6

Watch Your Step

Piecewise defined-functions and the greatest integer function are useful in modeling the growth of a business. In this individual work, you will consider several growth situations and examine the use of transformations in defining appropriate step-function models.

1. Sketch graphs of each of the following functions in the window [–10, 10] x [–10, 10]. Comment on how each of your graphs in parts (b)-(g) is related to your graph in part (a). Be as specific as possible, being sure to describe the graphs, not the equations.

   Note: It is customary to indicate with a solid dot that the endpoint of a segment is included; an open dot indicates that the endpoint is not included. Use that convention in your graphs. For example, in part (a), the point (2, 2) should be solid; the point (2, 1) should be open.

   a) $y = \text{int}(x)$

   b) $y = \lfloor x \rfloor$

   c) $y = \left\lfloor \dfrac{x}{2} \right\rfloor$

   d) $y = 4\text{int}(x/3)$

   e) $y = \lfloor -x \rfloor$

   f) $y = -\lfloor x \rfloor$

   g) $y = 3\text{int}(x/2.5) + 1$

2. The **ceiling function**—the smallest integer greater than or equal to a given number—is defined much like the floor function, except that it takes all non-integer values up (instead of down) to the next integer. As you might guess, the notation for ceiling of x is $\lceil x \rceil$. With this definition, then, $\lceil 2.1 \rceil = 3$.

   a) Graph $y = \lceil x \rceil$ on the window [-10, 10] x [-10, 10]. Indicate clearly which endpoints are included in the steps. (Note that ceiling is not a built-in function on most calculators, so create this graph by hand.)

   b) Write a formula using the greatest integer function, int(x), that is exactly equivalent to $y = \lceil x \rceil$, even at the endpoints. (Hint: look back at your work in Item 1.)

c) Write a formula for a function that looks like the greatest integer function, but which has its closed endpoints on the right ends instead of on the left.

3. **Figure 4.18** is a graph of a monthly cost model for a delivery service. (Following the endpoint convention described in Item 1, an open dot at the end of a segment means that the point is not included in the segment. Thus, the cost for 100 deliveries is $5000, not $8000.)

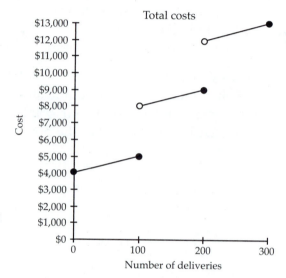

Figure 4.18.
Graph of monthly cost model for a delivery service.

a) The service has fixed office costs of $1000 per month. Each delivery vehicle that the company operates is capable of making 100 deliveries per month and has $3000 per month in vehicle and driver expenses. Moreover, each delivery costs $10 for packaging, gasoline, tolls, and other expenses. Show how each of these four values is visible in the graph.

b) For each of the three steps of the graph in Figure 4.18, write an equation of a line containing the step.

c) Develop a total-cost model that has a graph like the one in Figure 4.18. Verify that your model has the same graph.

d) If the company charges customers $50 per delivery, graph your cost model and a revenue model together. Interpret the graph in this context.

e) Combine your cost and revenue models to obtain a profit model. Use the profit model to create a model for the company's profit margin. Graph your profit margin model and interpret it in this context.

4. A charter company sells seats on an excursion trip. Expenses include bus leasing costs of $1500 per bus and driver costs of $225 per bus. There are $1100 in office and advertising costs for each trip. Each bus holds 70 passengers. For some trips, the company includes free meals for each passenger at a cost to the company of $15 per passenger. **Figure 4.19** shows two graphs of total costs.

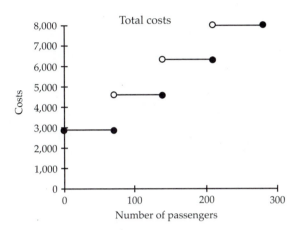

Figure 4.19(a).

Figure 4.19(b).

a) Determine which graph represents a trip with meals included and which represents a trip without meals. Explain.

b) Create a symbolic expression that models total costs for each type of excursion.

5. A new carpet-cleaning business is being established. Estimated monthly costs include $2000 in office expenses and $4500 for each van and employees to operate the van. Each van and crew is capable of making 120 calls a month. Each call has $5 in chemical expenses associated with it.

a) Use a piecewise-defined function to model the total costs for 1, 2, and 3 vans in terms of the number of calls made.

b) Use the ceiling or greatest integer function to model total costs.

c) Graph the total cost model.

d) Can the business operate at a profit if the market rate for a cleaning call is $60? Explain.

e) Models that are based on the greatest integer function sometimes cannot increase above a certain amount. For example, consider the function $y = \dfrac{3x + \mathrm{int}(x)}{x}$. The graphing calculator graph in **Figure 4.20** appears to show that the function is never above 4.

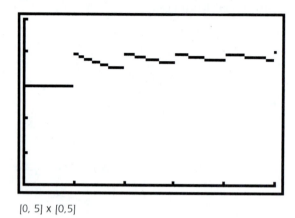

[0, 5] x [0,5]

Figure 4.20.

By thinking about the function's symbolic form, you can confirm that the function is never larger than 4: since $\mathrm{int}(x)$ is never larger than x,

$\dfrac{3x + \mathrm{int}(x)}{x}$ can never be larger than $\dfrac{3x + x}{x} = \dfrac{4x}{x} = 4.$

Is there a value that the profit margin of the cleaning company can't exceed if the company charges $60 per call? Explain.

6. In Activity 6, you developed models for growth of the company in the BIZ1/BIZ2 simulations. Revisit the average RMU cost model you developed in Lesson 2 and revise it to reflect a situation in which the company expands to a monthly production level of 4000 units of finished product.

7. In Item 5 of Individual Work 5, you considered the dinner-roll operation in a small bakery. Production costs included $600 in office expense, $2100 for a delivery truck and driver capable of delivering 36,000 rolls a month, $2500 for machinery and salaries to bake a maximum of 100,000 rolls a month, and $60 per 1000 rolls in production costs. The bakery gets a market price of 18¢ each for the rolls.

For each additional $2100 the company spends, delivery capacity can be increased by 36,000 rolls. For each additional $2500 the company spends, baking capacity can be increased by 100,000 rolls. Use the ceiling or the greatest integer function to create models that can be used to analyze potential growth. Discuss the implications of your models. (Hint: you will need to use a step function twice to model total costs since two different quantities step up.)

8. The greatest integer function can be used to model quite a few common situations. For example, charges for long distance phone calls are usually based on the number of minutes you talk. A model based on the greatest integer function enables a communications company's computer to quickly determine the amount you should be billed.

Figure 4.21 is a table of phone rates for a long-distance carrier. The charge is based on a connect fee of 30¢ and a per-minute fee of 20¢.

Time, t	Total charge
$0 < t \le 1$	$0.50
$1 < t \le 2$	$0.70
$2 < t \le 3$	$0.90

Figure 4.21.
Telephone charges.

Show how to transform the greatest integer function to model these phone charges. Include a graph of your model.

9. Supermarkets often price turkeys differently depending on their weight: small turkeys cost more per pound than large ones.

   a) Use the greatest integer function or a piecewise-defined funtion to model the cost of a turkey in terms of its weight if turkeys up to 8 pounds cost 89¢ a pound, turkeys between 8 and 14 pounds cost 69¢ a pound, and turkeys over 14 pounds cost 49¢ a pound.

   b) Use your model to determine the size turkey a person with $7.00 to spend can buy.

   c) What is interesting about this pricing scheme?

10. A college allows a maximum of 20 students in each section of a course and schedules enough sections to accommodate all students who enroll in the course. The college charges $500 tuition for the course and incurs expenses of $8000 for each section.

   a) Write a mathematical model of the amount of money the college makes from all sections in terms of the number of students enrolled.

b) Prepare a graph of your model in a reasonable window if enrollment in the course never exceeds 200 students. Interpret the graph in this context.

11. An item in Course 2 of *Mathematics: Modeling Our World* described a situation in which the parents of three children aged 5, 7, and 8 divided $20 weekly allowance in proportion to the ages of the children. As the years passed, the total amount of the allowance remained the same, but the amount received by each child changed.

    a) Use rational functions to model the portion of the allowance received by each child in terms of years since the youngest child was born.

    b) Graph the three models together. Interpret the graphs in this context.

12. Show how to find the optimal raw material ordering strategy for a manufacturing company whose average raw material costs are modeled by $\dfrac{40}{t} + 4t + 10$, where t is the number of months for which raw materials are ordered.

LESSON FOUR
Slow Growth

KEY CONCEPTS

Gradual growth

Arithmetic series

The Image Bank

PREPARATION READING

Barriers to Growth

The mathematical modeling process is cyclic: often it is repeated several times because the model must be improved or adapted. Your experience in this unit has demonstrated the cyclic nature of the modeling process. The original models you developed had to be adapted to a situation in which the business could not control the price of its product and to a situation in which the business was considering expansion.

Each time you revisited your models, you questioned some of the original assumptions and made new ones. For example, your models for the growth of a business assume that increased capacity is used immediately. That is often not the case because a business that increases its capacity cannot immediately sell all the product it is capable of producing. Frequently growth is gradual because a business must work hard to attract new customers.

A more realistic interpretation of your growth models would consider gradual growth. What can your models tell a company that does not expect to use all of its additional capacity immediately?

GROWING GRADUALLY

In Activity 6, you developed models for the growth of the company in the BIZ1/BIZ2 simulations. Recall that prior to the company's expansion, a total-cost model was $32.19x + 38726.5$, where x is the number of units of finished product manufactured in a month. Expansion of the company's manufacturing capacity from 2000 units to 4000 units increased costs by $25,000 monthly.

Assume the market price of the company's product has fallen to $55 per unit, which has resulted in a decline in profits. The company is considering a strategy of increasing capacity to 4000 units together with an aggressive campaign to increase sales. The company predicts that increasing the monthly sales from the current 2000 units to 4000 units is possible, but at a gradual rate of increase of 150 units per month.

Your task in this activity is to consider the feasibility of expansion. Below are several questions the company wants answered before making its decision. When you have finished your analysis, prepare a report that shows how you obtained your answers to each question. Include any observations or recommendations you would make to the company.

1. Will the company operate at a loss because of the expansion? If so, for how many months will the company incur a loss, and how much will it lose each month?

2. How long will it be before the company's profits return to their current level?

3. During the time that profits are below their current level, what is the total value of the lost profits?

4. If the company succeeds in increasing its sales to 4000 units, how will the profits compare to those at the current 2000 unit capacity? How will the profits during a year of operating at 4000 units compare to the profits in a year of operating at 2000 units?

Breaking Better Than Even

1. Whether to increase the capacity of a business can be a difficult decision because growth sometimes requires a sacrifice of short-term profits. **Figure 4.22** describes the profits of a business for the first three months after expansion.

   a) If profits continue to increase at the same rate, for how many months does the company operate at a loss?

   b) The total losses can be found by adding them individually. However, since the losses form an arithmetic series, the total can also be found by means of a shortcut you have used before. (See Item 4 of Individual Work 3. Recall that an arithmetic series is a sum in which the terms increase or decrease by a constant amount.) Show how to find the total of the losses without adding them individually.

   c) If the company's monthly profits were $3000 before expansion, what is the total of lost profits during the months the company operated at a loss? Explain.

Months after expansion	Profits
1	–$11,500
2	–$9,500
3	–$7,500

Figure 4.22

2. Reconsider your analysis of gradual growth for the company in Activity 7 if the company can increase its sales by 200 units per month instead of 150.

   a) Determine the number of months for which the company will operate at a loss and for which it will experience a decrease in profits.

   b) Determine the total losses and total lost profits.

3. In Item 3 of Individual Work 6, you developed a model for the growth of a carpet cleaning company with monthly office expenses of $2,000, chemical expenses of $5 per call, and monthly equipment expenses of $4500 for each van it operates. (A single van can do a maximum of 120 calls per month.) Suppose the company is started with just a single van serving 115 customers a month, each of which pays $85 per cleaning. The company decides to purchase a second van and believes it can expand its business at the rate of 5 calls a month.

   a) How much money does the company need to finance its losses during expansion? Explain.

b) How long will it be before the company's profits return to pre-expansion level, and what is the total of the profits the company can expect to lose during that time?

c) The company feels that new service calls can be generated at the rate of 10 per month if $15,000 is spent on the services of an advertising agency. Do you feel the cost of hiring the agency's services is justified? Explain.

4. Mathematicians sometimes use their knowledge of arithmetic series to find a sum quickly.

a) According to one story, the young Karl Gauss (1777–1855), who is considered one of the greatest mathematicians of all time, once amazed his elementary school teacher by quickly finding the sum of all whole numbers from 1 through 100. Show how this sum can be found quickly.

b) Show how to find the sum of all the odd numbers from 1 through 100 quickly.

5. Recall that the aspect ratio of a rectangle is the ratio of its length to its width. **Figure 4.23** is a 2 cm x 3 cm rectangle.

a) What is the rectangle's aspect ratio?

b) Use a rational function to model the aspect ratio of the rectangle if the length and width increase by the same amount. Graph your model and interpret the graph in this context.

c) How do the model and your interpretation change if the length increases twice as rapidly as the width?

Figure 4.23.
A 2 cm x 3 cm rectangle.

6. Because of expansion, if a company loses $10,000 one month, $9000 the next, and continues to improve losses by $1000 a month, what will the total of its losses be? Explain how the answer can be found quickly.

7. If a company invested $10,000 in stocks that earned 2% on the first year, but 24% the second year, would the company have made the same amount of money from an investment paying $\frac{2 + 24}{2} = 13\%$ compounded annually? Explain.

ACTIVITY

UNIT PROJECT

8

Timber Ridge Woodworking is the manufacturer of high quality handcrafted dining tables. Timber Ridge has a small niche market of upscale clients and an excellent business reputation. They have been in business in the same small town for ten years and have good working relationships with their suppliers, their wholesalers, and their local bank.

Although their product is top notch and commands a high price, demand for their furniture is sensitive to price. Their records of the relationship between price and monthly sales are shown in **Figure 4.24.**

Current overhead costs for the company's office and the manufacturing plant are $85,000 per month. The company operates only one shift consisting of two master carpenters, four carpenters, and three apprentices. Salary costs for the shift are $28,000 per month. Working at full capacity, a shift can produce up to 140 tables per month. The workers are willing to work an extra 10 hours per week if they are paid time-and-a-half overtime. The cost for raw materials for

Price	Sales
$1,200	260
$1,500	200
$1,600	182
$1,800	139
$1,900	120

Figure 4.24

each table is $650. The lumberyard, which supplies Timber Ridge, is in the same town; thus Timber Ridge keeps very little raw material inventory. Timber Ridge currently has $149,000 in cash reserves that earn 4% annual interest compounded monthly.

There are enough qualified carpenters in the area that Timber Ridge could staff a second shift and double their output. However, it would take one month for the shift to learn the ropes and become productive. The expected cost for this month-long training period is $40,000 for salaries and materials.

ACTIVITY

8

1. What price should Timber Ridge set for their product in order to maximize their profit? What production level is required for this price? Justify your answer. Make sure you consider three options:

   a) one shift

   b) one shift with overtime

   c) two shifts.

2. A chain of exclusive hotels contacts Timber Ridge. The chain is embarking on an extensive refurbishing of their hotels and wishes to purchase 900 tables per year. The chain offers $1,350,000 for the contract and expects to renew the contract for at least four more years. Their hotels are located significantly outside Timber Ridge's current market, thus the contract is unlikely to affect the demand for Timber Ridge's regular production. The bank will loan Timber Ridge capital at 9% interest, but requires a business plan for the next three years.

   Should Timber Ridge accept the contract with the hotel? If they do, how would the contract affect the optimal selling price for current customers? What production level should be set? Justify your answers. Make sure you consider three options:

   a) one shift

   b) one shift with overtime

   c) two shifts.

If Timber Ridge must borrow money in order to accept this contract, write a proposal to the bank that includes how much you wish to borrow, and how you will repay it. Include a business plan that tracks your expected costs, revenue, profit, and cash flow for the next 4 years.

Wrapping Up Unit Four

1. A rock band is giving a concert. The hall rents for $5500 and seats 2000 people. There are additional fixed costs of $5000 for travel, salaries, etc. Local regulations require a security guard for every 250 tickets sold. Each security guard is paid $200.

   a) Create a model for total costs.

   b) If the band charges $10 per ticket, graph a revenue model and a cost model together. Interpret your graph.

   c) Develop a profit model. Use the model to determine the band's profit if the stadium fills.

2. a) Show how a rational function can be used to model the addition of acid to 2 liters of a solution that is half water and half acid.

   b) Graph the model. Explain the meaning of any asymptotes in this context.

   c) Show how to use the model to determine the amount of acid that must be added to increase the acid concentration of the original solution to 70%.

   d) How does the model change if water and acid are added to the original solution simultaneously in the ratio of 2:1? Interpret the new model in this context.

3. The geometric mean of two numbers is a function of two variables. For example, a symbolic description of the geometric mean of two numbers might be $gm(a, b) = \sqrt{ab}$.

   a) Use function symbolism to express the arithmetic mean of two numbers.

   b) Graphing the geometric mean or arithmetic mean relationship for two numbers requires a three-dimensional graph. However, you can graph the relationship in two dimensions if you hold one of the two numbers constant, which is a practice mathematicians often use when studying functions of more than one variable. Pick a constant for one of the numbers and graph the arithmetic mean and geometric mean relationships together. Be sure to state the constant you used.

   c) Interpret your graph. You may want to try one or two additional graphs with a different constant before stating your conclusions.

   d) Do you detect any asymptotes in your graph? Explain.

4. **Figure 4.25** shows the records of price charged and monthly sales of a non-seasonal product.

Price	Sales
$55	1270
$75	850
$68	1004
$52	1356

Figure 4.25

a) Model the relationship between price and sales.

b) The fixed costs associated with manufacturing this product are $22,000 monthly. There are additional costs of $28 per item. Show how to re-express the costs in terms of the price charged.

c) Develop models that can be used to maximize the profit associated with this item. Use your models to give a recommendation.

d) If the company's costs increase by $2 per item, would you advise the company to increase the price it charges by the same amount? Explain.

e) Use your profit model from part (c) to determine the price that maximizes profit margin.

5. The area and perimeter of a rectangle are functions of two variables: the rectangle's length and its width. For example, the relationship among the area, the length, and the width can be expressed symbolically as $a(l, w) = lw$.

a) Express the perimeter, length, and width relationship symbolically.

b) Show how to re-express the length in terms of the width if the area of the rectangle is fixed at 50 square units.

c) Show how your re-expression in (b) can be used to express the perimeter in terms of the width when the area is fixed at 50 square units.

d) Show how to use your answer to (c) to determine the dimensions of a rectangle with an area of 50 square units constructed with the smallest possible perimeter.

6. In 1998, postage on a first-class letter was 32¢ for the first ounce and 23¢ for each additional ounce. A graph of first-class postage is shown in **Figure 4.26.**

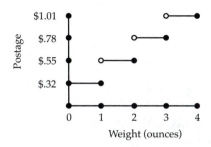

Figure 4.26

Does $0.32 + 0.23\text{int}(w)$ model the relationship between weight (in ounces) and first-class postage (in dollars)? Explain. If not, correct the equation.

7. Discuss the merits of measuring the success of a business by profit margin instead of total profit.

8. Describe the graph of $y = \dfrac{1}{x}$. Show how it can be transformed to produce the graph of $y = \dfrac{7x+3}{2x}$.

9. Item 6 of Individual Work 3 described a summer camp that had fixed expenses of $67,000 and per child expenses of $487 for food, supervision, and transportation. Since a supervisor is usually responsible for several children, and because quite a few children can be transported in a single bus, better models can be developed if the per-child expenses are broken down into categories. Food for each child costs the camp $247. One person supervises 15 children and is paid a salary of $2850. Each bus transports 40 children and costs $2000 in rental and driver expenses.

   a) Show how to use the greatest integer function to model the camp's costs.

   b) The camp usually draws between 400 and 500 children, but its facilities can handle no more than 500. The camp is run by a non-profit group whose only financial interest is breaking even. Use your models to discuss what you feel is a reasonable amount to charge each child.

10. A company pays $23 per unit of raw material plus shipping of $600 regardless of the size of the order. If the company orders raw materials in advance, it loses about $180 in interest for each month in advance it orders its raw materials. Can the company save money by ordering less frequently than once a month if it uses about 900 units of raw materials monthly? Explain.

11. A small manufacturing company currently produces and sells 11,000 units of finished product monthly. The market price of the product is $7.80 per unit. The company has $24,000 in monthly fixed costs and additional costs of $2.90 per unit of finished product. A consultant has been hired to analyze possible expansion. The consultant's report estimates that expanding manufacturing capacity by 5000 units will increase the company's fixed costs by $8000 monthly. The consultant also estimates the company's per unit cost will increase by 50¢ to pay for promotional efforts needed to sustain sales at a level near the new capacity.

   a) Use this information to develop a recommendation in favor of or opposed to expansion. Support your recommendation.

   b) If the company is unsure it can achieve maximum capacity after expansion, what level of sales must it reach in order to match pre-expansion profits? Explain how you got your answer.

   c) What level of sales will the company have to reach to return its profit margin to the pre-expansion level?

   d) Is there a possibility that expansion will cause the company to operate at a loss for a time? Explain.

Mathematical Summary

The primary mathematical goal of this unit is to develop mathematical models that can be used to optimize the performance of a small business. Measures of business performance used in the unit are total profit and profit margin. One advantage to the latter is that profit margin is a rate and, therefore, is a more useful way to compare one business to another business of a different size or to its own past performance. Several types of models are used to optimize performance.

LINEAR AND QUADRATIC MODELS

Data gathered from spreadsheet or calculator simulations show there is often a linear relationship between the price a business charges for its product, and sales. The costs a business incurs are often a linear function of the number of items it produces, but costs can be re-expressed in terms of price when there is a linear relationship between price charged and sales. Therefore, profits can often be expressed as a function of price alone, and the relationship in such instances is quadratic. Since a graph of a quadratic price/profit model is a downward opening parabola (see **Figure 4.27**), graphical and/or symbolic methods can be used to determine a price that maximizes profit.

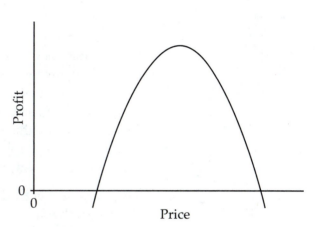

Figure 4.27.
Graph of a quadratic price/profit model.

RATIONAL FUNCTION MODELS

Since profit is the difference between revenue and costs, a company can sometimes find ways to improve its profits further by reducing costs. One way is by taking advantage of reduced per-unit costs associated with quantity purchases. A mathematical model of average raw material cost is often a rational function: one that is the ratio of two polynomial functions. Rational functions often have asymptotes: lines the graph approaches. These asymptotes can be vertical, horizontal, or diagonal (see **Figure 4.28**). Vertical asymptotes divide the graph into two or more sections called branches.

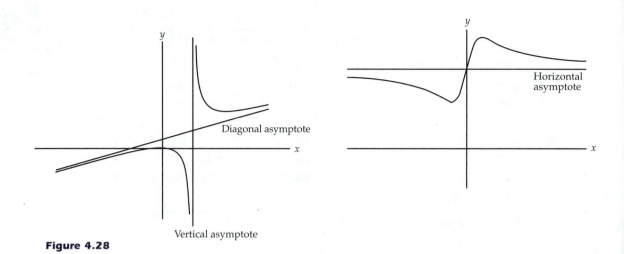

Figure 4.28

When one branch of a rational function's graph has both a vertical and diagonal asymptote, there can be a point on the curve that is lower than any other point on that branch. (For example, note the right branch in the graph on the left in Figure 4.28.) In average raw material cost models, this point corresponds to a minimum average raw material cost. A graphing calculator's zoom feature or minimum-finder can be used to approximate this point closely.

In some cases, an exact value can be determined by applying a technique based on the fact that the geometric mean of two numbers is less than or equal to their arithmetic mean. Thus if the product of two quantities is constant, their sum is minimized when the two quantities are equal. The general result obtained from this technique is useful in other situations that are modeled by functions of the form $\frac{a}{x} + bx + c$, where a, b, and c are constants. Since $\frac{a}{x} \times bx = ab$, which

is a constant, the minimum sum occurs when $\frac{a}{x} = bx$.

Since a horizontal asymptote represents a value that the response variable approaches as the explanatory variable gets large, rational function models can tell a business that some measures of performance (that is, profit margin) have limits–values that cannot be exceeded even if sales increase considerably.

Because rates and ratios are common, rational functions are used in mathematical models in many situations other than business. Many rational function models are transformations of the function $y = \frac{1}{x}$, whose graph is a hyperbola (see **Figure 4.29**).

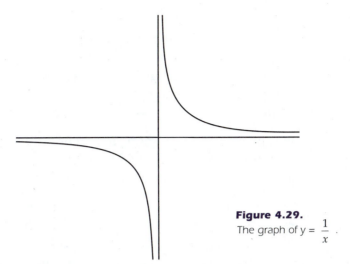

Figure 4.29.
The graph of $y = \dfrac{1}{x}$.

There are many factors that affect the success of a business, even a small business. Therefore, mathematical models used to optimize the performance of a business are often functions of several variables. Since functions of more than one variable can be difficult to analyze, mathematicians often hold one or more variables constant while observing the behavior of the others. In a modeling context, this means that mathematicians simplify the situation so models are manageable.

STEP FUNCTION MODELS

One way in which mathematicians simplify a business model is by assuming the size of the business remains constant over a period of time. In reality, however, businesses are often in the process of growing. Growth means costs, revenues, and profits all change over time.

To model the profits of a business during a period of growth, mathematicians often find that more than one model is necessary. These models can be combined into a single piecewise-defined function or represented by a function defined in a single piece based on the greatest integer function. Graphs of both piecewise and greatest integer function models are characterized by distinct pieces that resemble steps (see **Figure 4.30**).

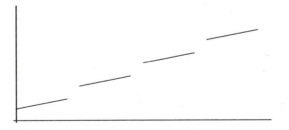

Figure 4.30.
A graph of piecewise-defined and greatest integer function models.

Step functions typically have either all right-hand endpoints included in the respective steps, or all left-hand endpoints included. Included endpoints are usually shown in graphs as solid dots; excluded endpoints are usually seen as open circles. The greatest integer function, $\text{int}(x)$ or $\lfloor x \rfloor$, has left-hand endpoints included.

The ceiling function, $\lceil x \rceil$, has right-hand endpoints included. The ceiling function may be written as a transformation of the greatest integer function as $\lceil x \rceil = -\text{int}(-x)$.

Models designed to reflect the growth of a business often predict that growth results in a period of time during which the business must be able to withstand reduced profits, or perhaps even a loss, before returning its profits to a level that exceeds pre-expansion. In order to predict the cumulative effect during the period of reduced profits that follows the expansion of a business's capacity, mathematicians often employ simple shortcuts such as summing an arithmetic series by averaging its first and last terms, then multiplying by the number of terms in the series.

Glossary

ASYMPTOTE:
A line that a graph approaches. Asymptotes are often vertical or horizontal, but do not have to be either.

AVERAGE UNIT COST:
The cost associated with one unit of product. Average unit cost is found by dividing the total cost by the number of items produced.

CEILING FUNCTION:
The smallest integer greater than or equal to a given number. The ceiling function of x is denoted as $\lceil x \rceil$.

CONIC SECTION:
A curve produced by intersecting a plane and a cone. The hyperbola, parabola, circle, and ellipse are all conic sections.

FUNCTION OF MORE THAN ONE VARIABLE:
A quantity is a function of more than one variable if its value depends on at least two other variables. For example, the revenue a company obtains from a product is equal to product of sales and price charged. Thus, revenue is a function of sales and price. A symbolic expression of this relationship is $r(p, s) = p \times s$.

GREATEST INTEGER FUNCTION:
A function whose value is the largest integer less than or equal to a number. For positive numbers, the greatest integer function's value is the whole-number part of a number. For example, the greatest integer function assigns the value 3 to 3 and to any number between 3 and 4. The graph of the greatest integer function resembles a set of steps. It is also known as the floor function.

HYPERBOLA:
A curve characterized by two sections or branches. Two intersecting lines serve as asymptotes for both branches. The simplest symbolic equation that produces

a hyperbolic graph is $y = \dfrac{1}{x}$.

MARGINAL COST:
The cost of producing one additional unit of product.

MARGINAL REVENUE:
The revenue obtained from producing and selling one additional unit of product.

POLYNOMIAL:
An expression composed of one or more terms in which the variable is raised to one or more of the powers 1, 2, 3, ... A polynomial may also include a constant term. For example, $2x^3 - x + 7$ is a polynomial.

PROFIT MARGIN:
The ratio of profit to revenue. Profit margin is usually expressed as a percent.

PROFIT:
The difference between a business's revenues (money it takes in) and its costs (money it pays out).

RATIONAL FUNCTION:
A function formed by writing the ratio of one polynomial to another.

STEP FUNCTION:
A function that is a transformation of $y = \text{int}(x)$.

UNIT

5

Oscillation

In this unit, you will encounter situations in which quantities oscillate over time. Situations that involve oscillating behavior include the waxing and waning of the moon, your height above the ground when you ride a ferris wheel, and the demand for electricity.

Initially, you will concentrate on developing descriptions that characterize periodic phenomena. Then you will study two important simple periodic functions—the sine and cosine functions. You will learn to adapt these functions and/or combine them with functions that you've learned previously in order to model the behavior of quantities that oscillate in more complex ways.

PLANNING FOR THE FUTURE

Many companies planning for the future must predict how particular quantities vary over time. Often, these quantities are affected by the seasons. For example, owners of department stores expect to do brisk business between Thanksgiving and New Year's. Holiday sales must be sufficient to offset sales slumps that occur at other times of the year. Understanding the oscillating pattern of sales and slumps helps stores plan their economic futures.

Seasonal Affective Disorder (SAD) affects approximately 10 million Americans. For some SAD sufferers, shorter hours of daylight can trigger severe depression, while longer hours can produce a heightened sense of well-being. Understanding the oscillating pattern of hours of daylight can help some SAD sufferers plan for and control their moods.

To avoid brownouts and blackouts, electric companies must predict their customers' demand for electricity on a weekly, daily, and even hourly basis and then plan how they will supply enough electricity to meet that demand.

Each of the previous examples involves planning. Sometimes this planning is formal, and sometimes it is just a memory from the years before. This unit focuses on deepening your understanding of oscillating patterns at both a formal and informal level. At the formal level, you will learn to build models describing oscillating behavior and use them to make predictions.

LESSON ONE
Life's Ups & Downs

KEY CONCEPTS

Periodic data

Amplitude

Period

Relationship between
revolutions per minute
and velocity

The Image Bank

PREPARATION READING

To Oscillate

A pendulum inside an old grandfather clock oscillates steadily back and forth. In some parts of the country, temperatures oscillate between hot in the summer and frigid in the winter. Water in the ocean appears to oscillate up and down in the form of waves. Length of daylight oscillates from short days in the winter to long days in the summer.

So, what does it mean to oscillate? According to *The American Heritage College Dictionary* it means:

1. To swing back and forth with a steady uninterrupted rhythm.
2. To waver, as between conflicting opinions or courses of action.
3. To vary between alternate extremes, usually within a definable period of time.

In this lesson, you will work with several data sets that can be characterized by oscillation. Later in the unit, you will learn how to model oscillating patterns.

CONSIDER:

What other phenomena produce oscillating patterns?

ACTIVITY

WOULD YOU REPEAT THAT?

1

You've no doubt been affected by life's periodic ups and downs. Do you get the wintertime blues, feeling trapped by the short winter days? Or perhaps you experience spring fever. Do you play a seasonal sport? When the season is over, you have to wait through the rest of the year until your sport starts up again. Do you hear adults periodically complain about exorbitant wintertime heating bills or summertime electrical bills due to air conditioning? Have you ever ridden on a jumper horse on a carousel? If you can answer yes to any of these questions, then oscillation has touched your life.

In some cases, understanding oscillating patterns can help you better plan for or cope with life's little (and sometimes not so little) ups and downs. For example, planning daily walks (no matter how cold) could help reduce wintertime blues. People probably plan for increased utility bills in the winter or summer. Anticipating when an amusement park ride will reach its maximum height can add excitement.

This activity focuses on developing mathematical descriptions of such patterns in a variety of contexts.

1. Most of the time (except during a lunar eclipse), essentially half the moon is illuminated. However, from the earth, we can usually see only a portion of the illuminated half. When you look up at the moon, it appears as a circular disk with a portion of the visible disk illuminated. The shape of the illuminated portion and its size relative to the circular disk change from night to night. For example, **Figure 5.1** shows how the moon looked at midnight on January 5th, 10th, 15th, and 20th, 1997.

   a) Describe how the size of the illuminated visible surface of the moon oscillates over time.

   b) Predict how the moon appeared February 9th and February 17th, 1997. On what did you base your prediction?

January 5

January 10

January 15

January 20

Figure 5.1.
Illumination of the moon on four nights in January.

ACTIVITY

1

WOULD YOU REPEAT THAT?

c) You may have had some difficulty in answering (b) in the absence of additional moon data. The visible portions of the moon's illuminated surface for the first three months in 1997 are presented in **Figure 5.2**.

Date	1/5	1/10	1/15	1/20	1/25	1/30	2/4
Day of year	5	10	15	20	25	30	35
Visible portion illuminated	0.20	0.02	0.43	0.89	0.98	0.66	0.17

Date	2/9	2/14	2/19	2/24	3/1	3/6	3/11
Day of year	40	45	50	55	60	65	70
Visible portion illuminated	0.04	0.48	0.91	0.97	0.63	0.12	0.07

Date	3/16	3/21	3/26	3/31
Day of year	75	80	85	90
Visible portion illuminated	0.52	0.92	0.96	0.57

Figure 5.2.
Visible portion of moon illuminated 1/5/97–3/31/97.

Graph the visible portion of the moon that is illuminated versus the day of the year. Draw a smooth curve that follows the pattern of your data. Interpret your graph in the context of the changing moon.

d) Use your graph to predict the visible portion of the moon's surface that is illuminated on February 9th and 18th, 1997. Compare these estimates with your predictions in (b).

e) Extend your graph so that you can use it to predict the portion of the moon's surface that is illuminated on April 15th (day of year, 105) and April 27th (day of year, 117).

2. Suppose you pedal your bicycle so the pedals revolve once a second. Each pedal is 5 inches from the ground at its lowest

and 18 inches from the ground at its highest. Suppose you start with the right pedal in its lowest postion.

   a) Make a plot showing the height above the ground for the right pedal every 0.25 second for 4 seconds.

   b) Use these data to draw the graph of a function you think best represents the relationship of height versus time.

3. Imagine that the data in **Figure 5.3** were collected in your mathematics class during an activity in Course 2, Unit 7, *Motion*. As part of the activity, a student walked in front of a motion detector that recorded his distance from the detector every second for 8 seconds.

Time (seconds)	0	1	2	3	4	5	6	7	8
Distance from sensor (feet)	2.0	3.3	4.2	6.7	9.8	13.5	17.8	22.7	28.2

Figure 5.3.
Data collected using a motion detector.

   Make a graph of the distance versus the time for the data in Figure 5.3. Describe the pattern of your graph.

4. Over the course of a year, the length of the day (the number of hours from sunrise to sunset) changes every day. **Figure 5.4** shows the length of day every 30 days for Boston Massachusetts from 12/31/97 to 3/26/99.

Date	12/31	1/30	3/1	3/31	4/30	5/30	6/29	7/29
Day number	0	30	60	90	120	150	180	210
Length (hours)	9.1	9.9	11.2	12.7	14.0	15.0	15.3	14.6

Date	8/28	9/27	10/27	11/26	12/26	1/25	2/24	3/26
Day number	240	270	300	330	360	390	420	450
Length (hours)	13.3	11.9	10.6	9.5	9.1	9.7	11.0	12.4

Figure 5.4.
Data on length of day.

ACTIVITY

WOULD YOU REPEAT THAT?

1

a) If you want to predict the length of day based on the day number, which is the independent (explanatory) variable and which is the dependent (response) variable?

b) Draw a set of axes using the scaling in **Figure 5.5**. Then plot the data from Figure 5.4.

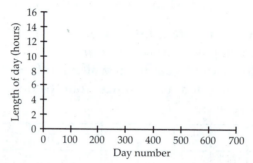

Figure 5.5.
Axes for length of day versus day number.

c) Draw a smooth curve through the points on your graph. Extend your graph to show what you think the pattern will look like over a period of two years.

d) Over this two-year, 730 day interval, on approximately what days was the length of daylight 12 hours? In what way are the first two occurrences related to the second two occurrences?

e) Describe in words what the graph of length of day versus day number will look like over a period of four years.

5. A homeowner has been keeping track of her utility costs for the last 2 years. The table in **Figure 5.6** gives the cost (dollars) of natural gas used by this homeowner during each month over the 2-year period. Plot these data using months as the independent variable.

Figure 5.6.
Monthly heating costs over a two-year period.

Month	Jan	Feb	Mar	Apr	May	June	July	Aug	Sept	Oct	Nov	Dec
Cost ($)	85	87	72	44	25	20	18	17	19	35	79	87

Month	Jan	Feb	Mar	Apr	May	June	July	Aug	Sept	Oct	Nov	Dec
Cost ($)	75	84	58	50	23	15	16	17	20	36	65	85

ACTIVITY

WOULD YOU REPEAT THAT?

1

6. At some high schools, students operate concession stands during school events to earn money for class projects. Suppose that at one high school, the profit on each hot dog is 50 cents. Draw a graph that represents the profits on hot dogs versus the number of hot dogs sold.

7. Jumper horses on carousels move up and down as the carousel spins. Suppose the back hooves of such a horse are six inches above the floor at their lowest point and two-and-one-half feet above the floor at their highest point.

a) Draw a graph that could represent the height of the back hooves of this carousel horse during a half-minute portion of a carousel ride.

b) What assumptions did you make for (a)?

8. All but two of the graphs in Items 1–7 involve patterns that repeat themselves over and over. Any function that repeats itself on intervals of equal length is called **periodic**. Which two items are not periodic?

9. Compare the graphs from Items 1–7 that are (approximately) periodic. Describe similarities and differences in these graphs. What characteristics did you use in determining similarities and differences? For example, if you were to describe each to a friend over the telephone, what phrases would you find yourself using for in all your descriptions?

10. **Figure 5.7** shows graphs of three periodic functions. Each function's graph repeats some basic shape over and over.

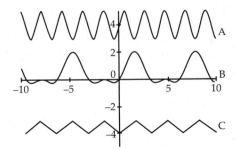

Figure 5.7.
Graphs of three periodic functions.

ACTIVITY 1

WOULD YOU REPEAT THAT?

a) The shortest horizontal length of a basic repeating shape is called the fundamental period, or just the **period**. Determine the approximate period for each of these functions. (Note that there are many periods for any periodic function, so be sure to distinguish between "the" period and "a" period.)

b) For a function that oscillates up and down, the **amplitude** is half of the fixed vertical height of the basic repeating shape; that is, half of the vertical difference between the maximum and minimum values of the periodic graph. What is the amplitude for each of these functions?

c) Even when reporting the amplitude of a function, the description is still not quite complete. After all, oscillations between 0 and 4 and between 21 and 25 both have an amplitude of 2 units. One additional feature distinguishes these two oscillations. The **axis of oscillation** is the central level of the function. This center of oscillation is determined as the horizontal line midway between the maximum and minimum values of the periodic graph. In the first example, it is 2; in the second, it is 23. Identify the axis of oscillation for each of the functions in Figure 5.7.

11. Return to Items 1–7.

a) Estimate the period for each of the periodic functions in Items 1–7.

b) Approximately what are the **amplitude** and axis **of oscillation** for each of the functions in (a). How sure are you that you have the correct values for each situation?

c) Which repeating patterns in Items 1–7 do you think will continue indefinitely? Which patterns will change over time? Which patterns will terminate?

12. **Figure 5.8** gives the total electrical power consumption by bakeries in 1988–1989. In this table, power consumption is recorded as the percentage of January 1987 usage. This

ACTIVITY

WOULD YOU REPEAT THAT?

1

enables the bakery to compare its power consumption with a benchmark level set in January 1987.

	Jan	Feb	Mar	Apr	May	June	July	Aug	Sept	Oct	Nov	Dec
1988	94.6	92.6	93.7	92.6	96.2	106.3	109.2	114.7	114.1	105.1	101.0	99.5
1989	99.5	93.6	95.5	98.3	99.1	110.8	114.7	110.8	115.0	109.7	98.9	

Figure 5.8.
Electric power consumption by bakeries 1988-1989.

a) Plot these data. Do they appear to be approximately periodic? If so, approximate the period and amplitude.

b) Could you predict the electrical power that was needed by bakeries in March of 1990? How much error do you think is in your prediction? Explain.

INDIVIDUAL WORK 1

Play Ball!

Sometimes the motion of a ball produces a periodic pattern, but often it does not. For Items 1–5, decide whether a ball's motion is periodic in the given situation.

1. A ball is tossed up to start a basketball game. If the height of the ball is plotted with respect to time, does the plot represent a periodic function? If so, how would you determine its period and amplitude?

2. A basketball dropped from 5 feet is allowed to bounce on the gymnasium floor. If you plot the height of the ball with respect to time, is the resulting graph periodic? If so, how would you determine the amplitude and period?

3. Suppose you bounce a basketball taking care to push on the ball with enough force to ensure that it rebounds to the same height after each bounce. If you plot the height of the ball with respect to time, is the resulting graph periodic? If so, how would you determine the amplitude and period?

4. You hit a tether ball and then stand to watch it swing as the tether wraps around the pole. If you plot the distance between you and the ball over time, will the resulting graph be periodic? If so, how would you determine the amplitude and period?

5. Suppose a paddle-ball champion hits a ball with a paddle 500 times without missing. If you plot the distance of the ball from the paddle over time, will the resulting graph be periodic? If so, how would you determine the amplitude and the period? If the graph is not periodic, is there some way the champion could hit the ball so that the distance-versus-time graph would represent a periodic function?

Items 6–9 deal with a variety of contexts, none of which involve playing ball.

6. On the Swings. Suppose you're pushing your little brother as he swings in the park. If you plot his distance from you over time, will the resulting graph be periodic? If so, how would you determine the amplitude and period? If the graph is not periodic, is there some way you could push so that the distance-versus-time graph would represent a periodic function?

7. Housing Starts. Data on housing starts are of interest to city planners, to real-estate agents, and most of all to building contractors and
   construction workers. Housing-start data (in thousands) for one year
   beginning March 1983 are presented in **Figure 5.9**.

Month	Mar 83	Apr	May	June	July	Aug
Starts (x1000)	124.3	122.1	161.5	160.1	148.0	159.8

Month	Sept	Oct	Nov	Dec	Jan 84	Feb
Starts (x1000)	139.6	147.8	122.1	103.2	102.7	120.2

Figure 5.9.
Housing starts 3/83-2/84.

a) Graph these data. Then assume that the pattern is periodic and
   extend your graph so that it represents the pattern of housing
   starts for a two-year period.

b) Based on your graph, in what months do you expect the fewest
   housing starts? In what months do you expect the largest number
   of housing starts? Do your answers to these two questions make
   sense from what you know about home-building? Explain.

c) Can you offer an explanation for why the number of housing
   starts in July might be less than for June or August?

d) Do you think that it is reasonable to assume that housing starts
   are approximately periodic? Why or why not? What information
   would you need to check the reasonableness of this assumption?

8. Traffic Patterns. Imagine that you are studying the traffic patterns at
   a particular traffic light. Plot the (hypothetical) number of cars
   stopped at this traffic light, beginning at 8:00 AM. What assumptions
   or information was needed to make your plot? Is the graph periodic?
   If so, what are the period and amplitude, and what do they tell you
   about the situation?

9. Your Choice. Describe a situation that would produce periodic data.
   How would you determine the period and amplitude of such data?
   What would a scatter plot of these data look like?

Be ready to share your answer to Item 9 with your class.

ACTIVITY

2

CIRCLE GAME

In Activity 1, you examined a number of different situations, many of which exhibited periodic behavior. As was indicated there, and as you have seen in other units, it is frequently useful to be able to predict behavior based on past experience. Predictions can be made blindly; those are usually called wild guesses and are not considered very valuable. Another approach is to predict directly from a scatter plot of past data, without creating any formulas or equations from the data. You might call these eyeball predictions. They are better than wild guesses, but are somewhat subjective. In order to make more consistent predictions, most people like to have equations.

In seeking the best possible predictions for periodic phenomena, the usual modeling advice still applies. Start simple. Examine the context carefully to understand its properties; those properties need to be inherited by your model. Work with familiar descriptions before trying to invent new ones. Again, match properties of the context to properties of your mathematical descriptions.

This activity takes you to an amusement park and asks you to begin the modeling process necessary to make predictions for some of its rides.

1. Draw a set of axes similar to the ones in **Figure 5.10**. Make a graph of your guess at average temperature versus season over a two-year period for your region. Is your graph approximately periodic? If so, what are the period and amplitude?

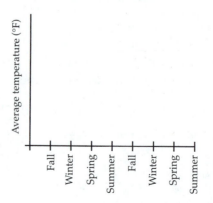

Figure 5.10.
Average temperature versus season.

ACTIVITY

CIRCLE GAME

2

2. The graph in **Figure 5.11** represents the height above the floor of a carousel horse's back hooves versus time during a carousel ride.

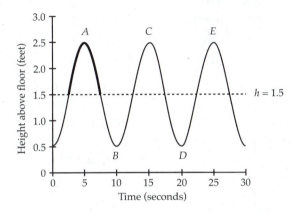

Figure 5.11.
The height of the hooves of a carousel horse versus time.

Write a formula to model the oscillating behavior shown in Figure 5.11 by piecing together quadratic functions as outlined below.

a) Write an equation in the form $y = a(t - h)^2 + k$ that describes loop A (the approximately parabolic section labeled A). For what values of t does this equation apply? How did you determine your equation?

b) What modifications would you make to your equation in (a) in order to describe loops C and E? Over what intervals would each of these equations apply?

c) Use the periodic nature of the graph in Figure 5.11 to write formulas for the upper loops in the graph over an extended time interval of 2 minutes. Specify the interval over which each formula applies.

d) Write an equation in the form $y = a(t - h)^2 + k$ that describes loop B. For what values of t does this equation apply?

e) Adapt your equation describing loop B to describe loop D. What constants in the equation $y = a(t - h)^2 + k$ did you

ACTIVITY

2

CIRCLE GAME

have to change? Over what interval does your adapted equation apply?

f) Use the periodic nature of the graph in Figure 5.11 to write formulas for the lower loops in the graph over an extended two-minute interval. Be sure to specify the time interval over which each equation applies.

g) Explain how you would enter the equations corresponding to loops *A-E* into your calculator to produce a graph similar to the one in Figure 5.11. Use your calculator to test your approach. Does your graph resemble Figure 5.11? If not, revise your approach and try again.

FYI

The Dentzel Carousel Company

The Dentzel Carousel Company was one of the country's foremost carousel builders from 1860 to 1929. Dentzel carousels were known for their graceful, elaborately carved animals. The partially restored Dentzel carousel in Glen Echo Park, Washington, D.C. (the only carousel owned by the U.S. Government) can be ridden May through September. It has three rows of animals—40 horses, 4 rabbits, 4 ostriches, a giraffe, deer, lion, and tiger. The carousel turns to the music of a Wurlitzer band organ that operates much like a player piano, using perforated paper rolls.

The Image Bank

CIRCLE GAME

3. When you ride a carousel, in addition to moving up and down, you get to spin around. The Dentzel carousel in Glen Echo Park is 48 feet in diameter and turns counter-clockwise, making about five revolutions per minute. Suppose that you have chosen to ride the intricately carved lead horse, located in the outer row approximately two feet from the edge.

   a) Each time the carousel makes a complete turn, how far (in feet) have you ridden around? (Ignore any up-and-down distance.)

   b) How fast, in feet per minute, are you riding? How fast would this be in miles per hour?

   c) Imagine that your friend is riding on an inside horse that is approximately 6 feet from the edge. In terms of miles per hour, how much faster are you moving than your friend?

   How do you measure the speed of a spin? In the carousel example, you converted between two different methods when you changed from revolutions per minute (rpm) to feet per minute or miles per hour. In Item 4, you explore movement around a circle on a different amusement park ride, a ferris wheel.

4. Assume that the ferris wheel pictured in **Figure 5.12** rotates at a constant speed of 30 seconds for one complete rotation. The ride lasts approximately 5 minutes and 3 seconds from the time it picks up the last rider until it begins stopping to let riders off.

   a) How fast are the riders spinning in revolutions per minute (rpm)? How fast are they moving in feet per second?

   b) Your friend Thia is the last person to board the ferris wheel. Plot Thia's height above the ground every 7.5 seconds for the first two minutes of the ride. Then draw a smooth curve (no corners) connecting the points on your graph.

   c) At approximately what times during the first half-minute of the ride is Thia 30 feet above the ground?

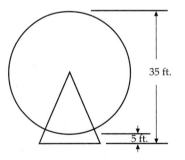

Figure 5.12.
Ferris wheel rotating at a constant speed.

ACTIVITY

2

CIRCLE GAME

d) Use the periodic nature of your graph to determine the approximate times when Thia is 30 feet above the ground during the entire ride. How are the these times related to the times in (c)?

e) In part (b) you were asked to draw your curve with no corners. How do you know that such instruction is appropriate?

5. How would your graph in Item 4(b) change under each of the following conditions? Overlay a graph of height versus time for the altered situation on a copy of your answer graph in Item 4(b).

a) The ferris wheel is slower and makes one revolution every minute instead of every half minute.

b) The ferris wheel is faster and makes one revolution every 15 seconds instead of every half minute.

c) The ferris wheel is turning at the original speed, but is 10 feet off the ground instead of five.

d) The ferris wheel is turning at the original speed, is five feet off the ground, but has a diameter of 50 feet instead of 30.

e) The ferris wheel is making two revolutions per minute, is 2 feet off the ground, and 40 feet in diameter.

CONSIDER:

In the last two items, you've seen that the graph of height versus time for a rider on a ferris wheel produces a periodic graph.

1. What feature of the ferris wheel controls the period of this graph?

2. What feature of the ferris wheel controls the amplitude of this graph?

3. What feature of the ferris wheel controls the axis of oscillation of this graph?

INDIVIDUAL WORK 2

Nights at the Amusement Park

1. Plot graphs that represent each of the following situations. Tell whether each graph is periodic. If a graph is periodic, list its period and amplitude.

   a) Your height above the ground as you ride a roller coaster.

   b) The height of the first car on a roller coaster if it is plotted all day. Assume that the roller coaster is a popular ride and runs continuously all day.

   c) Explain the difference between situation (a) and situation (b).

   d) Your distance from the ticket booth as you ride a horse on a carousel.

2. Holland-based Nauta-Bussink sells amusement park rides which include giant 33-meter, 44-meter, and 55-meter ferris wheels. These dimensions refer to the height of the top of the wheel. Assume that the wheels rotate at constant velocities (ignoring start-up and slow-down times).

   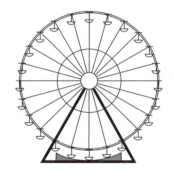

   a) The 33-meter ferris wheel has a wheel diameter of 29.5 meters and turns at a rate of 2.6 revolutions per minute. How fast do its riders move, in meters per second, around the circle?

   b) The 44-meter ferris wheel has a wheel diameter of 40.7 meters and turns at a rate of 1.5 revolutions per minute. In terms of meters per second, would a rider be moving faster or slower on the 44-meter ferris wheel than on the 33-meter ferris wheel? How much faster or slower?

   c) The 55-meter ferris wheel has a wheel diameter of 52.0 meters and turns at a rate of 1.5 revolutions per minute. How fast do its riders move (in meters per second) around the circle?

   d) If you plotted a rider's height versus time for each of these ferris wheels, what would be the period and amplitude of each of your graphs?

   e) Suppose that one of the lights on the outside of the 55-meter ferris wheel has burned out. Imagine starting your stop watch the instant the light is at the bottom of the wheel. How high off the ground is the light at the start of the ride? Approximately how high off the ground will this light be 10 seconds later? 20 seconds later? 30 seconds later? Explain.

f) If the ride in (e) continues for another 4 minutes after you start your stop watch, at what times will the burned-out light be at the top of the wheel? How are your answers to this question related?

3. Eclipsing binary stars are two stars in close orbit around each other. The stars are often so close that they appear to be one point of light in the night sky. If the plane of their orbit is oriented to contain the earth, the brightness of the star system will vary over time. A light curve is a graph of the brightness of the star system over time. Suppose that Pam has observed such a star system and measured its brightness every night during an unusual run of cloudless nights. A plot of her data appears in **Figure 5.13**. (The larger the Luminosity number, the brighter the star system.)

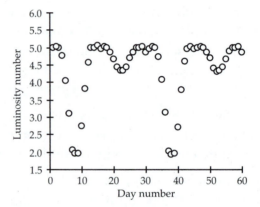

Figure 5.13.
Luminosity versus day.

a) Would you consider these data to be (approximately) periodic? If so, what are the period and amplitude?

b) Use the pattern of the graph in Figure 5.13 to predict the Luminosity number of the star system on Days 80 and 100. How can your answer to (a) be used to help you answer this item?

c) What do you think might explain the shape of this light curve (the graph of luminosity versus time)?

LESSON TWO
A Sine of the Times

KEY CONCEPTS

Unit circle

Radian measure

Translations

Scale-change transformations

Sine function

Trigonometric graphs

Solving equations involving sinusoidal functions

Rates of change

The Image Bank

PREPARATION READING

Round and Round It Goes, Where It Stops Nobody Knows

*I*n the previous lesson, you represented the height above the ground of someone on a ferris wheel over time. In drawing your graphs, you plotted only a few points per period and then joined them using a smooth curve. Ideally you could avoid the data step and use some kind of equation (function) to describe such motion. In fact, you built a piecewise-parabolic model in Activity 2. That model currently has two difficulties. First, you have not checked that it is really accurate. And second, it is really cumbersome to use because of the need to check to see which piece to use for a particular prediction.

The key to dealing with these two problems is looking more closely at the context—more data! Of course, you can't fit a full-size ferris wheel in your classroom, so you need something smaller to model a ferris wheel rider's height above the ground versus time.

A bicycle wheel looks, and could act, like a ferris wheel. So, in this lesson, you use it (or some other circular object) as the physical model. After studying the motion of the bicycle wheel, you return to the ferris wheel and apply your new knowledge to model someone's height above the ground over time. You also revisit several of the other situations presented in Lesson 1 and determine which can be modeled by the same type of function used to model a person's height above the ground while riding a ferris wheel.

CONSIDER:

How could a bicycle wheel be used to collect data relevant to a ferris wheel rider's height above the ground during the ride? Describe the details of a relevant experiment or exploration.

WE'RE JUST ROLLING ALONG

For Item 4, Activity 2, you plotted a person's height above the ground every 7.5 seconds during the ride on a 35-foot ferris wheel.
The plot of your data should have resembled **Figure 5.14**.

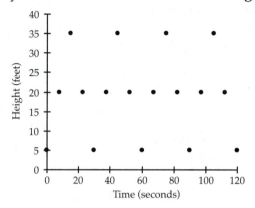

Figure 5.14.
Height-versus-time data from
Item 4, Activity 2.

Then you were asked to connect these data with a smooth curve to produce a graph that could represent height versus time.

CONSIDER:

You argued in Activity 2 that a smoth curve was better than a piecewise-linear graph. You also used a piecewise-parabolic model for the similar motion of a carousel horse. How can you determine for sure whether the graph really is piecewise quadratic or not? Explain in detail.

Your goal in this activity is to determine, through experimentation, the shape of the graph of height versus time as a person rides a ferris wheel. Instead of an actual ferris wheel, for this activity you will need a bicycle wheel (with or without the bicycle) or some other round object such as a Frisbee, hoola hoop, or round garbage can lid. In addition you will need a tape measure, meter stick, and some masking tape.

ACTIVITY

3

WE'RE JUST ROLLING ALONG

PART 1: Data Collection

1. Lay the tape measure on the ground in front of the bicycle wheel, but along its path. Mark the zero location on the floor with a piece of masking tape that is perpendicular to the tape measure at its zero reading. Roll the wheel up to and directly on top of the masking tape. The tire should sit on the masking tape with its axle centered directly above the tape.

2. Place a dot on the tire (a sticker or piece of tape will do) at the point where the tire sits on the masking tape.

3. Roll the wheel forward beside the tape measure, stopping frequently to make measurements. When you stop, measure and record the height of the dot above the floor and the horizontal distance the wheel has traveled. (See **Figure 5.15**.) Record your data in Figure 5.1, Handout H5.3. Be sure to specify your units of measurement.

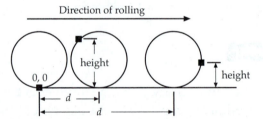

Figure 5.15.
Measuring the distance the wheel rolls and the height of the dot.

4. Collect these data until the wheel has made at least three complete revolutions. Be sure that you stop and take measurements frequently enough that when you plot these data you will be able to determine the shape of the graph of height versus distance. (Since one purpose of these data is to allow checking the piecewise-parabolic approach from Activity 2, collect 6 to 10 measurements corresponding to the first upper loop of the height graph. These positions are those in which the dot is above the height of the axle.)

Note: Save your data for use in later activities.

ACTIVITY

WE'RE JUST ROLLING ALONG

3

PART 2: Modeling the Motion

5. Plot your data. Then sketch a smooth graph that you think best represents the relationship between your two variables. Which is the independent variable and which is the dependent? Explain.

6. Explain why these data should be periodic. Explain how you know the period and amplitude before you look at the data. Use your graph to verify the period and amplitude.

7. Will the pattern in your graph continue indefinitely? Explain.

8. Extend your graph to include negative values for the independent variable. What do these negative values mean? Explain how you could (or did) gather data corresponding to this situation.

9. You took a sample of relatively few measurements and plotted these points. Then you drew a smooth curve connecting your points. Is this a legitimate thing to do? Is the domain of the relationship height, *h*, versus distance, *d*, continuous or discrete? Explain.

10. a) Use your understanding of the geometry of the contextual setting to identify the three points that mark the start, middle, and end of the first loop of the graph of height versus distance. For consistency, define this first loop as beginning when the dot first reaches the height of the axle on its way up and as ending when the dot next reaches the same height on its way down.

b) Use your three points to write an equation for the parabola passing through them.

c) Use your equation and data from your experiment to determine whether a piecewise-parabolic model does a good job describing the height of the dot.

INDIVIDUAL WORK 3

Going in Circles

*A*ctivity 3 shows that parabolic models for the tire data are fairly close over a limited domain, but are consistently wrong even there. The fact is, the graph of your tire data is *not* parabolic. A new kind of function is needed! This assignment introduces you to this new function.

1. In Activity 3, you and your classmates obtained graphs of periodic behavior by plotting the heights of dots as you rolled circular objects. Circles come in only one shape, but they occur in many sizes. That means there are many different graphs, at least according to their scales.

   a) How does changing the radius of the rolling circle affect a height-of-the-dot graph? Be specific.

      For (b)–(f), suppose your wheel has a radius of exactly one foot.

   b) How far would the wheel have to roll to go one complete revolution? Provide both an exact answer (involving π) and a decimal approximation.

   c) How far would the wheel have to roll for the mark on the tire to move from the bottom of the wheel to the top for the first time? Provide an exact answer and a decimal approximation.

   d) How far would the wheel have to roll for the marked dot to be level with the axle the first time? and then the second time? Give both exact and approximate answers.

   e) How far would the wheel have to move for the marked dot to be level with the axle the third and fourth times? How are these answers related to your answers in (d)? What about for the fifth and sixth times?

   f) Draw a smooth curve that represents the pattern of height-versus-distance data for this one-foot wheel. (The shape of this curve should be similar to the one that you drew for Item 5 of Activity 3.) Complete the graph for distances from 0 to 25 meters. What are the period and amplitude of your graph?

2. You can determine the position of a rider on a ferris wheel if you know the distance the rider has traveled since boarding the ride. Suppose, for example, your friend boards a ferris wheel that has a

30-meter diameter. After your friend has traveled 71 meters, how many revolutions has he made, and what is his approximate position (possible positions—near the top, near the bottom, level with the axle, midway between the axle and the top, etc.)? What about after 236 meters?

In riding a ferris wheel, progress can be measured by how far around the circumference of the wheel you have moved. With the tires in Activity 3, progress was recorded as how far forward the wheel had rolled. However, since the amount of forward progress for a rolling wheel is exactly equal to the amount of its circumference that has rolled past the contact point, these two methods of measuring the turning of a circle are identical. This means that results from the tire experiment apply directly to the ferris wheel situation, except that radii differ.

Your work in Item 1 should convince you that circles having a radius of 1 unit make calculations fairly easy. For that reason, in the quest to keep things simple, mathematicians generally base their study of periodic phenomena on the **unit circle**—a circle with a radius of one unit and centered at the origin. The unit is not specified—it could be an inch, or a half-inch, or a centimeter, or even a mile. So, a particular unit circle can be of any size as long as the length of its radius is specified as the unit. To convert from one kind of unit to radius units, divide all originial length measures by the length of the radius. Radius units, when used to measure portions of a circle's circumference, are called **radians**—the directed length of an arc that begins at (1,0) on the unit circle.

3. **Figure 5.16** shows an ant walking the circumference of a unit circle.

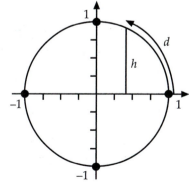

The ant's position on the unit circle can be determined by the directed distance of its walk. The direction is positive for a counterclockwise walk and negative for a clockwise walk. For example, if the ant walks 2π radians, then it has walked once around the circle (because the circumference of the circle is 2π radii) in the counterclockwise direction; but if the ant walks $-\pi$ radians, then it has walked half way around the circle in the clockwise direction.

Figure 5.16.
Ant walking around the circumference of a unit circle.

In each of (a)–(c), two radian measures are given. Each measure corresponds to a possible journey for the ant. Make a copy of the unit circle (you can trace the one in Figure 5.16) and using separate colors, draw arcs corresponding to the radian measures in (a)–(c). Draw one unit circle for each pair. Indicate which arc corresponds to each radian measure. (It may be helpful to determine the fraction of the circle's circumference that corresponds to a particular radian measure.)

a) $3\pi/4$, and $-\pi$.   b) 3π, and $\pi/2$.   c) -2.3, and 6.0.

The reason you are able to determine the length of an arc on the unit circle is because you know the radius of the unit circle is one unit, whatever the unit happens to be. So, if the ant walks an arc of 3 radians, that means the ant has traveled an arc equivalent to three radii (each of one unit) placed end-to-end. Using radians to measure arc length allows you to generalize the concept of arc length to larger circles. As can be seen from **Figure 5.17**, an arc of 3 radians (3 radii) will extend nearly halfway around the circle, regardless of the circle's size; while an arc of $-3\pi/4 \approx -2.4$ radians will extend 3/8th of the way around the circle in the opposite direction, regardless of the circle's size.

4. Return to your data from Activity 3. Convert all your measurements to radius units. Thus, the rolled distance will be in radians. Be sure to state how you make the conversions.

5. Return to the ferris wheel in Item 2. Assume that the 30-meter diameter ferris wheel turns in a counterclockwise direction. Suppose that your friend boards the ferris wheel and as soon as he reaches the height of the wheel's axle (midway between the bottom and top of the ferris wheel), you begin measuring the distance that he travels around the wheel.

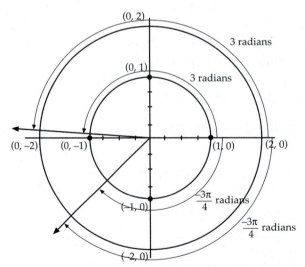

Figure 5.17.
Arcs measuring 3 radians and $-3\pi/4$ radians on circles with different radii.

a) After he has traveled 71 meters (from a position level with the wheel's axle), how many radians has he turned?

b) After he has traveled 236 meters, how many radians has he turned?

c) After he has traveled $7\pi/2$ radians, where is he on the wheel?

The conversion to radian measure makes it possible to treat all circles in a similar fashion—each as though its radius were 1 unit. That's a step in simplifying all periodic motion into a single description since it makes the period for motion around any circle be exactly 2π units.

Look back at your descriptions of periodic functions from Activity 1 in Lesson 1. The three main features of your descriptions of oscillations are period, amplitude, and axis of oscillation. Changing to radian measure standardizes the period. Another transformation can standardize the axis of oscillation, and the simplest case uses an axis at the 0 level.

6. The heights in the graph for Item 1(f) oscillate between 0 to 2 feet. Thus the amplitude is 1, about an axis of oscillation of 1. Translating the graph down exactly 1 unit makes its axis of oscillation 0.

a) What are the period and amplitude of the translated function?

b) Sketch the translated graph.

c) Make a scatter plot of your data from Item 3, above. Describe how it compares to your graph in Item 1(f), then explain how you could transform your data from Item 3 to adjust its axis of oscillation to be 0.

d) Carry out that transformation, and compare the scatter plot of the transformed data to your graph from part (b).

e) Explain how the wheel could be rolled or measured differently so that you could collect original data that would have this same graph.

f) Make a graph of the height versus distance walked for the ant in Item 4. Measure both heights and distances in radius units.

7. Suppose a friend has periodic data obtained by measuring a horse's distance from the ticket booth at a carousel and the horse's distance around the carousel. Explain the kinds of geometric transformations that could standardize these periodic data to radian input and axis of oscillation 0.

A sketch of a graph of the ant's height versus the distance it walked (see Item 4) looks exactly like the translated graphs that you drew for

Items 6(b) and 6(d). The only difference between the situations is that in one case the circle is stationary and the ant moves around the circle, and in the other case the circle does the turning. In each case, though, by standardizing measurements by using raduis units and measuring from the center (rather than from the floor or ground), the resulting graphs are identical.

As the ant (or rotating dot, or ferris wheel rider) moves from its initial position, the point (1,0) on the unit circle, a graph of its height versus the directed distance (radian measurement) of its walk produces the oscillating graph that you constructed in Item 6. This new function is called the **sine function**—the vertical displacement from the horizontal axis of a point on the unit circle. That is, the value of the sine is the y-coordinate of a point on the unit circle. The corresponding input is the arc distance along the circle, starting at (1, 0) and going counterclockwise to the point in question.

8. a) To graph the sine function on your calculator, set your viewing window to match the one that you used in Item 6(d). Next, check that your calculator is in Radian mode, and turn off all scatter plots. Finally, use your calculator's SIN key to enter and graph the function $y = \sin(x)$. Compare the graph in your calculator's screen to the one that you sketched for Item 6(b).

   b) Next, change your window settings to your calculator's trig window. (The window [-6.28,6.28] x [-3,3] will do.) Sketch the graph over this interval. Does the wavy pattern of the sine function extend to both positive and negative values for x?

   c) In Item 2, Activity 2, Lesson 1, you modeled a wavy curve by piecing parabolas together. In Activity 3, you checked that fit with more data, so you should have a good idea of how one loop of the sine function compares to a parabola. What are the three key points defining the first loop of the sine function? (Use the definition of sine; don't approximate.)

   d) Determine the equation of a quadratic function that has exactly the same x-intercepts and vertex as the sine loop. Then adjust your window settings to [0,3.14] x [0,1] and graph both functions (the sine and the parabola) together.

   e) Compare the graph of the sine function to a graph of the quadratic function that you determined for (d). Describe any apparent differences in the curves.

f) Remove the parabola from your graphing screen and add the scatter plot of your transformed data from Item 6(d). Comment on the fit.

9. Suppose you had a partial set of data. When plotted, these data appeared to lie on an upper loop from the graph of a sine function; on second thought, perhaps these data appeared to lie on a downward-opening parabola. How could you tell whether these data should be modeled with a sine function or a quadratic function?

10. Suppose a ball is dropped from the same height as the top of a ferris wheel. How would the height-versus-time graphs describing the motions of the falling ball and a rider's descent from the top to the bottom of a ferris wheel differ? Explain the physical significance of this difference.

11. The sine function relates vertical displacement on a unit circle to the radian measure around its circumference. For most arcs along the unit circle, your calculator is essential to finding the corresponding height. However, for some special arcs, you can do the mathematics without using your calculator.

Figure 5.18 shows a unit circle superimposed on a coordinate plane.

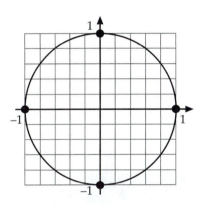

Figure 5.18.
Graph of unit circle.

a) Copy and complete the table in **Figure 5.19** using geometric relations you already know, recording exact answers. Then use the graph in Figure 5.18 to verify (approximately) the entries in your table. (It may help to convert radians to the fraction of a complete turn around a circle.)

Radian measure of arc beginning at (1,0)	$-\pi$	$-3\pi/4$	$-\pi/2$	$-\pi/4$	0	$\pi/4$	$\pi/2$	$3\pi/4$
Height (vertical displacement from horizontal axis)								

Radian measure of arc beginning at (1,0)	π	$5\pi/4$	$3\pi/2$	$7\pi/4$	2π	$9\pi/4$	$5\pi/2$	$11\pi/4$
Height (vertical displacement from horizontal axis)								

Figure 5.19.
Height-versus-radian data from a unit circle.

INDIVIDUAL WORK 3

b) Graph the height-versus-radian data from your table in (b) using the scaling shown in **Figure 5.20**.

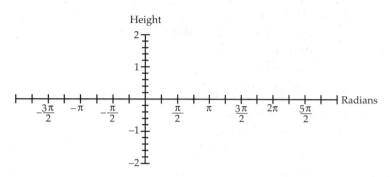

Figure 5.20.
Axes with scaling used for
Item 11(b).

c) Demonstrate symbolically that the points corresponding to $x = -\pi, -3\pi/4,$ and $-\pi/2$ do not lie on a line.

d) Do the points corresponding to $-\pi, -3\pi/4, -\pi/2, -\pi/4,$ and 0 lie on a parabola? Support your answer using an argument based on second differences.

e) Enter the data from (a) into your calculator. Plot these data in the same viewing window that you used for (b). Then overlay the graph of $y = \sin(x)$. Does this function appear to describe the pattern of your plotted points? Draw a smooth curve through the points that you plotted in (b) so that your graph matches what you see in your calculator screen.

Units of Measurement: Inches

Distance wheel moves	108	114	120	126	132	138
Height above the floor of dot	18.75	23.25	25.75	25.5	22.75	17.875

Figure 5.21.
Data collected from rolling
a wheel with a 26-inch
diameter.

12. During Activity 3, a group of students collected data by rolling a wheel that had a 26-inch diameter. **Figure 5.21** shows a partial set of their height-versus-distance data. (The heights are recorded to the nearest eighth of an inch.)

a) What should be the period and amplitude for the entire data set? How are they related to the dimensions of the wheel?

b) Using second differences, verify that the data in Figure 5.21 are not contained on a parabola.

c) If these were all the data, would a parabola make a good model for the relationship between distance and height over the distance-interval from 108 to 138 inches? Explain.

13. Challenge. You know that the equation $y = \sin(x)$ is a good model for the transformed tire data you created in Item 6(d). Write an equation that is an equally good model for the untransformed, original tire data from Activity 3.

ACTIVITY

IN THE LIGHT OF THE MOON

4

According to *The Old Farmer's 1997 Almanac*:

"The best time to plant flowers and vegetables that bear crops above the ground is during the *light* of the Moon; that is, between the day the Moon is new to the day it is full. Flowering bulbs and vegetables that bear crops below ground should be planted during the *dark* of the Moon; that is from the day after it is full to the day before it is new again."

Imagine it is 1997 and you plan to plant a garden. Why 1997? Figure 5.2, Activity 1, Lesson 1 presents data on the visible portion of moon illuminated every five days from 1/5/97 to 3/31/97. (You can update to the present year after you have completed this assignment.) **Figure 5.22** gives planting times for carrots and flowers in three planting zones in the United States.

Inch by inch, row by row

Gonna make this garden grow

All you need is a rake and a hoe

And a piece of fertile ground...

from *The Garden Song* by Dave Mallet

	Zone A northern section	Zone B middle section	Zone C southern section
Carrots Early planting Late planting	5/15–5/31 6/15–7/21	3/7–3/31 7/7–7/31	2/15–3/7 8/1–9/7
Flowers	5/17–6/21	4/15–4/30	3/15–4/7

Figure 5.22. Recommended planting times.

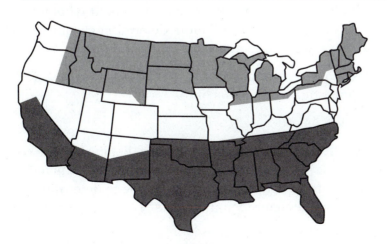

Figure 5.23. Planting zones in the United States.

ACTIVITY

IN THE LIGHT OF THE MOON

4

The question is, what are the best planting dates for the three zones? Remember, according to the *Farmer's Almanac*, you want to plant the flowers when the moon is waxing (increasing in illumination from day to day) and carrots when the moon is waning (decreasing in illumination from day to day).

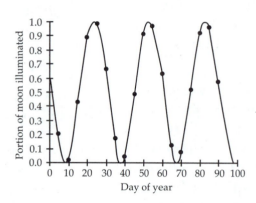

Figure 5.24.

Graph of portion of illuminated moon surface versus day of year.

How can you use the data from Figure 5.2 to determine the days during each of the planting periods when the moon is waxing or waning? The data alone are sufficient only for their domain. Extending to later dates requires tedious extension of the table, or precise drawing of a graph, or a formula. **Figure 5.24** presents a plot of the moon data with a smooth curve fit to the data. (Figure 5.24 should be similar to the graph that you drew when you answered Item 1(c) in Activity 1.)

This curve looks very much like a sine curve. So, perhaps a **sinusoidal function**—a function that can be expressed in the term, an equation of the form $y = A\sin(B(x - C)) + D$, could be used to describe this situation. You have studied translations and scale changes with other functions. Once again, it will be helpful to do a preliminary general investigation to find out what the control numbers A, B, C, and D do before determining a sinusoidal model for the specific moon-illumination data.

1. Use your graphing calculator or the program SINGRAPH.GSP to investigate equations of the form

    $$y = A\sin(B(x - C)) + D.$$

    Be systematic in your investigation. Begin with the equation $y = \sin(x)$ (so, $A = 1$, $B = 1$, $C = 0$, and $D = 0$). Then change the value of one control number at a time to determine how changing this number affects the graph. Write a summary of

ACTIVITY

IN THE LIGHT OF THE MOON

4

the results of your investigation. Include in this summary sample sketches of graphs that illustrate how changing the values of A, B, C, or D, separately, affects the sine wave. (Note: Your calculator should be in Radian mode for this investigation.)

Then consider cases in which two control numbers have been changed.

2. Based on the results of your investigation, answer the following questions. (If you can't answer these questions, you may need to do additional investigative work.)

   a) Which control number shifts the graph horizontally? How far? Left or right?

   b) Which control number shifts the graph vertically? How far? Up or down?

   c) Which control number affects the graph's amplitude? How is the graph's amplitude related to this number?

   d) Which control number affects the graph's period? How is the graph's period related to this number?

3. How would you modify $\sin(x)$ so that the period of the modified function is:

   a) 4π?

   b) 3π?

   c) 2?

   d) 10?

4. Describe how each of the following modifications to the sine function affects the graph. (In other words, does the modification change the amplitude, period, vertical, or horizontal position of the sine wave?) Then sketch the graph of the modified function and $y = \sin(x)$ on the same set of axes.

   a) $y = 3\sin(x) + 2$

ACTIVITY

IN THE LIGHT OF THE MOON

4

b) $y = 0.5 \sin(x - \pi/2)$

c) $y = \sin(2(x + \pi/2))$

5. Now, it's time to apply what you have learned about modifying the sine function to develop a model that describes the moon data.

   a) Enter the data from Figure 5.2 into your calculator and then plot illuminated portion versus day number. What are the approximate period and amplitude for these data? How did you determine your answer?

   b) Graph the untransformed sine function in the same window as your data. Does $y = \sin(x)$ do a good job in modeling the oscillating pattern of the moon data?

   c) Modify the equation $y = \sin(x)$ so that the amplitude and period of the graph of the modified equation match the amplitude and period in (a). On your calculator, graph your modified function together with the original data. Does this sinusoidal function do a good job in describing the moon data?

   d) What additional modifications will you need to make to your function in (c) in order to create a model that describes these data? Make these modifications. What is your function? Explain how you decided on this function. (You will need this function again in Individual Work 5.)

Recommended Planting Dates According to the Moon		
Zone A northern section	Zone B middle section	Zone C southern section
Carrots Early planting Late planting		
Flowers		

Figure 5.25.
Best planting times according to the phase of the moon.

6. Now that you have a model that describes the moon data, use it to predict the best days to plant flowers and carrots in each of the three planting zones. Divide the calculations among group members. Record your results in a table similar to **Figure 5.25**. Explain how you arrived at your prediction.

INDIVIDUAL WORK 4

What's Your Sine?

In Activity 4, you explored the effects of four control numbers in the general sinusoidal model $y = A\sin(B(x - C)) + D$. A determines the size of the amplitude, and the sign of A indicates whether the sinusoid is right side up or upside down. The period of the model is $2\pi / |B|$, and the axis of oscillation is the line $y = D$.

The value of C controls the horizontal translation of the graph and is called the **phase shift** of the sinusoidal function $y = A\sin(B(x - C)) + D$. It is the horizontal shift required to translate the graph of $y = A\sin(Bx) + D$ so that it coincides with the graph of $y = A\sin(B(x - C)) + D$. Another way to think of C is that $x = C$ marks the start of the first loop of the sinusoid since it is the value of x that makes the input of the sine function exactly 0.

It is also important to remember that in the description above, scale change operations must be done before translations. That is, adjust the period and amplitude before locating the start of the first loop and the axis of oscillation.

1. a) Without using a graphing calculator, sketch the graphs of $y = 3\sin(2x)$ and $y = \sin(x)$ on the same set of axes. Choose a scaling for the x-axis that involves multiples of π. What are the amplitudes and exact periods of these two functions? (After you have completed your sketch, use your calculator to check that your graphs are correct.)

   b) Without using a graphing calculator, sketch the graphs of $y = 3\sin(0.5x)$ and $y = \sin(x)$ on the same set of axes. Then use your calculator to check that your graphs are correct.

   c) How are the graphs for $y = 3\sin(2x)$ and $y = 3\sin(0.5x)$ the same? How are they different?

2. Write equations of sinusoidal functions having the amplitude, period, phase shift, and axis of oscillation given below. Then sketch a graph of your function without the aid of a graphing calculator. Scale your x-axis in multiples of π. (After you have sketched your graphs, use your calculator to check that your graphs are correct.)

   a) An amplitude of $3/4$, period of 4π, phase shift of $\pi/2$, and axis of oscillation 0.

b) An amplitude of 1, period of 3π, phase shift of $-\pi/2$, and axis of oscillation 0.

c) An amplitude of 2, period of 2π, phase shift of π, and axis of oscillation 2.

3. Write equations of sinusoidal functions having the amplitude, period, phase shift, and axis of oscillation given below. Then sketch a graph of your function. Use the scaling shown in **Figure 5.26**.

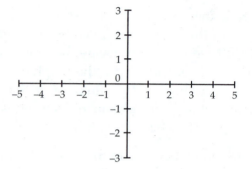

Figure 5.26.
Axes with scaling appropriate for Item 3.

a) An amplitude of 0.5, period of 5, 0 phase shift, and axis of oscillation 2.

b) Amplitude of 1.5, period of 2.5, phase shift of 1, and axis of oscillation −1.

4. Write an equation that describes each of the graphs in **Figures 5.27–5.29**. Check your answers with your calculator.

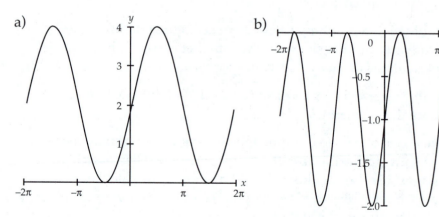

Figure 5.27.
Graph of a sinusoidal function.

Figure 5.28.
Graph of a sinusoidal function.

c)

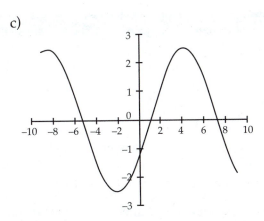

Figure 5.29.
Graph of a sinusoidal function.

5. The graph in **Figure 5.30** represents the height above the floor of a carousel horse's back hooves versus time during a carousel ride. (You first saw this graph in Activity 2, Lesson 1.)

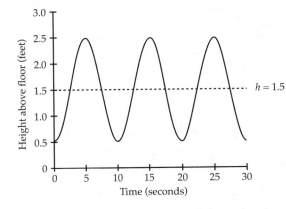

Figure 5.30.
The height of the hooves of a carousel horse versus time.

a) What are the period and amplitude of the function graphed in Figure 5.30?

b) In Lesson 1, you wrote a piecewise quadratic model describing this function. Now determine a sinusoidal model. After writing the equation for your model, use your calculator to check that its graph matches the one in Figure 5.30.

c) Which do you think is a better model for height versus time in this situation? Explain.

6. Use what you know about the geometry of your tire and sinusoidal graphs to solve the challenge problem (Item 13) from Individual Work 3. That is, find an appropriate sinusoidal model for your tire data from Activity 3, based on contextual reasoning.

FERRIS WHEEL FUN

CONSIDER:

1. A rider on a ferris wheel travels in a circle at a constant rate. As she circles, her height above the ground changes. Does her height above the ground change at a constant rate?

2. What features of a ferris wheel ride make it thrilling? In particular, what elements make one ferris wheel ride more thrilling than another?

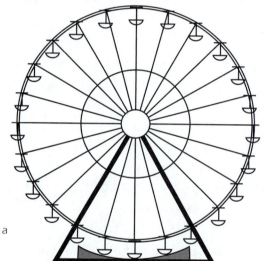

Figure 5.31.
Schematic drawing of a
33-meter ferris wheel.

You've no doubt thought of several features of a ferris wheel ride that add to its excitement. This activity explores several possible definitions of fun rides. Ferris wheels come in a variety of sizes and rotate at a variety of speeds. Technical details for three of Nauta-Bussink's most popular ferris wheels appear in **Figure 5.32**.

Figure 5.32.
Technical details for three
popular ferris wheels.

Wheel height (meters from ground to top of wheel)	Wheel diameter (meters)	Revolutions per minute
33.00	29.50	2.6
44.00	40.70	1.5
55.00	52.00	1.5

FERRIS WHEEL FUN

You will need the information contained in Figure 5.32 for Items 1, 6, and 7.

1. Suppose Anna is the last rider to board the 33-meter ferris wheel before the ride starts. Write a sinusoidal function that describes her height above the ground over time during the ride. Explain how you determined your model. What assumptions did you make in your model?

Use a spreadsheet for the remainder of this activity. Handout 5.5, "Zooming With Tables," contains some suggestions for setting up the tables in your spreadsheet efficiently.

2. Set up a table with the first two columns labeled Time and Height. (Here time is in seconds, and height in meters.) In the Time column, enter times from 0 to 70 seconds in one-second increments. Then enter a formula to compute Anna's height corresponding to each of these times.

3. Make a scatter plot of the height-versus-time data. Use this scatter plot to sketch a graph of your model over the time interval from 0 to 70 seconds.

4. Certainly one of the more exciting times on any ferris wheel is when you are high above the ground.

   a) Use the data in your spreadsheet to approximate when Anna is more than 30 meters above the ground. (Use at least one-decimal precision.) You should get three intervals. Approximately, how are these intervals related?

   b) How would you determine the answer to (a) from your graph?

5. Recall that slope measures rate of change. After the initial start up, a ferris wheel revolves at roughly a constant rate (in terms of circumference per unit time). Even though Anna travels at a constant rate *around* the wheel, her *height* above the ground does not rise or fall at a constant rate. Moments when her height above the ground changes most rapidly, as well as moments when she feels suspended in midair due to the fact

ACTIVITY

5

FERRIS WHEEL FUN

that her height above the ground is changing very slowly, add excitement to her ride.

a) Based on your graph in Item 3, how do you know that the rate of change in Anna's height above the ground over time is not constant?

b) Indicate on your graph from Item 3 when Anna's height is changing most rapidly. What feature of your graph tells you the times when this occurs?

c) Estimate the rate at which Anna's height is increasing at the time when it is increasing least rapidly. (Use a zoom-in approach to improve the precision of your answer.) Where is the location of her seat on the wheel at this time?

6. Suppose that next Anna boards the 44-meter ferris wheel. Write a sinusoidal function that describes her height above the ground over time during this ride.

7. What if Anna decides to board the 55-meter ferris wheel? What constants in your model from Item 6 must change to describe her height over time on this ferris wheel? What constants stay the same?

Time, t seconds	Height, h (meters)	Approximate rate at $t = 6$
5	20.2	
6	21.1	1.2
7	22.6	

Figure 5.33.
Data from ferris wheel ride.

In Course 2, Unit 7, *Motion* you approximated the instantaneous velocity of a falling book at various times by using a symmetric difference quotient. You can use the same approach for determining the instantaneous rate of change of Anna's height above the ground at a specified time. For example, suppose that the data in **Figure 5.33** were collected from a ride on a ferris wheel.

The average rate of change in height from $t = 5$ to $t = 7$ is given by the symmetric difference quotient $(h(7) - h(5))/(7 - 5)$. This value approximates the instantaneous rate at $t = 6$.

ACTIVITY

FERRIS WHEEL FUN

5

8. Return to Anna's ride on the 33-meter wheel. Use symmetric difference quotients to approximate Anna's rate of change in height above the ground with respect to time at one-second intervals for one revolution of the wheel. Then use a zoom-in process to approximate the time during that revolution when Anna's height above the ground is increasing most rapidly. How fast is her height changing at that time? Where is her seat located at that time?

9. a) Generate height-versus-time data for Anna's ride on the 44-meter ferris wheel. Use one-second increments for the times over an interval long enough for the wheel to make two revolutions. Then create a column of approximations for the rate of change in height with respect to time using symmetric difference quotients.

   b) On the same set of axes, make scatter plots of height versus time and rate-of-change-in-height versus time. Describe the pattern of the scatter plot of rate versus time. What does it tell you about how the rate-of-change-in-height over time is related to the height-versus-time graph?

   c) Anna loves heights, the higher the better, and Anna loves the sensation of falling, the faster the better. During the first two revolutions on the 44-meter ferris wheel, at approximately what times will Anna find her ride most thrilling? How high will she be and how fast will she be descending at these times?

10. a) During the first two revolutions of Anna's ride on the 55-meter ferris wheel, at what times will she be at the top of the wheel? At what times will she be descending most rapidly? How fast will her height above the ground be changing at these times?

    b) Will the most thrilling parts of the 44-meter ferris wheel occur at the same *times* as those for the 55-meter ferris wheel? Explain why you should not be surprised by your answer.

INDIVIDUAL WORK 5

Bicycles, Daylight, and Tides

*I*tems 1–3 and Item 6 in this assignment revisit situations described in Lesson 1. The data in Item 1 are perfectly periodic while the data in Items 2, 3, and 6 are considerably more scattered. In each case, you are asked to use your understanding of control numbers to write a sinusoidal model describing the data.

1. Suppose you pedal your bicycle so that the pedals revolve at a constant rate once a second. The pedal is 5 inches from the ground at its lowest and 18 inches from the ground at its highest. In Item 2, Activity 1, Lesson 1, you were asked to make a plot showing the height of the right pedal from the ground every 0.25 seconds for 4 seconds. If you begin pedaling with your right pedal at its lowest point, your plot probably resembled **Figure 5.34**.

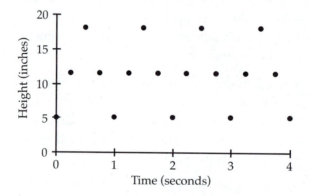

Figure 5.34.
Height of bicycle pedal over time.

   a) Write a sinusoidal model describing the height of the right pedal from the ground from the time you begin pedaling until you get off the bicycle. How did you determine your model? (Use your calculator to check that your model produces a graph that would describe the pattern of the points in Figure 5.34.)

   b) Pedaling at a constant rate of one complete cycle per second, is the height of the pedal rising and falling at a constant rate? Explain.

2. Over the course of a year, the length of the day (the number of hours from sunrise to sunset) changes every day. **Figure 5.35** shows the length of day every 30 days for Boston, Massachusetts, from 12/31/97 to 3/36/99.

Date	12/31	1/30	3/1	3/31	4/30	5/30	6/29	7/29
Day number	0	30	60	90	120	150	180	210
Length (hours)	9.1	9.9	11.2	12.7	14.0	15.0	15.3	14.6

Date	8/28	9/27	10/27	11/26	12/26	1/25	2/24	3/26
Day number	240	270	300	330	360	390	420	450
Length (hours)	13.3	11.9	10.6	9.5	9.1	9.7	11.0	12.4

Figure 5.35.
Data on length of day.

a) Write an equation of the form $y = A\sin(B(t - C)) + D$ expressing the number of daylight hours, y, as a function of time, t. Explain how you determined each constant in your model.

b) If your calculator has a regression feature that fits sinusoidal models to data, use that feature to fit a model to these same data. Compare this model to the one that you determined for (a).

c) Rosita, who lives in Boston, suffers from SAD (seasonal affective disorder). During the winter she gets very depressed, but by the first day of spring, March 21st, she feels wonderful. She has been advised to use light therapy during the winter. Assuming that one hour of light therapy replaces one hour of natural daylight, write a model that Rosita could use during the fall and winter of 1998/99 (September 21, 1998–March 21, 1999) to determine how much light therapy she needs on a particular day in order to have an equivalent amount of daylight until March 21st. Draw a graph of this model over the interval corresponding to the days when she would use this model.

d) Use your model to determine how long Rosita should apply light therapy on January 15, 1999.

e) Like Rosita, Sasha lives in Boston and also suffers from SAD. However, her depression is triggered at times when the length of daylight is changing most rapidly. At what times of the year will she be most likely to suffer from depression? How did you obtain this information from your graph?

f) During the week that the length of daylight in Boston is increasing most rapidly, approximately how rapidly is it changing? Estimate how many more minutes of daylight there would be at the end of this week than at the beginning. Do you think you would notice this amount of change?

INDIVIDUAL WORK 5

3. Recall the homeowner from Lesson 1 who has been keeping track of utility costs for the last 2 years. **Figure 5.36** gives the cost of natural gas that was used by this homeowner each month over the 2-year period.

Month	Jan	Feb	Mar	Apr	May	June	July	Aug	Sept	Oct	Nov	Dec
Cost ($)	85	87	72	44	25	20	18	17	19	35	79	87

Month	Jan	Feb	Mar	Apr	May	June	July	Aug	Sept	Oct	Nov	Dec
Cost ($)	75	84	58	50	23	15	16	17	20	36	65	85

Figure 5.36.
Fuel costs over a two-year period.

a) On a piece of graph paper, plot the cost for natural gas versus the month.

b) Write an equation that models utility costs as a function of time. On the graph that you drew for (a), overlay a sketch of the graph of your model.

c) Make a residual plot. Based on this plot, is this model adequate for describing the fluctuations in utility costs?

d) How useful do you think your model is for predicting next year's costs? (How close do you expect your predictions to be?) What could you do to obtain a more useful model?

4. The Potomac River flows through Washington, D.C. Tide levels for the Potomac are approximately sinusoidal and range from a height of 5 feet to a low of 1.5 feet when measured against a post at Harbor Place (a small plaza with a dock at which boats can land).

a) Suppose on July 1, high tide is at 6:30 AM and low tide is at 12:45 PM Write an equation describing the height of the water for every hour after midnight on July 1. Explain how you arrived at your model.

b) How high will the water be at noon on July 4?

    c) At what times on July 4 will the tide levels be rising most quickly? Falling most quickly?

    d) If the owners of Harbor Place need to hire someone to help people docking when the water is below 3 feet, for about how long every day should they hire help?

5. Pat and Terry are turning a long jump rope for Tracy, who is waiting to jump in. Pat and Terry turn the rope one time per second. The maximum height is 7 feet while at its lowest, it just touches the ground. Assume that the rope was on the ground moving up and away from Tracy at starting time.

    a) Write an equation expressing the height of the rope as a function of time since Pat and Terry started turning it. Explain how you arrived at your equation.

    b) Tracy is 5 feet 3 inches tall. When will the rope be higher than Tracy's head? (Write an expression that would describe all the times that this occurs.)

6. Write a sinusoidal model for the electricity usage for bakeries during 1988-1989. (See Figure 5.8 and your answers to Item 12 in Lesson 1, Activity 1, for data and graph.)

LESSON THREE
Connections

KEY CONCEPTS

Rates of change

Cosine function

Reference angle

Relationship between radians and degrees

Connections between right-triangle and circular trigonometric functions

The Image Bank

PREPARATION READING

Sine Off

*I*n Lesson 1, you examined periodic data, and in Lesson 2 you determined sinusoidal models of the form $y = A\sin(B(x - C)) + D$ that described some of the periodic data from Lesson 1. The sine function, the basis for sinusoidal models, was defined as the vertical displacement (height) as you wrapped around a unit circle. Many of the real-world situations described in Lesson 1 also involved circular motion. Given, for example, the orbital motion of the earth around the sun, the moon around the earth, and the spinning of the earth around its axis, it's not surprising that data such as the hours of daylight, daily temperature, or visible portion of illuminated moon surface over time can be modeled using sinusoidal functions.

In Activity 5, "Ferris Wheels," you began investigating the rate of change of sinusoidal functions. Most likely you noticed that the rate-of-change-versus-time function appeared to oscillate with the same period as the original sinusoidal function. In this lesson, you investigate further the connection between sinusoidal functions and their associated rate functions. In the process, you develop a new function called the cosine.

The sine and cosine are not new to you. You've worked with these functions before in Unit 1, *The Geometry of Art*. However, in that unit you determined values for the sine and cosine based on angles and ratios of sides of triangles. In this lesson, you explore the connection between the definitions of sine and cosine developed in Unit 1 and the definitions used in this unit.

CONSIDER:

1. How were the sine and cosine functions defined in Unit 1, *The Geometry of Art*?

2. **Figure 5.37** illustrates the definition of $\sin(\pi/4)$ as the y-coordinate of the point at the end of the arc of $\pi/4$ radians. (Remember, that the y-coordinate gives the height of this point above the x-axis.) How might you turn this situation into one involving an angle in a right triangle?

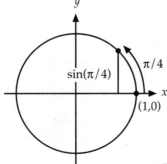

Figure 5.37.
Unit circle showing sin(π/4).

ACTIVITY

WHAT ARE YOUR RATES?

6

Suppose you board one of Nauta-Bussink's 55-meter ferris wheels. Once the wheel is up to speed, you rotate one-and-one-half times around the wheel every minute. During the ride, your height above the ground oscillates between 3 meters to 55 meters and can be modeled by a sinusoidal function. The rate at which your height changes over time is not constant. At certain times during the ride, you ascend or descend farther in one second than at other times. **Figure 5.38** shows part of a spreadsheet that gives your height above the ground and the approximate rate of change in height at one-second intervals. The model $h(t) = 26 \sin(0.16(t - 10)) + 29$ is used to compute the heights.

	A	B	C	D
1	Start =	0	Increment =	1
2				
3	Time	Height	Rate	
4	0	3.011086		
5	1	3.222083	0.54025066	
6	2	4.091588	1.18765278	
7	3	5.597389	1.8047158	
8	4	7.701019		
9	5	10.34874		
10	6	13.47292		

Figure 5.38.
Portion of spreadsheet.

1. In Activity 5, symmetric difference quotients were used to approximate the rate of change in height at particular times. For example, based on the increment value of 1, you can estimate the rate of change in height at time t using the quotient:

$$(h(t + 1) - h(t - 1))/2.$$

a) In Figure 5.38, check that the rate entry corresponding to $t = 2$ is correct. What are the units for this entry?

b) Use Figure 5.38 to complete the rate entries corresponding to $t = 4$ and $t = 5$. Why can't you compute a symmetric difference quotient for $t = 6$ from the data in Figure 5.38?

The spreadsheet in Figure 5.38 was extended to $t = 80$ seconds and used to create **Figure 5.39**, showing height-versus-time and

ACTIVITY

WHAT ARE YOUR RATES?

6

rate-versus-time data. (Note the height-versus-time graph is the one that oscillates from $y = 3$ to $y = 55$.)

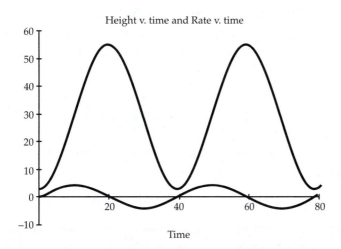

Figure 5.39.
Height and rate versus time for the 55-meter ferris wheel.

2. Base your answers to Items (a)–(c) on Figure 5.39.

a) When you are at the top of the ferris wheel, what is the approximate rate of change of your height above the ground with respect to time? (Include the appropriate units in your answer.) What about when you are at the bottom of the wheel?

b) What about when you are midway between the top and the bottom of the wheel?

c) What's the same about the height-versus-time and rate-versus-time graphs? What's different?

d) Make a convincing argument that the rate of change for a sinusoid must be periodic with the same period as the sinusoid itself. What other conjectures about sinusoidal models and their corresponding rate-of-change graphs seem reasonable?

Is it a fluke that the rate function for the sinusoidal model $h(t) = 26 \sin(0.16(t - 10)) + 29$ also appears to be a sinusoidal function with the same period? In order to answer this question,

WHAT ARE YOUR RATES?

6

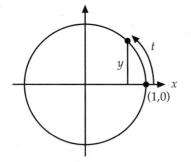

y

(1,0)

Figure 5.40.
Dot rotating about the unit circle.

it will be helpful to examine the rate of change graph for the simplest sinusoid of them all—$y = \sin(t)$.

Imagine a dot is spinning around the unit circle. It begins at (1,0) and travels an arc of t radians. The y-coordinate of the dot's location (that's its vertical displacement or height) is $\sin(t)$. (See **Figure 5.40.**)

3. a) Copy **Figure 5.41**. For each t-value, approximate (using a symmetric difference quotient based on a very small increment) the rate of change in $y = \sin(t)$. For example, the second entry in the rate column was computed using an increment of 0.01 as follows:

$$(\sin(1 + 0.01) - \sin(1 - 0.01))/0.02 \approx 0.54$$

Radians, t	Rate of change in y	Increment
0	1.00	0.01
1	0.54	
2	−0.42	
3	−0.99	
4		
5		
6		
7		
8		
9		
10		
11		
12		

Figure 5.41.
Rate versus radian data.

b) Enter these data into your calculator and make a scatter plot of rate versus radians. If you were to connect the

ACTIVITY

WHAT ARE YOUR RATES?

6

points on your scatter plot with a smooth curve, how would your graph be related to the graph of $y = \sin(t)$?

c) Assume that the period of your data is 2π, the same as for $y = \sin(t)$. Write a sinusoidal model that describes these data. Explain how you determined your model. Then, graph your model to check that it fits the data.

d) The name of the rate function that you have determined in (b) is called the **cosine** (short for the *complement of the sine*). Use your calculator: Press the COS-key to graph $y = \cos(t)$. Check that its graph follows the pattern of your data and matches the graph of your model from (c).

Return to the dot spinning around the unit circle in Figure 5.40. The sine function is defined as the y-coordinate of the dot (the dot's height or vertical displacement) versus the t-value of its arc. Go back to your table in Item 3. There, $t = 0$ when rate of change is 1.00; $t = 1$ when rate of change = 0.54; and so on. Since y is the height, $y = 0$ when $t = 0$; $y = 0.84$ when $t = 1$. (Check **Figure 5.42.**)

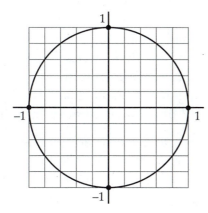

Figure 5.42.
Graph of unit circle.

ACTIVITY

6

WHAT ARE YOUR RATES?

It is easy to see the sine function; it's just y. But how do you see the rate of change, or cosine? What if, instead of y-coordinates, you plotted the dot's x-coordinate (its horizontal displacement) versus the t-value of its arc? That's what Item 4 investigates.

4. a) Make a copy of **Figure 5.43**. (The dot's t-value is the radian measure of its arc. The dot's x-coordinate is its horizontal displacement from the y-axis.) Use the graph in Figure 5.42 to complete the entries in your table to one-decimal precision. (It may help to convert radians to the fraction of a complete turn around a circle.) Three of the entries have been completed for you.

Dot's t-value	$-\pi$	$-3\pi/4$	$-\pi/2$	$-\pi/4$	0	$\pi/4$	$\pi/2$	$3\pi/4$
Dot's x-coordinate	-1.0				1.0	0.7		

Dot's t-value	π	$5\pi/4$	$3\pi/2$	$7\pi/4$	2π	$9\pi/4$	$5\pi/2$	$11\pi/4$
Dot's x-coordinate								

Figure 5.43.
Horizontal displacement-versus-radian data from a unit circle.

b) Explain how to use $\sin(t)$, the definition of $\sin(t)$ as a y-coordinate, and the Pythagorean theorem to obtain x-values with greater precision than you can see in Figure 5.42. In general, how are $\sin(t)$ and the x-value of the dot related? Illustrate your answer with a drawing.

c) Use your answer to (b) to determine the x-coordinate of a point t units around the unit circle for each given value of $\sin(t)$. Assume each point is in the first quadrant.

   i. $\sin(t) = 3/5$

   ii. $\sin(t) = 3/8$

d) Repeat (c) without the restriction that both points lie in the first quadrant. Illustrate your answers using a copy of Figure 5.42.

WHAT ARE YOUR RATES?

5. Look back at the table you made in Item 4(a). Graph the horizontal displacement-versus-radian data using the scaling shown in **Figure 5.44.** Then draw a smooth curve through the points on your scatter plot.

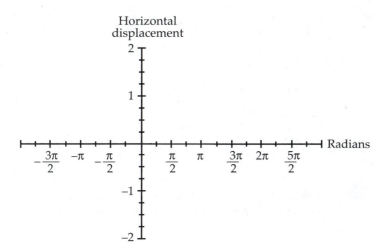

Figure 5.44.
Axes with scaling used for Item 5(a).

     b) Compare your graph in (b) to the graph of $y = \cos(x)$.

So far, you have generated the cosine function in two ways—first, as the rate of change function for $y = \sin(t)$, and second as the relationship between the x-coordinate and t-value of a dot rotating about the unit circle. The **cosine function** is the horizontal displacement versus the radian measure of an arc made by a dot rotating around a unit circle. Graphs of the sine and cosine functions have the same period and amplitude. You can translate one graph to coincide with the other by shifting horizontally $\pi/2$ units left or right.

6. Some of the equations that follow are true for all values of t and some are not. Describe in words what each equation says about the graphs of the functions involved. (Use words such as horizontal shift and reflection in your descriptions.) Then state whether the equation is true for all values of t and hence an **identity**—an equation that is true for all values of the variable.

ACTIVITY

6

WHAT ARE YOUR RATES?

For example, $\sin(t + \pi/2) = \cos(t)$ indicates that by shifting the graph of $y = \sin(t)$ $\pi/2$ units to the left, it will coincide with the graph of $y = \cos(t)$. Since this is true, this equation is an identity.

a) $\cos(t - \pi/2) = \sin(t)$.

b) $\cos(t + \pi/2) = \sin(t)$.

c) $\cos(t - 2\pi) = \cos(t)$.

d) $\sin(t - \pi/2) = \cos(t)$.

e) $\cos(t + \pi) = -\cos(x)$.

f) $\sin(t + \pi) = -\sin(t)$

7. Rewrite your answer to Item 4(b) in terms of $\sin(t)$ and $\cos(t)$. Then make up two additional identities of your own that involve sine and/or cosine functions. (Be ready to share them with the class.)

8. You can modify the cosine function the same way you modified the sine function to get cosine functions of the form $y = A\cos(B(x - C)) + D$. In each of the items below, determine a cosine function whose graph is the same as the given sinusoidal function. In each case, explain how you arrived at your answer. Then use your calculator to check your answers.

a) $y = \sin(x - 1)$.

b) $y = \sin(2x)$.

c) $h(t) = 26 \sin(0.16(t - 10) + 29$. (Recall this was the model used to describe a ferris wheel rider's height above the ground over time, which was discussed at the beginning of this activity.)

9. The rate function for $y = \sin(t)$ is $y = \cos(t)$. In answering the items that follow, think how the given modification to the sine function will affect its rate of change. In particular, think about how the modification would affect the symmetric dif-

WHAT ARE YOUR RATES?

ference quotients used to approximate the rate function, or think about how the modification would affect the steepness of the sinusoidal graph. (If you have difficulty, you may find it helpful to create symmetric difference tables for some of these functions.) In each case, give your answer in terms of the cosine function and explain how you determined your answer.

a) What is the rate function for $y = \sin(t) + 5$?

b) What is the rate function for $y = 3\sin(t)$?

c) What is the rate function for $y = \sin(t - 2)$?

d) What is the rate function for $y = \sin(2t)$?

10. Return to the model
$y = 26 \sin(0.16(t - 10)) + 29 = 26 \sin(0.16t - 1.6) + 29$.

a) Based on what you have learned in Item 9, what is the rate function for this model?

b) Graph both the model and your rate function from (a) in a window that matches the one used in Figure 5.39. Does your graph resemble the one in Figure 5.39? If not, make appropriate adjustments until it does.

c) Suppose, once again, that you have boarded the 55-meter ferris wheel. At $t = 30$ seconds, you are on your way down, approximately midway between the bottom and top of the wheel. Based on your rate function, approximately how fast are you descending at this time? What about at $t = 35$ seconds? What about at $t = 38$ seconds?

INDIVIDUAL WORK 6

What's My Equation?

1. In Item 1, Activity 5, you used technical details on Nauta-Bussink's 33-meter ferris wheel to determine a model for a rider's height above the ground over time. Your model was based on the sine function. Write a second model, this time based on the cosine function. Check with your calculator that your new model produces the same graph as your sinusoidal model from Item 1, Activity 5.

2. Suppose you have a sinusoidal model of the form $y = A\sin(B(x - C)) + D$. How would you re-express this model using the cosine function?

3. **Figure 5.45** displays the graph of $y = \cos(x)$ over the interval from -2π to 2π. Without using your calculator, sketch the graphs of each of the modified cosine functions below on sets of axes that use the same scaling as Figure 5.45. Describe in words how the modification alters the graph of $y = \cos(x)$. (After you have completed each graph, use your calculator to check your work.)

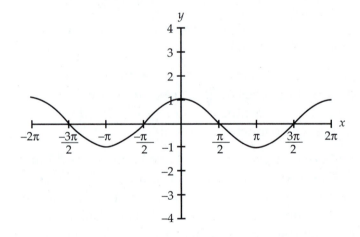

Figure 5.45.
Graph of $y = \cos(x)$.

a) $y = 2\cos(2x) + 2$.

b) $y = \cos(2(x - 3))$.

c) $y = 0.25\cos(4(x - \pi)) - 1$.

4. a) Write two equations for the mystery graph in **Figure 5.46**, one using sine and the other using cosine. Check your answers with a calculator.

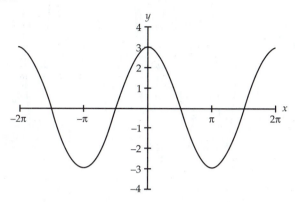

Figure 5.46.
Mystery graph #1.

b) Repeat (a) for **Figure 5.47**.

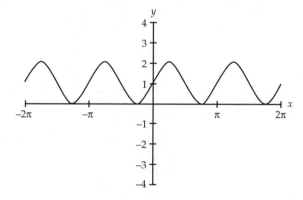

Figure 5.47.
Mystery graph #2.

5. For each of the graphs in **Figures 5.48–5.54**, determine a sine or cosine equation that has (approximately) the given graph. Also state the exact period, amplitude, and axis of oscillation for your equation.

a)

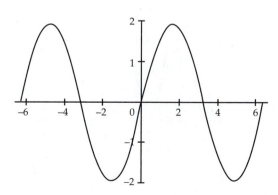

Figure 5.48.
Graph of a periodic function.

INDIVIDUAL WORK 6

b)

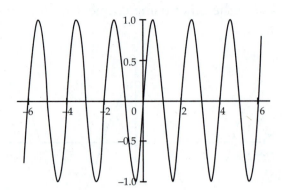

Figure 5.49.
Graph of a periodic function.

c)

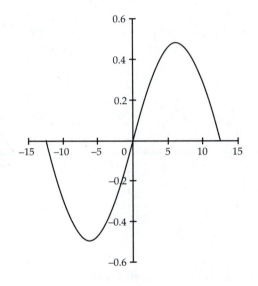

Figure 5.50.
Graph of a periodic function.

d)

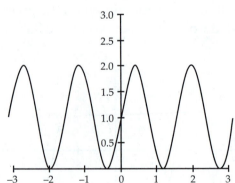

Figure 5.51.
Graph of a periodic function.

e)

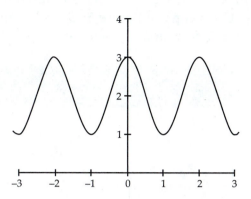

Figure 5.52.
Graph of a periodic function.

f)

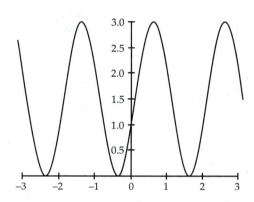

Figure 5.53.
Graph of a periodic function.

g)

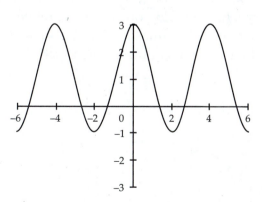

Figure 5.54.
Graph of a periodic function.

INDIVIDUAL WORK 6

6. Repeat Item 3 of Activity 6, this time to find the rate of change of the cosine function. Use a copy of **Figure 5.55**, and symmetric difference quotients based on a very small increment.

Radians, t	Rate of change in cos(t)
0	
1	
2	
3	
4	
5	
6	
7	
8	
9	
10	
11	
12	

Figure 5.55.
Rate versus radian data.

b) Enter these data into your calculator and make a scatter plot of rate versus radians. If you were to connect the points on your scatter plot with a smooth curve, how would your graph be related to the graph of $y = \sin(t)$? $y = \cos(t)$? Write formulas for this graph, first in terms of the sine function and then in terms of the cosine function.

POINT OF REFERENCE

ACTIVITY

7

In this unit, the sine and cosine have been
defined in terms of the length of arc as you
traverse a unit circle. For example, imagine you
are walking a unit circle starting at the point (1,0). Every now and
then you stop and record in radians the directed length of your
arc. These recordings, based on the definitions of sine and cosine,
can be used to find the coordinates of your location.

In Unit 1, you also studied sine and cosine. There, however, they
were defined in terms of shape ratios (ratios of sides) in right triangles. Are the two definitions of sine (and of cosine) consistent?
This activity answers that question.

1. If you know you have walked t radians, how can you determine the coordinates (x,y) of your location?

Continue to imagine you are walking around a unit circle. Add a
spotlight at the center of the circle. Its operator tracks you in its
beam during your walk. Your starting location is (1,0). When you
stop, the ray made by the spotlight beam has turned a certain
number of degrees as it followed you along your arc (see **Figure
5.57**). Your location on the unit circle can also be determine by
this angle θ, called the **central angle**—an angle whose vertex is
the center of a circle.

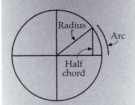

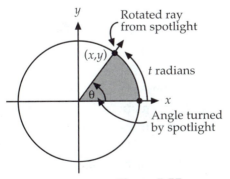

Figure 5.57.
Arc length and corresponding central angle.

FYI

**From sinus
to sine**

Interestingly, the
term *sine* actually
developed from
an error. The Hindu
term *jya*, meaning
half-chord became
jyb in Arabic. A
translator,
translating from
Arabic to Latin,
incorrectly read *jyb*
as *jayb* (Arabic for
pocket). Thus, the
Latin *sinus* was
used by mistake
and we now use
this in the form
sine.

Figure 5.56
Function *jya* of an
arc: half chord in a
circle of radius *r*.

ACTIVITY

POINT OF REFERENCE

7

2. A 360° rotation of the spotlight will sweep out one circumference of the circle, or an arc of 2π radians. What fraction of the circumference will be swept out by a 180° rotation of the spotlight? How many radians is this?

3. a) Use proportional reasoning to write a method for determining the radian measure of an arc, t, given the degrees of the corresponding central angle, θ. Then write a method for determining the degrees of a central angle, θ, if given the radian measure of the corresponding arc, t.

   b) Use your method from (a) to complete the entries in **Figure 5.58**.

Central angle	Arc's radian measurement
360°	2π
180°	
	$\pi/2$
45°	
	$\pi/3$
30°	
	$5\pi/8$
270°	

Figure 5.58.
Radian and degree equivalents.

The table you completed in Item 3 provides a natural way to define sine and cosine for angles outside the context of triangles. Unit circle definitions of sine and cosine for radian measures are extended to their corresponding central angles. For example, with your calculator in radian mode, $\sin(5\pi/6) = 0.5$. In degree mode, $\sin(150°) = 0.5$. Of course, 150° is not an angle in a right triangle, so you cannot apply the opposite/hypotenuse definition from Unit 1. However, you can draw natural right triangles based on all given central angles.

ACTIVITY

POINT OF REFERENCE

7

4. a) Explain how you can use the unit circle and your knowledge of right-triangle sines and cosines from Unit 1 to determine the exact values for $\sin(\pi/4)$ and $\cos(\pi/4)$. Use a unit circle similar to the one in **Figure 5.59** and a triangle to illustrate your answer. Clearly identify the triangle you use. (Hint: If you are not sure how to change this radian measure into an equivalent central angle, recall that both the central angle and the arc length can be related to fractions of a full trip around the circle.)

   b) Repeat (a) to determine the exact values for $\sin(\pi/6)$ and $\cos(\pi/6)$.

5. In Unit 1, the sine and cosine functions were only defined for angles between 0° and 90° because they were applied only to angles in right triangles. The unit circle, however, can be used to define the sine and cosine of angles greater than 90° and even for negative angles.

   a) An angle of 150° cannot exist in any right triangle. Why not?

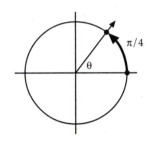

Figure 5.59.
The unit circle with shaded arc $t = \pi/4$.

Figure 5.60 illustrates a 200° angle on a unit circle (recall the spotlight illustration). Remember that one way to compute $\sin(200°)$ and $\cos(200°)$ is to convert the 200° angle to its equivalent radian measure and then compute the sine and cosine of that arc. However, the figure suggests how you can draw a reference right triangle to use the right triangle definitions from Unit 1 to compute $\sin(200°)$ and $\cos(200°)$. A **reference right triangle** is a triangle made by dropping a perpendicular to the x-axis from a point on the terminal side of a central angle whose initial side lies on the positive x-axis.

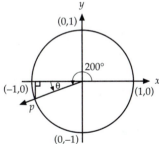

Figure 5.60.
Reference right triangle for 200° angle.

A reference right triangle always has one leg along the horizontal axis, and the hypotenuse coincides with a radius of the unit circle. In the illustration in Figure 5.60, the acute angle θ marked in the shaded triangle measures 20°. (Check it!) The unit circle definition says that $\sin(200°)$ is the y-coordinate and $\cos(200°)$ is the x-coordinate of point P. The right triangle definition applied to the

ACTIVITY

POINT OF REFERENCE

7

reference triangle can be interpreted as
sin(200°) = opposite/hypotenuse, as in Unit 1, except that
now the opposite side is negative (namely, *y*). Likewise,
cos(200°) = adjacent/hypotenuse, where adjacent is *x*. The angle θ
is called the **reference angle**—the acute angle in a reference right
triangle that has its adjacent side along the horizontal axis.

> b) Draw the reference triangle, and find the reference angle,
>   θ, for a central angle of 150°. How do the signs of sin(θ)
>   and cos(θ) compare to the signs of sin(150°) and cos(150°)?
>   How do their absolute values compare?
>
> c) Draw an angle of 300° in a unit circle. What is the refer-
>   ence angle for 300°? How is sin(300°) related to the sine of
>   the reference angle? How is cos(300°) related to the cosine
>   of the reference angle?
>
> d) For what angles θ is sin(θ) negative? For what angles θ is
>   cos(θ) negative?

For the remainder of this activity, you will need the *Geometer's
Sketchpad* program and the CD-ROM program file SINCOS.GSP.

In the *Geometer's Sketchpad* sketch on your computer screen, the
two legs of the triangle (horizontal and vertical) are color-coded
(blue and red) to the two graphs (cosine and sine). As the point
revolves around the circle, graphs of the sine and cosine functions are generated.

> 6. a) Click the Fast Graph and then the Slow Graph button sev-
>   eral times and watch the animation to get a feel for the
>   relationships among the circular motion, the lengths of the
>   red and blue legs of the reference triangle, and the graphs
>   of sine and cosine.
>
> b) Next, point to the dot that rotates around the circle. At the
>   bottom of your screen, you should see the message Select
>   Point C. (If you don't, try pointing and clicking again until
>   you do.) Click on this point, and check that the message
>   Translate Point C appears at the bottom of your screen.

ACTIVITY

POINT OF REFERENCE

7

When it does, drag Point C slowly once around the circle, counterclockwise.

c) Click on Point C and drag it to the starting location (1,0). Clear your graph by clicking once on the graph window. You should be left with red and blue points located at (0,0) and (0,1), respectively. What do these two coordinates have to do with the sine and cosine functions?

7. a) Click on Point C and drag it around the circle in the counterclockwise direction until the graphs of $y = \sin(t)$ and $y = \cos(t)$ intersect for the first time. Approximate from the graphs of $y = \sin(t)$ and $y = \cos(t)$ the coordinates of Point C.

   b) Examine the reference right triangle. What kind of triangle is it? What is the reference angle? How do you know?

   c) What is the radian measure of the arc traced out by the rotating dot?

   d) Imagine reflecting this triangle about the y-axis to produce a reference right triangle in quadrant II. Click and drag Point C to produce the triangle you have imagined. Approximately what are the coordinates of Point C? What is the central angle swept out by rotating Point C to this location? What is the reference angle of this triangle?

   e) Continue dragging Point C until the graphs of $y = \sin(t)$ and $y = \cos(t)$ intersect for a second time. Approximately what are the coordinates of Point C? How is this reference right triangle related to the one observed for (a)? What is the central angle associated with this reference triangle?

8. Reposition the dot at (1,0) and clear your graph. Slowly move the dot counterclockwise once around the unit circle. How do the graphs of $y = \sin(t)$ and $y = \cos(t)$ change as Point C sweeps around the circle through quadrant I? What about as Point C moves through quadrant II? Through quadrant III? Through quadrant IV?

POINT OF REFERENCE

9. Reposition Point C at (1,0) and clear the graphs. Again, slowly drag Point C counterclockwise once around the circle.

a) As Point C sweeps through quadrant I, what happens to the lengths of the red and blue legs of the reference triangle? What does this tell you about the graphs of $y = \cos(t)$ and $y = \sin(t)$?

b) As Point C sweeps through quadrant II, what happens to the red and blue legs of the reference triangle?

c) What about when Point C sweeps through quadrant III? Quadrant IV?

10. a) Experiment for a while longer. What other discoveries did you make? Be ready to share them with the class.

b) If you can't think of anything to investigate, try dragging Point C to form some familiar right triangle in quadrant I. Then drag Point C so that you reflect this triangle into each of the other three quadrants. Approximate the coordinates of Point C corresponding to each of your reference right triangles. How are these four sets of coordinates related? (For example, can you make an approximate 30°-60°-90° right triangle in quadrant I and then reflect it into the other three quadrants?)

INDIVIDUAL WORK 7

The Angle's Central

1. Sketch the central angle of 140° on a copy of the unit circle (see **Figure 5.61**). Then sketch the reference right triangle and determine the acute reference angle θ associated with the central angle of 140°. Use a calculator (in degree mode) to approximate cos(θ), cos(140°), sin(θ), and sin(140°). How are cos(θ) and cos(140°) related? How are sin(θ) and sin(140°) related?

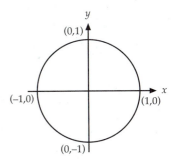

Figure 5.61.
Graph of the unit circle.

2. Sketch a central angle of –110° on the unit circle. What is the acute reference angle, θ, associated with a central angle of –110°? Use a calculator to approximate cos(θ), cos(–110°), sin(θ), and sin(–110°). How are cos(θ) and cos(–110°) related? How are sin(θ) and sin(–110°) related?

3. Find the reference angles for the following central angles. In which quadrant does the corresponding reference right triangle lie?

    a) 250°.   b) 390°.

    c) 760°.   d) –80°.

    e) –175°.   f) –390°.

    g) 160°.

4. Set your calculator to Degree mode. Set the viewing window to [–360,360]x[–3,3] (or use your calculator's trig viewing window).

    a) Graph $y = \sin(x)$ and $y = \cos(x)$ on the same set of axes. Sketch what you see in your calculator screen.

    b) Express $y = \cos(x)$ as a sine function that has been shifted to the left. Use your calculator to graph both $y = \cos(x)$ and your translated sine function. If the graphs do not appear the same, adjust the value for the horizontal shift (the phase shift).

    c) Express $y = \sin(x)$ as a cosine function that has been shifted to the right. Verify using your calculator that your translated function has the same graph as $y = \sin(x)$.

5. Use your calculator to graph $y = \sin(x)$ and $y = \cos(x)$. Then find two central angles whose sine and cosine are (approximately) equal to the values given below. (In each case, only one of the central angles can be between 0° and 360°.)

    a) $\sin(\theta) = 0.642$ and $\cos(\theta) = 0.766$.

b) $\sin(\theta) = -0.588$ and $\cos(\theta) = 0.809$.

c) $\sin(\theta) = 0.259$ and $\cos(\theta) = -0.966$.

d) $\sin(\theta) = -0.906$ and $\cos(\theta) = -0.423$.

e) Why do you need both the sine and cosine of the angle?

6. Set your calculator to Radian mode. Graph the function $y = 2\sin(2(x - \pi/3)) + 2$ over the x-interval -2π to 2π. Suppose you want to change the independent variable from radians to degrees, but want to view a graph that matches the one presently in your calculator screen. How would you change the formula and window settings? Use your calculator to verify your answer.

7. Set your calculator to Degree mode. Graph the function $y = 3\cos(0.5(x - 45°))$ over the x-interval from $-720°$ to $720°$. Suppose you want to change the independent variable from degrees to radians, but want to view a graph that matches the one presently in your calculator screen. How would you change the formula and window settings? Use your calculator to verify your answer.

8. Leave your calculator in degree mode. Below are sine and cosine functions that have been modified. Graph each equation with a graphing calculator and then discuss how the modification has translated the sine or cosine curve.

a) $y = \sin(x + 45°)$.

b) $y = \cos(x - 90°)$.

c) $y = \sin(x) + 3$.

d) $y = \sin(x - 45°) - 2$.

e) $y = \cos(x - 180°) + 1$.

9. Use your calculator to graph $y = 3\sin(2(x + 45°)) + 1$. Explain the effect of each of the constants in this equation on the graph of $\sin(x)$.

Now you have a choice. You can graph sine functions in Degree mode or Radian mode. However, you will need to ascertain from the context of the problem whether the independent variable is in terms of degrees or radians and set your calculator's mode accordingly.

LESSON FOUR
Fade Out

KEY CONCEPTS

Adding functions

Multiplying functions

Damped oscillations

Linear decay

Exponential decay

The Image Bank

PREPARATION READING

The Nature of Sound

Many of the periodic situations that you studied in earlier lessons were connected with circular motion—motion of the earth about the sun, the moon about the earth, or a ferris wheel about its axle. But there are other types of phenomena that produce periodic patterns and don't involve circular motion.

When you hear a sound, for example, you are really sensing changes in the air pressure against your eardrum. Even though weather causes changes in air pressure, you generally don't hear sound when a high pressure system replaces a low pressure system in your area. Strike a

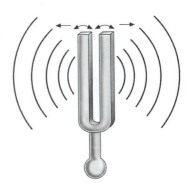

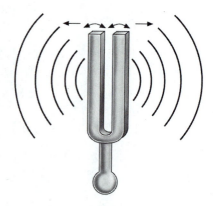

tuning fork, however, and you hear a sound. That's because the tines of the fork vibrate back and forth creating pressure waves. When the tine of the fork moves to the left, it presses on air molecules causing a high pressure zone on that side (because the molecules have been compressed). These molecules, in turn, press against other air molecules further away from the fork. When the fork moves to the right, it gives air molecules on the left more space, causing a low pressure zone. The rapid vibrations of the fork create alternating zones of high pressure followed by low pressure. Our ear picks up these alternating pressure zones and interprets them as sound.

The reason you don't hear weather systems is that human ears only hear pressure changes that occur within a specific range of speeds. Weather is too slow.

CONSIDER:

Suppose you could slow the process of the vibrating tuning fork and measure the air pressure at a specific location as it changes from high air pressure zones (moving rapidly away from the tuning fork) to low pressure zones. Suppose you were to graph pressure versus time. What might the graph look like?

DO YOU HEAR WHAT I HEAR?

Sound moves as a wave of pressure through the air. High-pitched sound (like a soprano voice) has a small period, while low-pitched sound (like a bass voice) has a longer period. Large amplitude (large differences in pressure between the high-and-low pressure zones) corresponds to loud sound; small amplitude corresponds to quiet sound.

So, how do you capture information from sound waves so you can represent them graphically? A microphone can be used to detect the changing pressure and transform it into a signal. Data from this signal can be transferred to your calculator or computer and you can graph it!

If a song begins with a G chord, three notes, G, B and D are struck at the same time. How would you represent a G chord graphically? For that matter, what would individual notes such as G, B, or D look like graphically? You'll find out in this experiment.

Signals from pure tones such as those produced by tuning forks have periodic graphs. The pitch of the tone is generally defined in terms of **frequency**, the number of waves (oscillations) per second (called hertz, Hz), rather than period. For example, middle C has a frequency of 256 Hz, which means that the period of middle C is 1/256 second.

CONDUCTING THE EXPERIMENT:

You'll need a microphone/amplifier that can translate the sound into a signal and transfer data from the signal into your calculator (or your computer). You should also have an assortment of tuning forks.

Set up the equipment and conduct the experiment as follows:

Place the microphone/amplifier on a table with the microphone facing up and connect it to a calculator (or computer), see **Figure 5.62**.

DO YOU HEAR WHAT I HEAR?

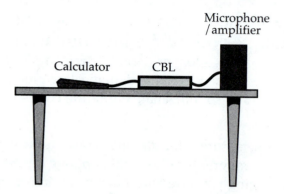

Figure 5.62.
An example of a micro-
phone/calculator set-up.

Calculator   CBL   Microphone
/amplifier

Execute the SOUND program. Select a tuning fork. (You will
get the best results if you choose a tuning fork whose frequency is between 200 and 300 Hz.) Hit the tuning fork with
a rubber hammer or strike it on the rubber sole of a shoe
(such as a sneaker). Hold the fork closely over the microphone and press Enter to begin collecting data.

1. a) Make a sketch of the graph of the pressure-versus-time
    data collected by the microphone. (If you choose a tuning
    fork whose frequency was higher than 300 Hz, you may
    want to zoom in on a few cycles of the graph to get a bet-
    ter idea of the shape of the graph.) Describe your graph.
    What does pressure 0 represent?

    b) What is the period of your graph? How did you determine
    the period? (Retain all decimal places that your calculator
    gives you. Do not round until you have completed (c).)

    c) Remember, frequency = 1/period. According to your data,
    what is the frequency of the tone produced by the tuning
    fork? How does it compare to the frequency stamped on
    the side of the fork?

    d) Write the equation of a sinusoidal function that you think
    best describes the pattern of your data. Explain how you
    determined your model. Then graph both the model and
    the data in the same viewing window. (If you used a

DO YOU HEAR WHAT I HEAR?

tuning fork whose frequency is higher than 300 Hz, change the *t*-interval for your graph by replacing *x*-max with a value that is one-half to one-third of that set by the SOUND program.) If your graph doesn't match the pattern of these data, adjust the formula for your model. (For example, you may find that you need to use more decimal places for the constants *A*, *B*, *C*, and *D*.)

2. How does the loudness of the sound affect the graph representing it? Design an experiment to find out. Then conduct your experiment and report on the results. (Note: If your program automatically fits a window to the data, then you will need to pay close attention to the scaling on the vertical axis.)

3. If you strike a G (above middle-C) tuning fork, it will vibrate at a frequency of 391 Hz. This means that if the sound continues for one second, the sine's wave shape repeats itself 391 times.

    a) What is the period of the sine wave this tuning fork produces?

    b) **Figure 5.63** shows a graph of air pressure versus time that could represent the sound produced by a G tuning fork. Make a copy of Figure 5.63 and add appropriate scaling to the horizontal axis.

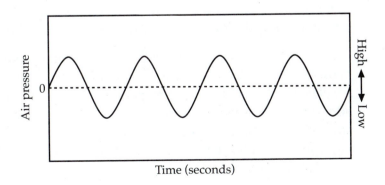

Figure 5.63.
Sine wave produced by a G tuning fork.

ACTIVITY

8

DO YOU HEAR WHAT I HEAR?

c) Suppose you strike the G tuning fork with more force than was applied in (b). Add to your graph from (b) a sketch of a sine wave that could represent this situation. Explain why your graph looks the way it does.

d) Write a general model that describes the relationship between air pressure and time when the G tuning fork is struck. List any assumptions you have made in designing your model. Use letters for any undetermined control numbers.

4. If a song begins with a G chord, three notes, G, B and D, are struck at the same time. B has a frequency of 492 Hz, and D a frequency of 586 Hz.

a) Write sinusoidal models describing the sine waves representing the pitches of B and D. (Assume the phase shift is zero in both cases.)

b) Assume each note is played at the same volume. Overlay graphs of your three models from 3(d) and 4(a) over the time interval from $t = 0$ to $t = 0.005$ second. Make a sketch of your graphs. State any assumptions you have made.

c) Suppose the three notes in the G chord, G, B, and D, are struck at exactly the same time. What do you think happens to the air pressure when three high air pressure zones (produced by the three notes) are combined? What do you think happens when a high pressure zone produced by one note combines with a low pressure zone from another?

d) When the three notes from the G chord are played simultaneously, each note's pressure waves radiate toward your ear. The net effect is that the respective pressure values are added to each other. Write an equation representing this sum of waves. Then graph your model over the time interval from $t = 0$ to $t = 0.01$ seconds. (Sketch the pattern you see.) Is it what you expected?

DO YOU HEAR WHAT I HEAR?

e) Explain the causes of the main features of your graph. That is, think about how the graph of the sum of three sinusoidal functions should look. If you find you can't answer it, suggest some questions that would be easier to tackle but that would provide information helpful in eventually answering the original question. (If you wish, you can return to this question at a later time.)

Early synthesizers made sound using simple repeating wave forms. The most popular wave forms are shown in **Figure 5.64**. Each has its own characteristic timbre (pronounced TAM-brr), or distinctive sound. More complex sounds were created by combining and filtering these wave forms.

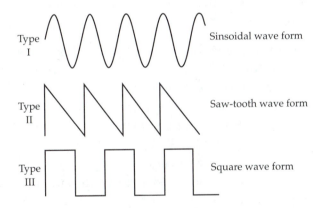

Type I — Sinsoidal wave form

Type II — Saw-tooth wave form

Type III — Square wave form

Figure 5.64.
Popular wave forms

It may be easier to picture what the graph of the sum of three sinusoidal functions looks like if you first analyze the sums of two functions represented by the type II or III wave forms used by the early synthesizers.

5. Two square waves are pictured in **Figure 5.65**. (The vertical lines are included for reference, but are not technically part of the graph of the model representing these sound waves.) The synthesizer can transform Models #1 and #2 into sound. In addition, by adjusting control numbers in the models, the amplitudes, frequencies, and phase shifts of the graphs can be altered.

ACTIVITY

DO YOU HEAR WHAT I HEAR?

8

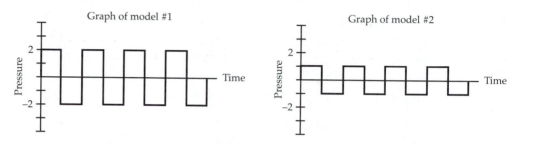

Figure 5.65.
Graphs representing
two sounds pro-
duced by synthesizer.

a) Suppose that each model produces a wave with a frequency of 300 Hz and that the synthesizer is programmed to
play both sounds simultaneously. Add scales to the horizontal axes in the figure. What is the width of one step of
one wave?

b) The resulting sound can be modeled by the sum of Model
#1 and Model #2. Draw a graph that represents that sum
by stacking the rectangles from the graph of Model #2 on
top of or to the bottom of the rectangles for the graph of
Model #1. For example, when $0 < t < 1/600$, the values of
Models #1 and #2 will be 2 and 1, respectively. The sum
will be 3. Put appropriate scaling on both axes. Explain the
details of how you constructed at least one additional step
of your graph.

c) Suppose Model #1 is adjusted so its phase shift C is $1/600$.
Model #2 is not adjusted (in other words, it's the same as it
was in (b)). Graphs for each of these models appear in
Figure 5.66. (The scaling on the t-axis has purposefully not
been provided.)

Draw a graph that represents the sound produced when
the synthesizer simultaneously plays these two sounds.
Explain how you determined your answer.

ACTIVITY

DO YOU HEAR WHAT I HEAR?

8

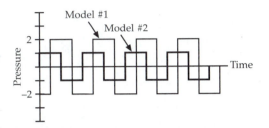

Figure 5.66.
Graphs of Model #1 with
phase shift of 1/1200 and
Model #2.

d) Suppose Model #2 is adjusted so its frequency is 600 Hz
and Model #1 is left as it was in (b). Draw a graph that
represents the sound produced when the synthesizer plays
these two sounds simultaneously.

Perhaps looking at sums of two functions represented by type-III
wave forms has shed a bit more light on why the graphical
representation of the G chord looks the way that it does.

CONSIDER:

Suppose you were trying to classify all the shapes of graphs of
sums of two type-III wave forms. For each type-III wave form,
you can change the amplitude, period, and phase shift. How
would you organize your investigation? How long do you think
this study might take?

INDIVIDUAL WORK 8

Music Fills the Air

1. **Figure 5.67** shows two graphs. The one on the left represents a pure tone and the one on the right represents noise. What graphical features distinguish noise from the pure tone?

Figure 5.67.
Representations of a
pure tone versus noise.

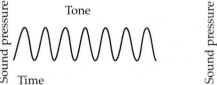

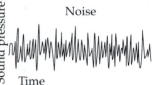

2. When you hit a tuning fork, the sound does not continue forever. Gradually it fades in volume. First, draw a graph representing the sound from a tuning fork soon after it is struck. Then, draw a graph representing its sound somewhat later, but before the fork has stopped vibrating. What feature(s) of your first graph changed in your second? What feature(s) stayed the same?

3. Suppose you are listening to a musician playing a steel guitar. The musician frets a string (presses the string against the neck of the guitar) in order to produce the note of B as she strums the string. Instantly she slides the bar down the string, shortening the portion of string that's vibrating and causing the sound to get higher in pitch. Draw a graph that could represent the sound you hear from the steel guitar. Describe how your graph shows what you hear.

4. The saw-tooth wave (type II in Figure 5.64) consists of parallel lines. (The vertical lines are for guidance and are not technically part of the function representing the sound.) In order to model the sound produced when a synthesizer plays two saw-tooth waves simultaneously, it's helpful to understand how to graph the sum of two linear functions from their graphs. **Figure 5.68** shows graphs of two linear functions, $f(x)$ and $g(x)$.

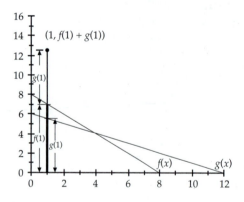

Figure 5.68.
Graphs of two linear functions.

a) Copy Figure 5.68. Without first finding the equations for $f(x)$ and $g(x)$, make a graph of their sum. One point is already plotted for you. It was determined by stacking vertical line segments with lengths $f(1)$ and $g(1)$.

b) Use information from Figure 5.68 to determine equations for $f(x)$ and $g(x)$. Then determine the equation for $f(x) + g(x)$. Check that the graph of $f(x) + g(x)$ produces the graph you made in (a).

5. Adding two sinusoidal models can produce complicated graphs. But what would the graph of the sum of a sinusoidal model and linear model look like? Work through (a)–(d) to find out.

a) Graph the functions $y = \sin(x)$ and $y = 0.5x$ separately on a sheet of graph paper. Based on your sketch, describe how you think the graph of their sum will look. Then graph the sum, $y = \sin(x) + 0.5x$. Does the graph in your calculator screen match your written description?

b) Next, consider the function $y = \sin(x) - 0.5x$. Describe in words how you think this function will look. Then use your calculator and compare the graph in your calculator's screen with your description.

c) Write formulas for a sinusoidal model and a linear model of your own choosing. Graph the sum of your equations. (You may have to adjust your viewing window in order to see key features of the graph.) Make a sketch of your graph.

d) Repeat (c), this time using a linear model with slope opposite in sign to that in (c). Graph the sum of your equations. Make a sketch of your graph.

e) Summarize your findings. Describe the graph of the sum of a sinusoidal model and a linear model. How does the slope of the linear model affect the graph?

6. In Item 5, you graphed the sum of a sinusoidal function and a linear function. Suppose a synthesizer were programmed to play two sinusoidal wave forms (type I in Figure 5.64) simultaneously. Suppose the sinusoidal waves have the same phase shifts and periods. Describe the graph representing the sound produced by the synthesizer. How is it related to the graphs representing the individual tones? What is the effect of playing these notes simultaneously?

ACTIVITY

9

DIMINISHING RETURNS

1. Suppose on your way to school, your bus hits a large speed bump while you are sitting in a seat over one of the back wheels. Draw a graph that represents the height of your head above the road before, during, and after the speed bump. Describe the features of your graph and tell what they mean about your ride.

2. Suppose you start a pendulum swinging and use a motion detector to record its motion. Initially, its distance-versus-time graph looks sinusoidal. When you plot these data, the amplitude appears fairly constant. However, eventually the pendulum stops swinging. Draw three graphs: One showing the distance-versus-time relationship within the first 20 seconds that the pendulum swings; a second, one minute later; the third, just before the pendulum stops swinging. What changes from graph to graph?

3. Imagine you are producing a soundtrack and you need to produce a tone that begins loud and then fades away within 0.02 second. **Figure 5.69** presents a graphical representation of what is needed. You have a graph; all that's left is to determine a model for the graph so you can program the synthesizer to produce this sound.

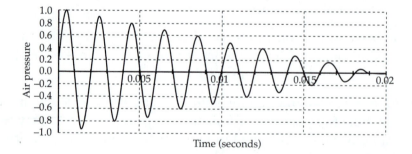

Figure 5.69.
Graphical representation
of a sound.

ACTIVITY

DIMINISHING RETURNS

9

Note (pitch)	Frequency (Hz)
G	391
A	440
B	492
C	522
D	586
E	658
F	698

Figure 5.70.
Notes and corresponding frequencies.

a) **Figure 5.70** gives a list of frequencies associated with a variety of notes. What is the pitch (approximately) of the sound represented by Figure 5.69? Write a model that describes the graph produced when this note is played at a constant volume.

b) For periodic functions, amplitude is defined as half the difference between the maximum and minimum. The function in Figure 5.69 is not periodic and does not have an amplitude according to the usual definition. How could you expand the definition of amplitude so it would make sense to say that in Figure 5.69 the amplitude is decreasing?

c) For periodic functions, the period is defined as the shortest horizontal length of a repeating pattern. Again, because the function in Figure 5.69 is not periodic, it does not have a period according to this definition. How would you expand the definition of period so it would make sense to say that in Figure 5.69, the period is constant?

d) For the sine and cosine functions, the amplitude can also be computed by subtracting D (the average of the maximum and minimum values) from the maximum value. In the fade-out situation, D would represent the level to which the air pressure will settle after the sound diminishes to silence. (This is $D = 0$ on the high-low pressure scale used in this lesson.) You could then define amplitude as the difference between the function of maximum values versus time, and the value of D, which is zero in this example. As you move from peak to peak in Figure 5.69, approximately how are the maximums changing? Is the change roughly constant, increasing, or decreasing? What type of function could describe the maximums versus time? Write a formula for this function.

e) How can you combine your formula from (d) and your model from (a) to produce a graph that matches the one in Figure 5.69? Experiment until you find a model that works. What is your model? How did you get it?

The graph in Figure 5.69 represents a situation in which the sound fades out. This phenomenon is called **damped oscillation**—an oscillation in which the amplitude decreases with time. The amplitude function in a damped oscillation is called the **damping factor**. For example, the model that you determined for Item 3(d), describing the changing maximums, is a damping factor.

The general form of a sinusoidal function is $y = A\sin(B(x - C)) + D$ where A is the amplitude. Think about the following questions as you work through Items 4–6.

What happens when you replace the amplitude A with a function $A(x)$?

How does the type of function used for the damping factor affect the oscillation?

How are the graphs of $y = A(x)$ and $y = -A(x)$ related to the graph of the damped oscillation?

4. a) Graph $y = (1/x) \sin(x)$ using an x-interval of 0 to 15. Describe what happens to the oscillation as the value of x increases. Sketch the graph and identify the axis of oscillation.

ACTIVITY

DIMINISHING RETURNS

9

b) Overlay the graph of the damping factor $A(x) = (1/x)$. Repeat for the opposite function, $y = -(1/x)$. What is the relationship between the graphs of $A(x)$, its opposite, and the graph of the function in (a)?

c) Apply the damping factor $(1/x)$ to $2\sin(x) + 5$. That is, replace $A = 2$ with $A(x) = 2(1/x)$. Sketch your graph, and describe the oscillating pattern in words. What is the axis of oscillation?

d) Overlay the graphs of $A(x)$ and $-A(x)$ on your graph in (c). Describe the result. Modify the graphs of $A(x)$ and $-A(x)$ so they envelope the oscillation as was done in (b).

As you have seen in Item 4, if $y = D$ is the axis of oscillation for an oscillation, and if $A(x)$ is its amplitude function, then the graphs of $D + A(x)$ and $D - A(x)$ touch and surround the oscillation. These curves form what is called an **envelope** for the oscillation.

5. a) Graph $y = 0.8^x \sin(x)$ using an x-interval that shows the pattern of the oscillation for positive x-values. Sketch your graph. What is the relationship between the graphs of $y = (0.8^x)$ and $y = -(0.8^x)$ and the graph of the damped oscillation itself?

b) Try using the damping factor from (a) on the sinusoidal model $y = 3\sin(2x) + 5$. (In this case, replace $A = 3$ by $A(x) = 3(0.8^x)$.) Describe the pattern of the oscillation. Compare this graph to your graph in (a).

c) Write the equations defining the envelope for this damped oscillation.

6. Describe how to find a model that describes damped oscillation. Test your method by finding equations describing Mystery graphs 1 and 2 in Figures 5.71 and 5.72.

a) Mystery graph #1 appears in **Figure 5.71**. To help you determine its equation, here are the approximate

ACTIVITY

9

DIMINISHING RETURNS

coordinates of the first four peaks in the graph: (0.25,1.86), (1.25,1.40), (2.25, 1.05), and (3.25,0.79). Find an equation that describes this graph and explain how you did it.

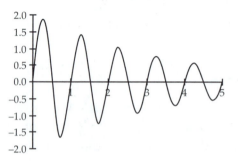

Figure 5.71.
Mystery graph #1.

b) Mystery graph #2 appears in **Figure 5.72**. To help you determine its function, here are the approximate coordinates of five points on the graph: (0.16,13.8), (0.46,–9.6), (0.78,13.2), (1.09,–9.1) and (1.41,12.6). Find an equation that describes this graph and explain how you did it.

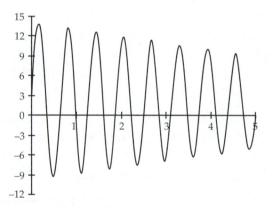

Figure 5.72.
Mystery graph #2.

CONSIDER:

1. Suppose you have the graph of a damped oscillation with axis of oscillation $y = 0$. How could you determine an approximate damping factor?

2. What if the axis of oscillation is the line $y = D$, where D is not zero. How does this change your strategy for finding the damping factor?

INDIVIDUAL WORK 9

Name that Graph

1. For each of the following graphs, decide if the damping factor is linear. If it is, find the equation of $A(x)$, the amplitude function. If not, suggest what type of equation the damping function might be.

a)

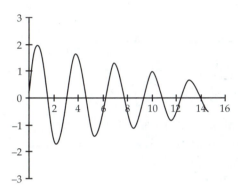

Figure 5.73.
Graph of damped oscillation.

b)

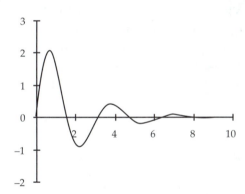

Figure 5.74.
Graph of damped oscillation.

c)

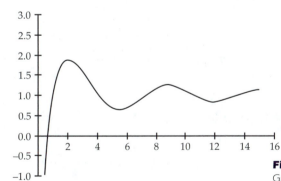

Figure 5.75.
Graph of damped oscillation.

d)

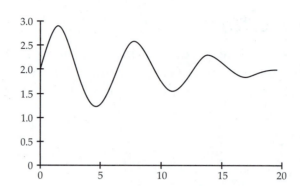

Figure 5.76.
Graph of damped oscillation.

2. Make up damping factors of your own and apply them to a sinusoidal function of your own choosing. Try one that is linear and compare it to one that is not linear. Describe the effect your damping
   functions have on the oscillation.

3. The graph in **Figure 5.77** was generated by a sine waveform signal
   editor. The time units are in μS (micro-seconds). The microphone
   converts the sound to voltage. (When you ran the sound experiment
   in Activity 8, your calculator converted the voltage values into pressure levels. The graphs of pressure versus time and voltage versus
   time look the same regardless of which units are used. They differ
   only by a scale change.)

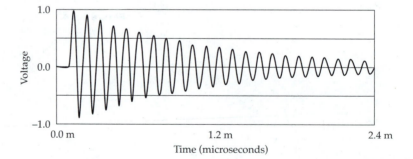

Figure 5.77.
Sine wave from signal editor.

a) Does the period of the oscillation appear to be constant? If so,
   approximately what is the period?

b) Could the damping factor be linear? Why or why not?

4. Return to the problem of adding (or subtracting) sinusoidal models. What happens if you take the difference between two sinusoidal models that agree in every way except that their phase shifts differ slightly?

a) Graph $y = \sin(x)$ and $y = \sin(x + 0.1)$ together in the trig viewing window. Predict how the graph of the difference of these functions will appear. After you have recorded your prediction, graph $y = \sin(x) - \sin(x + 0.1)$. Make sure that you adjust your viewing window so that you can see the key features of the graph.

b) Were the results in (a) just a fluke? Try several more pairs of sinusoidal functions that have slightly differing phase shifts. What does the graph of the difference of each pair look like? Summarize your findings.

M A T H   A T   W O R K

Whether you are at home listening to a CD of your favorite recording artist or in a large theater or hall attending a concert, play, or lecture, the mathematics of oscillation is the basis of the quality of the sound you are hearing. The study and control of sound waves is the specific business of acoustic engineers—sound specialists who collaborate with

The Image Bank

architects and clients to plan or remodel those spaces where the best sound possible is required. Many factors affect the behavior of sound waves in a specific place. These factors include the building materials used, the dimensions of the rooms, the background sound (for example, heating and air conditioning noises), and the placement and type of electronic amplifying equipment. Today, acoustic engineers can use computer modeling to make the measurement of sound waves more exact.

ACTIVITY

10

IT'S SLINKY TIME

Have you ever played with a Slinky®?

- Set it at the top of a set of stairs, help it down the first step, and then stand back and watch as it descends the stairs.

- Place one end of the Slinky in your right hand, the other in your left, and let the middle coils form an arch. Move your right hand up and your left hand down and then alternate. Watch as the middle coils in the Slinky pulsate back and forth.

- Hold the Slinky above the floor, release half of its coils, and watch as the bottom coil on the Slinky bobs up and down.

CONSIDER:

1. Suppose you held a Slinky above a motion detector, released half its coils, and recorded the end coil's distance from the detector as the Slinky oscillates up and down? How do you think its distance-versus-time graph would look during a 10-second data-recording session?

2. What if you recorded the motion over a longer period of time? What features on the graph might change?

In this activity, you will conduct the Slinky experiment and determine whether your data support or refute your predictions. You'll need to set up a motion detector and run the program SLINKY in order to gather your data.

CONDUCTING THE EXPERIMENT

Set up the equipment and conduct the experiment as follows:

Place the motion detector on the floor facing up (so it can measure the Slinky's height above the detector) and connect it to a calculator (or computer).

IT'S SLINKY TIME

Hold the Slinky directly above the motion detector. You will be letting the lower half of the Slinky coils drop so they start to bounce. Hold the Slinky high enough so that the bottom coil will always be at least 18 inches above the detector. (To help the detector track the bobbing Slinky, attach a piece of paper or an index card to the bottom coil of the Slinky with a paper clip or slip the paper between the last two coils and tape it in place.)

Execute the CD-ROM program SLINKY. (If you are using a CBL, you will have to press the Trigger button before it begins collecting data.)

Drop the lower coils of the Slinky. (Remember if the Slinky's coils drop closer than 18 inches above the motion detector, the detector may not record the true distance.) Hold the top half of the Slinky stationary.

When the Slinky starts to bounce in a well-controlled manner, have a partner press the Trigger key to begin the process of data-collection.

MODELING THE MOTION

After gathering the data, use your calculator to create a scatter plot of height versus time. If the experiment did not work properly (perhaps something was blocking the motion detector), try it again. When you have a good set of data, use them to answer Item 1.

1. a) Determine a pure sinusoidal equation that you think best models the displacement of the Slinky over time. Explain how you arrived at your model. In particular, how did you determine the amplitude, period, axis of oscillation, and phase shift from your data?

   b) Using your calculator, graph your equation on the same set of axes as your scatter plot. Does your model appear to describe the pattern of the data adequately? Make a residual plot. Do the points in your residual plot appear to be randomly scattered or do they exhibit a pattern?

IT'S SLINKY TIME

c) Return to the scatter plot of your data. Does the period remain relatively constant? How can you tell?

d) Does the amplitude remain constant?

2. If the amplitude is not constant, then it must be changing over time. As a result, it should be possible to create a model describing the amplitude (defined according to your expanded definition in Activity 9). What model summarizes the relationship of the amplitude versus time for your Slinky data?

3. Refine your model describing Slinky's displacement over time. Describe the process you used to find the equation and the method you used to tell if the equation was a good fit or not.

COWABUNGEE, DUDE!

If you were daring and looking for a unique experience, it would be exciting and fun to set up this next experiment over a ravine, with you on the end of a long bungee cord. However, in the interests of safety, a set of elastic bands and a water balloon will have to do. The principle is the same: The bungee cord allows the object at its end to bounce up and down. But if it were purely periodic, you would never stop bouncing above the ravine. Friction takes care of this problem. It ensures that you would eventually come to rest to be pulled to safety.

CONSIDER:

1. In this activity, you will drop a water balloon attached to a bungee cord over a motion detector. How do you think its distance-versus-time graph will look (provided the balloon doesn't burst over the motion detector)? Explain your prediction.

2. How do you think its graph might differ from the distance-versus-time graph of the Slinky in Activity 10? What might account for the differences, if any, in the two distance-versus-time graphs?

You'll have to conduct the experiment that follows in order to find out if your predictions are close to what happens in reality. You will need to set up a motion detector and run the CD-ROM program SLINKY. You will need a balloon containing some water, and either a bungee cord or some very thick elastic bands tied together. One person will hold the bungee cord firmly, one will hold (then drop) the balloon, and the remaining group members will need to work the calculator/computer and connecting devices.

ACTIVITY

COWABUNGEE, DUDE!

11

CONDUCTING THE EXPERIMENT

Set up the equipment and conduct the experiment as follows:

Put some water in a balloon. (About 1/4 water and 3/4 air will work well.) Be careful to not fill the balloon too much. The balloon needs to have some weight in order for the experiment to work well. However, spilled water over the motion detector would damage the equipment and could be a safety hazard.

Tie the bungee cord or the elastic bands to the balloon securely.

Set up the motion detector/calculator (or computer).

Once you have the bungee balloon set up, test it numerous times so you are confident the balloon is securely attached to the bungee and that it will not break because it is too full.

Hold the bungee balloon directly above the motion detector. You will be letting the balloon drop toward the motion detector. Hold the bungee high enough so the balloon will always be at least 18 inches above the detector.

Execute the CD-ROM program SLINKY. This program will set up the motion detector, but the motion detector will not record data yet.

Drop the balloon.

When the balloon starts to bounce in a well-controlled manner, press the Trigger key to begin the data collection process.

MODELING THE MOTION

1. Make a scatter plot of the vertical displacement of the balloon versus time. Describe the pattern in words.

2. Look at your scatter plot and determine the axis of oscillation. Call this level D. How did you determine this level? To confirm that your estimate is good, enter its equation, $y = D$, into your calculator and graph the horizontal line together with your scatter plot.

ACTIVITY

COWABUNGEE, DUDE!

11

3. a) Using the calculator's lists or a spreadsheet, put all the x-coordinates (time) in the first column and the y-coordinates (distance) in the second. In a third column, create a list containing the differences (distance – D).

   b) Predict the scatter plot of (distance – D) versus time (sketch it). Then construct the actual scatter plot. How good was your prediction? (Pay attention to the scaling on the vertical axis.)

   c) How do you think the scatter plot in (b) would look if you were able to collect data for a long time?

4. a) Estimate the amplitude of the balloon on its successive bounces, using the transformed data from Item 3(a). Enter your data in a table similar to **Figure 5.78**.

Peak number, n	x-coordinate, x_n time of nth peak	Peak height, h_n above D
1		
2		
3		
4		
5		
6		

Figure 5.78
Height of bounce versus time.

   b) Make a scatter plot of peak height versus time. Describe the shape of the graph. What type of damping function do you think you should use? If you can't decide on a best choice, then fit more than one model and decide which is best based on the residuals or some other factor.

   c) Write an equation that you think best describes the bungee data. Describe the process you used to find the equation and how you decided it was a good equation.

COWABUNGEE, DUDE!

In the experiments from this activity and the previous activity, the amplitude of an oscillating graph decreased. The Slinky experiences a smoother damping effect because, as the coil is constantly fighting against gravity, the friction created in the Slinky wastes some of its energy. Eventually, the Slinky and gravity come to a compromise position of the Slinky.

The amplitude of the bungee balloon, particularly in the beginning, is not as smoothly damped as the Slinky's. When you first jump off the bridge, the bungee cord is not fighting gravity at all. It is not until you have fallen to the length of the cord that the bungee cord is taut and must fight gravity. This is when the damping begins. On the way back up, the bungee cord will again be losing energy to friction, but eventually you will be in freefall again as the cord becomes slack once more.

CONSIDER:

1. When you look at the curves for the bungee balloon drop, what type of curve do you think the balloon is tracing near (just before and just after) its peak, when the bungee is slack?

2. What type of curve do you think the balloon is tracing at the bottom of its trajectory?

Now We're Cookin'

KEY CONCEPTS

Residual analysis

Modeling seasonal trends

The Image Bank

PREPARATION READING

Growing Concerns

For many companies, the number of employees changes with the seasons. A landscaping company may need a larger staff in the summer than in the winter; a ski resort needs a larger staff in the winter than in the summer. One thing all companies have in common is that, as the years go by, they hope to employ more people as their business grows. How can a manager of a growing business determine the number of people needed for each month in the coming year? This can be determined by developing a model that accounts for the growth trend in addition to the seasonal fluctuations.

PREPARATION READING

In a community, growth in business is frequently accompanied by a growth in population, an increased demand for electrical energy, and a need for new homes. In addition to planning for the short-term daily demand for electricity, electric companies must make long-range plans in order to meet the future needs of their consumers. In Lesson 1, you looked at data on electrical usage by bakeries. Based on only two years' data, the usage appears nearly periodic. In this lesson, you will study two more years of bakery data and discover that the pattern is more complex.

To conclude this lesson, you will return to the housing-start data (Individual Work 1, Lesson 1) for your final project. Will a single sinusoidal model be adequate to describe these data? Or will an upward turn in the economy require that you combine a model that describes the oscillation with a model that describes the trend? You'll need more housing-start data than was provided in Lesson 1 in order to see any patterns.

CONSIDER:

Suppose the electrical usage by bakeries oscillates over time. More electricity is used in the summer, in part to keep work areas reasonably cool, and less is used in the winter. Suppose each year in a community, a new bakery is established or an old bakery is expanded. Assuming that all previously-established bakeries remain in business, what effect will this expansion have on the graph of electrical usage by bakeries versus time?

DO(UGH) RE MI

Figure 5.79 presents the total electrical power consumption used by bakeries in 1988–1989. In this table, power consumption is recorded as a percentage of January 1987 usage. This enables the industry to compare its power consumption with the benchmark level set in January 1987.

	Jan	Feb	Mar	Apr	May	June	July	Aug	Sept	Oct	Nov	Dec
1988	94.6	92.6	93.7	92.6	96.2	106.3	109.2	114.7	114.1	105.1	101.0	99.5
1989	99.5	93.6	95.5	98.3	99.1	110.8	114.7	110.8	115.0	109.7	98.9	100.6

Figure 5.79.
Electrical usage data from bakeries 1988–1989.

1. Enter the data from Figure 5.79 into your calculator as two lists—month number and electric consumption.

   a) In Item 6 of Individual Work 5 in Lesson 2, you wrote a sinusoidal model for these same data. Review your work there and modify it as you think necessary. Then write what you believe to be a good sinusoidal model for bakery electricty consumption.

   b) Make a residual plot for your model. Based on the residual plot, does your model appear to be adequate to describe these data? Explain.

2. **Figure 5.80** shows a scatter plot of the bakery data over a period of four years, 1988-1991. The dots have been connected to help you see patterns more clearly.

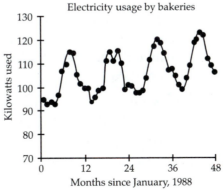

Figure 5.80.
Electrical usage by bakeries 1988–1991.

ACTIVITY

DO(UGH) RE MI

12

a) Draw a smooth curve that matches the pattern of the data in Figure 5.80. Then extend your graph to include what you think the pattern of data from the next three years would look like.

b) Describe in words any trends, other than oscillation, that you see in the data. (In other words, does the axis of oscillation remain constant?) Represent that trend on your graph in (a).

c) Can you explain why these data have a trend?

d) Suppose you were to use your equation from Item 1 to predict the pattern of the data pictured in the scatter plot of Figure 5.80. Describe how you think a residual plot based on these data and your equation from Item 1 would look.

Data from 1990–1991, graphed in Figure 5.80, are listed in **Figure 5.81**.

	Jan	Feb	Mar	Apr	May	June	July	Aug	Sept	Oct	Nov	Dec
1990	100.0	97.4	97.6	98.4	103.5	111.5	117.0	119.7	118.6	114.1	107.1	107.3
1991	104.7	100.5	99.0	103.6	109.1	120.4	119.9	122.6	123.4	111.7	108.7	105.9

Figure 5.81.
Electrical usage data from
bakeries 1990-1991.

e) Add these data to the data from Figure 5.79 that you have entered into your calculator. Then make a new residual plot based on your model from Item 1 and the four years of data from 1988–1991. Describe any patterns in your plot. Do they agree with your predictions from (d)? Is your model from Item 1 adequate to describe the pattern in bakery data?

f) What linear equation best describes the trend in the residuals? Fit a line to the data in your residual plot. What is your equation?

DO(UGH) RE MI

To model oscillating patterns with increasing trends, it is sometimes possible to create two separate models, one describing the oscillation and the other the trend, and then combine the two models by addition. You have a choice: find the trend, then the oscillation; or find the oscillation, then the trend.

3. Revise your model from Item 1 by adding your model from 2(f) (the trend).

   a) What is your revised model? Use your calculator to overlay the graph of your revised model on a scatter plot of the four years of bakery data. Does your revised model appear to describe the pattern of the bakery data reasonably well?

   b) Make a residual plot based on your revised model and the four years of bakery data. Does your model appear to describe adequately the pattern of these data? Explain.

4. Next, build a model by reversing the process. That is, first find a model that describes the trend, and then determine a model that describes the oscillation:

   a) Determine an equation for the axis of oscillation for the four years of bakery data. How did you determine your equation? Compute the residuals using only this equation as the model. Make a copy of the residuals for use in Activity 13.

   b) Now find a model for the oscillation (that is, the residuals from (a)). How did you determine this model?

   c) What is your final model? Make a residual plot for this model. Does your model appear to describe adequately these data? Explain.

ACTIVITY

12

DO(UGH) RE MI

5. Compare your models from Items 3 and 4.

a) How are the formulas alike and how are they different?

b) Use your graphing calculator to view graphs of both models in the same screen over the time interval from 0 to 48 months. Would predictions of power consumption based on these two models for the months 48–60 get farther apart or closer together ? What about for the months 60–72? Why might you expect this result based on the formulas for your two models?

c) Which is easier, modeling the oscillation first and then modeling the trend, or modeling the trend first and then modeling the oscillation? Which method do you think tends to give better results? Why?

CONSIDER:

1. Based on the residuals for the model in 4(b), how closely do you think you could predict the electrical expenses of bakeries for some month in the next year?

2. What about in the next five years?

3. What about in the next 50 years?

INDIVIDUAL WORK 10

The Remains of the Data

Miguel has been trying to fit equations to data that his mother made up for him. He thinks he has the general idea, but wonders if the fits to the data are good. Below are the equations Miguel came up with and the residuals for the equation when fit to the data.

For Items 1–3, look at the residuals and advise Miguel on how to improve the models. There are many kinds of functions you can use: linear, quadratic, exponential, logarithmic, cubic, and others. For each set of data, fit a model to the residuals and add that new equation to Miguel's equation to create a new model.

1. Miguel's model: $y = 7.3x^2 - 45.2$.

x	1	2	3	4	5	6	7	8	9	10
Residual	4.9	3.9	4.6	4.3	4.4	4.4	4.5	4.8	4.6	4.7

Figure 5.82.
Data set #1.

2. Miguel's model: $y = 5x^3 - 8$.

x	1	2	3	4	5
Residuals	0.5	1.2	1.6	2.4	2.9

Figure 5.83.
Data set #2.

3. Miguel's model: $y = 5x - 7$.

x	1	2	3	4	5	6	7	8	9	10
Residuals	19.9	19.6	19.1	18.4	17.6	16.5	15.2	13.7	12.1	10.2

Figure 5.84.
Data set #3.

4. Suppose a community keeps monthly water usage records. Data from these records for the last four years appear in **Figure 5.85**. (Year 1 contains the data from 4 years ago, year 2 from three years ago, etc.)

Year	Jan	Feb	Mar	Apr	May	June	July	Aug	Sept	Oct	Nov	Dec
1	168	154	153	156	182	187	207	214	213	219	209	197
2	176	170	165	171	193	208	224	233	233	23	220	214
3	198	188	183	192	196	226	226	243	255	253	237	229
4	218	197	187	211	213	235	254	268	278	270	247	240

Figure 5.85.
Water usage records.

a) Make a scatter plot of water usage versus time. Describe in words the pattern of these data.

b) Determine a model for these data by combining two models: one that describes the oscillating seasonal pattern of water usage and one that describes a general upward or downward trend. Explain how you arrived at your final model.

c) Make a residual plot based on your model from (b). Does the residual plot indicate that this model is adequate to describe the relationship between water usage and month? If not, revise your model until you get a good residual plot.

d) How accurate do you think your model will be for predicting the community's water usage for the coming year? Explain.

5. Clearly water usage in this community oscillates seasonally. Water usage is at a peak in the summer and at a low in the winter. Suppose that due to growth in nearby communities, this community's citizens have been asked to curtail their water usage by 5% a year over each of the next four years. Assume that the community is able to meet this goal. Sketch a graph that could represent water usage over time in this situation. Create a model you think can describe this situation.

ACTIVITY

CALENDAR EFFECTS

13

In Activity 12, you determined a model describing a combined linear trend and oscillating pattern in the bakery data. In this activity, you will explore these data a bit further, this time using a spreadsheet. In particular, you'll be looking for trends associated with individual years and with numbers of prime usage days in the month.

You will need your residuals (Electrical usage – linear trend) from Item 4(a), Activity 12.

Begin by setting up your spreadsheet and entering the data as follows:

Set up one column for month labels and four additional columns, one for each year (1988–1991).

Enter the month numbers (1–12) in the month column.

Enter the residuals from Item 4(a) into their corresponding year's column.

1. You should have five columns on your spreadsheet. One for month numbers, and the remaining four containing the departures of the data from the trend line, or the residuals, power consumption – linear trend.

   a) What do the numbers in columns 2–5 tell you about the electrical consumption of bakeries?

   b) Next, find an average residual for each month (1–12) by average the four values in each row. Enter them into a column named Monthly Prediction. A scatter plot of these values versus month number shows the average usage, month-by-month, in excess of the linear model from Activity 12. Thus, if the monthly average for, say, January, is –4.5, then consumption in Januarys tends to be about 4.5% below the axis of oscillation. Since this method looks at the data monthly across the years, these values can be used to predict usage even if the year-long pattern were not essentially sinusoidal.

ACTIVITY

CALENDAR EFFECTS

13

c) Add four more columns to your spreadsheet and name them Res88–Res91. In each of these columns, calculate new residuals for the actual data in columns 2–5 based on the monthly predictions you found in (b).

d) What do the numbers in Res88–Res91 tell you about the electrical consumption in a particular month of a given year? What does it mean if an entry is positive? Negative?

3. Find the six largest positive residuals. Record the month and year of each. Then find the six biggest (in absolute value) negative residuals and record the month and year of each. Interpret the results.

4. Which two days of the week do you think are busiest for bakeries? How many times do these days of the week occur in each of the month/year's corresponding to the most-negative residuals? What, if anything, does that tell you? **Figures 5.86–5.89** show the number of times each day of the week occurs during that month.

Month	Sun	Mon	Tue	Wed	Thur	Fri	Sat
1	5	4	4	4	4	5	5
2	4	5	4	4	4	4	4
3	4	4	5	5	5	4	4
4	4	4	4	4	4	5	5
5	5	5	5	4	4	4	4
6	4	4	4	5	5	4	4
7	5	4	4	4	4	5	5
8	4	5	5	5	4	4	4
9	4	4	4	4	5	5	5
10	5	5	4	4	4	4	5
11	4	4	5	5	4	4	4
12	4	4	4	4	5	5	5

Figure 5.86.
Number of days in months in 1988.

ACTIVITY

CALENDAR EFFECTS

13

Month	Sun	Mon	Tue	Wed	Thur	Fri	Sat
1	5	5	5	4	4	4	4
2	4	4	4	4	4	4	4
3	4	4	4	5	5	5	4
4	5	4	4	4	4	4	5
5	4	5	5	5	4	4	4
6	4	4	4	4	5	5	4
7	5	5	4	4	4	4	5
8	4	4	5	5	5	4	4
9	4	4	4	4	4	5	5
10	5	5	5	4	4	4	4
11	4	4	4	5	5	4	4
12	5	4	4	4	4	5	5

Figure 5.87.
Number of days in
months in 1989.

Month	Sun	Mon	Tue	Wed	Thur	Fri	Sat
1	4	5	5	5	4	4	4
2	4	4	4	4	4	4	4
3	4	4	4	4	5	5	5
4	5	5	4	4	4	4	4
5	4	4	5	5	5	4	4
6	4	4	4	4	4	5	5
7	5	5	5	4	4	4	4
8	4	4	4	5	5	5	4
9	5	4	4	4	4	4	5
10	4	5	5	5	4	4	4
11	4	4	4	4	5	5	4
12	5	5	4	4	4	4	5

Figure 5.88.
Number of days in
months in 1990.

ACTIVITY

13

CALENDAR EFFECTS

Month	Sun	Mon	Tue	Wed	Thur	Fri	Sat
1	4	4	5	5	5	4	4
2	4	4	4	4	4	4	4
3	5	4	4	4	4	5	5
4	4	5	5	4	4	4	4
5	4	4	4	5	5	5	4
6	5	4	4	4	4	4	5
7	4	5	5	5	4	4	4
8	4	4	4	4	5	5	5
9	5	5	4	4	4	4	4
10	4	4	5	5	5	4	4
11	4	4	4	4	4	5	5
12	5	5	5	4	4	4	4

Figure 5.89.
Number of days in
months in 1991.

OSCILLATION

Wrapping Up Unit Five

1. The average monthly temperatures in degrees Fahrenheit for Boston, Massachusetts from 1/95–12/97 are presented in **Figure 5.90**.

Year	Jan	Feb	Mar	Apr	May	June	July	Aug	Sept	Oct	Nov	Dec
1995	34.6	28.4	38.8	46.0	57.2	68.6	75.9	72.8	63.1	58.3	41.9	31.7
1996	30.1	30.9	36.5	47.9	57.4	68.1	71.8	70.9	64.1	53.2	40.3	39.2
1997	29.2	36.0	36.7	46.3	56.1	68.2	73.6	71.1	64.2	52.8	41.6	35.2

Figure 5.90.
Average monthly temperatures for Boston, Massachusetts.

a) Make a scatter plot of these data. How did you define the explanatory variable?

b) Your plot in (a) should appear (approximately) periodic. What is the period? Approximately what is the amplitude?

c) By hand, determine a model of the form $y = A\sin(B(t − C)) + D$ that you think best describes these data. Explain how you determined your model.

d) Overlay a graph of your model on a scatter plot of your data. Does your model appear to do a good job in describing these data?

e) If your calculator has regression capability of fitting sinusoidal models, use it to fit a model to these data. Compare your model from (c) to the one fit by sinusoidal regression. How are the equations for these formulas alike and how are they different? Are their graphs similar?

UNIT SUMMARY

2. Consider the function $y = 3\sin(2x − (\pi/3)) + 6$.

a) What are the period and amplitude of this function? What is its phase shift? Its axis of oscillation?

b) Without using a calculator, sketch a graph of this function. Use a scale on the *x*-axis that involves multiples of π. After you have completed your sketch, use your calculator to check it.

c) Write a function involving the cosine that produces the same graph as in (b).

3. What would you have to do to the graph of $y = \cos(x)$ to transform it into a graph that coincides with the graph of $y = 0.5 \cos(0.5\ x + \pi) - 2$?

4. Suppose that you are given the sinusoidal model $y = 4 \sin(3\pi(x - 1)) + 2$.

a) Use your calculator to graph this function. Make a sketch of the graph. Be sure to specify the settings of your viewing window.

b) Without using your calculator, describe the effect on the graph in (a) of modifying the model by replacing $A = 4$ with $A(x) = 4\ (3/4)^x$. Use your calculator to check your description, and make a sketch of the graph that results.

c) Without using your calculator, describe the effect on the graph in (a) of modifying the model by replacing $B = 3\pi$ with $B(x) = 0.5x$. Use your calculator to check your description and make a sketch of the graph that results.

d) Without using your calculator, describe the effect on the graph in (a) of modifying the model by replacing $D = 2$ with $D(x) = 2x$. Use your calculator to check your description and make a sketch of the graph that results.

5. **Figure 5.91** presents a mystery graph. Determine an equation that describes this graph. Explain how you arrived at your answer.

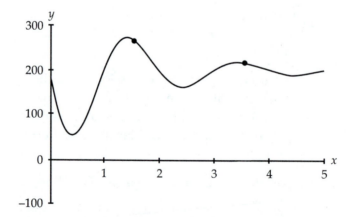

Figure 5.91.
Mystery graph.

6. Sales of snow blowers are seasonal. Fewer people buy snow blowers in the spring than in the fall. Suppose that snow blower dealers in one community began recording sales in November of 1995. The data are presented in **Figure 5.92**.

Nov	Dec	Jan	Feb	Mar	Apr	May	June	July	Aug	Sep	Oct
936	739	490	248	79	7	80	256	511	760	940	1008

Nov	Dec	Jan	Feb	Mar	Apr	May	June	July	Aug	Sep	Oct
960	757	513	275	90	38	88	285	533	772	957	1045

Nov	Dec	Jan	Feb	Mar	Apr	May	June	July	Aug	Sep	Oct
962	790	536	295	100	45	106	297	528	792	995	1051

Figure 5.92.
Data on sales of snow blowers.

a) Make a scatter plot of these data. Do they appear to be periodic?

b) Fit a model to the data in Figure 5.92. Explain the steps you used to determine your model. Based on a residual plot, explain why your model is adequate to describe the pattern of the snow blower data.

c) A business is thinking of adding, in the year 2000, snow blowers to the merchandise it already sells. However, it first wants to project the number of snow-blower sales in the peak selling season August–December. Use your model to estimate the number of snow blowers that will be sold from August to December in the year 2000.

Mathematical Summary

Τhis unit focuses on functions whose graphs oscillate. One important family of oscillating functions are periodic functions. Periodic functions have graphic patterns that repeat over fixed intervals. The period of a periodic function is the shortest horizontal length of the basic repeating shape of its graph. The amplitude is half the vertical height (top to bottom) of the basic repeating shape. Both the sine and cosine are examples of periodic functions.

The sine function is defined as the vertical displacement versus the radian measure of an arc made by a dot rotating around a unit circle. Any function of the form $y = A\sin(B(t - C)) + D$ belongs to the family of sinusoidal functions. The control numbers A, B, C, and D control the graph's amplitude, period, phase shift, and axis of oscillation, respectively.

The cosine function is defined as the horizontal displacement versus the radian measure of an arc made by a dot rotating around a unit circle. It also gives the rate of change of the sine function. The graph of the cosine function can be obtained by shifting the graph of the sine function $\pi/2$ units to the left. Hence, $\cos(t) = \sin(t + \pi/2)$. Similarly, shifting the graph of the cosine function $\pi/2$ units to the right, it coincides with the graph of the sine function. So, $\sin(t) = \cos(t - \pi/2)$. The two preceding equations are true for all t-values; they are identities.

Although sine and cosine are defined in terms of the radian measures of arcs of the unit circle, they may also be computed for angles measured in degrees, using the conversion $\dfrac{\theta}{2\pi} = \dfrac{\alpha}{360°}$.

When fitting a sinusoidal model to data by hand, you need to use the information contained in the data to estimate the values of the control numbers A, B, C, and D. Here is one method of estimating those values. Sometimes, however, a variant of this method will provide better results so, don't get locked into a single method.

- To estimate A: Average several of the maximum values in the data to get an estimate of the function's maximum value. Then do the same for the minimums. Let A be half the difference between the estimated maximum and minimum values.

- To estimate D: Let D be the average of the estimated maximum and minimum values.

- To estimate B: First, estimate the period. Select two data points associated with peaks, or maximums, but separated by several cycles of oscillation. Divide the time difference of these two data points by the number of cycles separating these maximums. This gives you an estimate of the period. Let $B = 2\pi/$(estimated period).

- To estimate C: The sine function $y = A\sin(Bt) + D$ should have its first maximum at $t = $ (period)$/4$. Locate the t-value associated with the first maximum in the data. Call it $t0$. To approximate the phase shift, set $C = t0 - $ (period)$/4$.

Many calculators have sinusoidal regression as one of their regression capabilities. If you have such a calculator, you can use sinusoidal regression to fit sinusoidal models to data. However, you may need to adjust the model fit by your calculator if the period or amplitude of the data are predetermined by the contextual considerations.

Not all oscillating patterns are periodic. Two important variations of purely periodic oscillations are those that include an underlying trend and those that represent damped oscillations. In the case of damped oscillation, the amplitude $A(t)$ is a decreasing function. Two commonly-used damping factors are linear and exponential functions. To create a model describing damped oscillation, replace A in $y = A\sin(B(t - C)) + D$ with the amplitude function, $A(t)$.

One way to fit these types of phenomena is to model the peaks and valleys separately with their own functions Max(t) and Min(t) first. Averaging these functions gives the axis of oscillation, or trend line. Then (Max(t) − Min(t))$/2$ approximates the amplitude function. Typically, one of these (trend or amplitude) will be constant.

You can create models for other non-periodic oscillating patterns by replacing the constants B, C, and D in the basic sinusoidal equation with functions $B(t)$, $C(t)$, and $D(t)$. When D is replaced by a function $D(t)$, the resulting graph will oscillate about the trend curve $y = D(t)$. One method of fitting a model to data that oscillate about a trend line is to first fit a linear equation to the data and determine the residuals. Then fit a sinusoidal model to the data in the residual plot. Create your model by adding the equation describing the linear trend and the equation describing the oscillation.

Glossary

AMPLITUDE (of a periodic function):
Half of the vertical height of the basic repeating shape; that is, half of the vertical distance between maximum and minimum values of the periodic graph.

AMPLITUDE (of an oscillation):
The difference between a model describing the oscillation's maximum values versus time and a model describing the axis of oscillation. Alternatively, half of the difference between models describing the oscillation's maximum and minimum values versus time.

AXIS OF OSCILLATION
(of a periodic function):
The center of oscillations, determined as the horizontal line midway between the maximum and minimum values of the periodic graph.

AXIS OF OSCILLATION
(of an oscillation):
The center of oscillations, determined as the function midway between the functions describing the maximum and minimum values of the oscillation versus time.

CENTRAL ANGLE:
An angle whose vertex is the center of a circle. (See **Figure 5.93.**)

COSINE FUNCTION:
The horizontal displacement versus the radian measure of an arc made by a dot rotating a unit circle counterclockwise from (1, 0). It also gives the rate of change of the sine function. (See Figure 5.93.)

DAMPED OSCILLATION:
An oscillation in which the amplitude decreases with time.

DAMPING FACTOR:
The amplitude function in a damped oscillation.

ENVELOPE:
The functions describing the maximum and minimum values of an oscillation, bounding the oscillation itself.

FREQUENCY:
The number of oscillations per second. The value of the frequency for a periodic function is 1/period.

IDENTITY:
An equation that is true for all values of the variable.

PERIOD (of a periodic function):
The shortest horizontal length of a basic repeating shape.

PERIODIC FUNCTION:
Function that repeats itself on intervals of a fixed length (equal to the period).

PHASE SHIFT:
A horizontal shift of a periodic function from a standard reference function. In particular, the phase shift for functions of the form $y = A\sin(B(x - C)) + D$ or $y = A\cos(B(x - C)) + D$ is C. This is the horizontal shift required to translate the graphs of $y = A\sin(Bx) + D$ and $y = A\cos(Bx) + D$ so they coincide with the graphs of $y = A\sin(B(x - C)) + D$ and $y = A\cos(B(x - C)) + D$, respectively.

RADIAN:
The directed length of an arc that begins at (1, 0) on the unit circle. If the arc turns in the counterclockwise direction, the radian measure is positive; if it turns in the clockwise direction, the radian measure is negative. You can extend this definition to any circle by defining its center as the origin and its radius as one unit.

REFERENCE ANGLE:
The acute angle in a reference right triangle that has its adjacent side on the horizontal axis. (See Figure 5.93.)

REFERENCE RIGHT TRIANGLE:
The triangle made by dropping a perpendicular to the *x*-axis from a point on the terminal side of a central angle whose initial side lies on the positive *x*-axis. (See Figure 5.93.)

SINE FUNCTION:
The vertical displacement, from the horizontal axis, of a point on the unit circle. The input for the sine is the radian measure from (1, 0) in a counterclockwise direction to the specified point. (See Figure 5.93.)

SINUSOIDAL FUNCTION:
Any function that can be expressed in the form $y = A\sin(B(x - C)) + D$, where neither A nor B is zero.

UNIT CIRCLE:
Circle with radius one unit and centered at the origin.

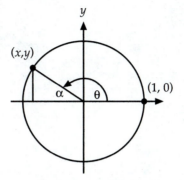

Figure 5.93.
An example of a reference right triangle corresponding to central angle θ. The reference angle is α.
$x = \cos(\theta)$
$y = \sin(\theta)$

UNIT

6

Feedback

In this unit, you will reexamine some simple models of growth and extend your understanding to more complex situations. Recursive and closed-form equations and graphs will be the backbone upon which you will build new ways of looking at situations that evolve over time. While earlier models have generally led to convenient closed-form representations, more complex systems typically are much harder to describe with such equations. Recursive methods now become even more effective. Most importantly, however, you will begin to notice and describe how things around you interact, and how they can affect each other to produce entirely new kinds of behavior than could be obtained by either one separately.

GROWTH: IT'S INTERACTIVE!

Wildlife managers are charged with the responsibility of understanding the natural world and with helping environmental systems survive. One facet of that work is observing and recording population data for various populations within a system. But no species lives in isolation; other species, both plant and animal, share the same space. How do the various populations affect each other? If a wildlife manager implements a plan to alter the growth or decline of one species, what will be the broader effect?

Many new communities grow rapidly in their early years. Families move into the area and tell their friends about how great things are. More and more people find it a good place to live and move in. But if community planners are not careful, this good word can spell disaster! Traffic increases, schools become crowded, trash does not get picked up as often, gas pressure drops in the coldest months of winter, and on and on. Now what happens to the community? How should planning take place in the early years?

A friend comes to school with a cold because class is too important to miss. How many classmates will have the cold over the next few days and weeks? Will everyone eventually get sick? What measures can be taken to lessen the impact of colds going around?

Each of these situations is mathematically similar, involving more than one quantity of interest. There are interacting phenomena involved. In this unit, you will develop successively more complex models of such situations so that you may recognize the many interacting components in your own daily life and begin to understand them quantitatively.

LESSON ONE
What Lies Ahead

KEY CONCEPTS

Causal-loop diagrams

Data analysis

Linear models

Exponential models

Piecewise-defined functions

Web diagrams

The Image Bank

PREPARATION READING

Modeling

*I*n your earlier studies of mathematics, you encountered a number of different types of functions. These functions described different types of behavior of phenomena in the world. Each function is based on some underlying assumptions. For example, if you assume that the number of moose born into a population of moose in a particular region in a particular year is proportional to the number of moose already there at the start of that year, then your assumption forces you into using an exponential model. On the other hand, assuming the moose population grows only by some constant number of moose migrating into the region leads to a linear model. Other models have corresponding, but different, underlying assumptions.

1. Do you think that either of the models mentioned in the preparation reading is a valid description of a moose population for long-term predictions? Explain.

The modeling process can lead to insight in either of two directions—good data can lead to good equations that help in understanding the underlying process, or a good understanding of the contextual processes can lead to good predictive equations. In either direction, of course, the strength of a model is only as good as the agreement between the assumptions behind the model and what's really going on in the actual situation. In each situation you have studied thus far, only one quantity was of any real interest, so pretty much everything else in the world was ignored. Are such models valid? Are there situations in which such approaches don't work well?

2. List several situations in which more than one quantity seems important. Include especially any situations you have modeled as though that were not the case. Name the quantities that you think are important in each situation you describe.

ACTIVITY

CATCHING A CLD

1

Sometimes it is helpful in modeling a situation to think qualitatively first, without worrying too much about specific numbers or arithmetic. That is, look at general relationships first, then move on to more specific details later. Remember, start simply. An early step in modeling anything is to identify what you think are the main features of the situation and to sort out the relationships among those features.

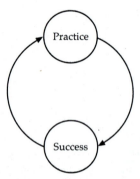

Figure 6.1.
A CLD for practice and success.

One tool that can help clarify your thinking is a causal-loop diagram. As the name implies, a **causal-loop diagram (CLD)** shows the identified main quantities in a situation and indicates the direction of changes that each quantity causes in others if all other factors were held constant. For example, **Figure 6.1** is a possible CLD for the relation between practice and success in a sport.

Note that the diagram includes named circles to indicate the main quantities in the system. The arrows denote causal relationships, not the flow of information, or stuff. Thus, this diagram claims that increased practice causes increased success and that increased success causes increased practice. It also implies that decreased practice will lead to decreased success and that decreases in success lead to decreases in practice. Again, remember, these claims are for all other factors being held constant.

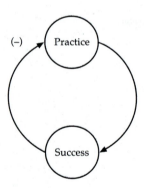

Figure 6.2.
Another CLD for practice and success

Many athletes may disagree with the second claim. They might say that with more success there is less need to practice and that if success falls off, then that should lead to more practice. That is, the direction for success causes practice is somehow opposite to the direction for practice causes success. To show that in the diagram, add a minus sign, as shown in **Figure 6.2.** Note that the minus sign is placed near the arrow end of the relationship in which increase in one thing (success) causes decrease in the other (practice).

ACTIVITY

CATCHING A CLD

1

Figure 6.3 shows a slightly more complex CLD. It represents one way of thinking about the speed of a skydiver.

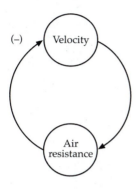

Figure 6.3.
A CLD for skydiving.

Again, the small negative sign (–) near the arrow connecting air resistance to velocity indicates that increasing air resistance causes a *decrease* in the velocity. There is no negative sign on the other arrow, so that indicates that increasing velocity causes an *increase* in the air resistance. The decrease in velocity due to air resistance does not mean that the skydiver slows down. Rather, it means that the velocity is less than what it would be if there were no air resistance. Remember, there is one other main factor in the skydiver situation that is not shown in the CLD—the force of gravity! So, if air resistance could be made large enough, then it could slow the skydiver, but speed alone is not capable of causing that large an increase in resistance. However, that is what a parachute does; it greatly increases the air resistance!

Each of the causal-loop diagrams discussed so far have involved two interacting quantities. For most real-world systems, you expect more than one main quantity. However, especially in creating simplified models, you may want to think about systems involving only one quantity. **Figure 6.4** is a possible CLD for a moose population that changes only through births.

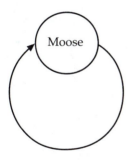

Figure 6.4.
A CLD of moose population growth.

This diagram indicates that the more moose there are at one time, the more there will be later. This is a simple example of **feedback**, the influence of some quantity *on itself*. Increasing the moose population leads to *more* increase in the moose population! Of course, this is not a very exciting diagram. After all, the assumption of change by births only means the only quantity that determines how many moose there are next year is the number of moose this year. However, you might make arguments that such an assumption is not valid, especially if the model is to be used for many years.

1. Name one or more quantities you might want to include in Figure 6.4 if it were to apply for a long period.

ACTIVITY

1

CATCHING A CLD

2. Several situations are described below. For each situation, create a plausible CLD. Use as few quantities in each diagram as you can and still have it make sense. (For some items, suggested quantities are given.) Include negative signs to indicate that increases in one quantity cause decreases in another. Write a sentence or two explaining why you think your diagram makes sense.

a) Cold season begins. Quantities: cumulative (total) number of people who catch a cold this season, and the number of people who are left who can get sick.

b) A few stray moose wander into a park in which there were none. Quantities: moose population in the park, and moose population in neighboring regions.

c) A candle burns in a candleholder. Quantity: height of candle.

d) A relative gives you a sum of money to put into a long-term savings certificate.

e) You step into the shower and realize the water is too hot. Quantities: degrees above comfortable, and amount of cold water turned on.

f) A new CD is released by a popular recording group. Quantities: cumulative (total) sales for the CD and potential purchasers.

g) A new joke is spread around the school.

h) A large number of deer inhabit some of the coastal islands of Georgia. Several years ago, a number of bobcats were brought to one such island to help to control the deer population.

INDIVIDUAL WORK 1

Behind the Scenes

1. The situations described in Activity 1 are listed again below, together with exactly one quantity from that situation. Sketch a rough graph of what you think the long-term time-series graph of the named quantity would look like, and explain your reasoning. List as carefully as possible all assumptions you made in reaching your conclusions. Use your CLDs to guide your thinking.

   a) A new CD is released by a popular recording group. Quantity: cumulative (total) sales for the CD.

   b) A few stray moose wander into a park in which there were none. Quantity: moose population in the park.

   c) A candle burns in a candleholder. Quantity: height of candle.

   d) A relative gives you a sum of money to put into a long-term savings certificate. Quantity: value of certificate.

   e) A skydiver jumps from an airplane. Quantity: speed of descent.

   f) You step into the shower and realize that the water is too hot. Quantity: water temperature.

   g) Cold season begins. Quantity: cumulative (total) number of people who have had a cold this season.

   h) Your best friend hears a great joke. Quantity: number of people in school who have heard the joke.

   i) A large number of deer inhabit some of the coastal islands of Georgia. Several years ago a number of bobcats were brought to one such island to help control the deer population. Quantity: number of deer on island.

   j) Same facts as (i). Quantity: number of bobcats on island.

2. Examine the graphs you drew in Item 1. Identify any that seem to have the same basic shape. Do the situations that have similarly shaped graphs have any common contextual features? Explain.

3. Look at the following list of simple assumptions about the behavior of some quantity. For each assumption, identify the kind of growth (linear, quadratic, exponential, mixed) it yields if you have studied it before. Sketch a typical time-series graph of that kind of growth, and indicate whether it seems appropriate for any of the situations in Item 1.

   a) There is no change. Things stay exactly as they are.

   b) The amount of change does not depend on any other quantity; it is constant for all similar time periods.

   c) The amount of change is proportional to how much stuff there is at the moment; more stuff means more change.

   d) The amount of change changes, but not proportionally to the amount of stuff present. Instead, the change depends only on how much time has passed; the change in the amount of change is constant for equal time periods.

   e) The amount of change is proportional both to how much is present and also to how much of something else is present, too.

   f) The amount of change is the result of two separate processes, one of which changes by a constant amount each time period, and another which changes proportionally to how much is present.

4. Each of the assumptions in Item 3 is related to a particular kind of recursive representation. Although you may not have studied situations representing all of these assumptions, write what you think is a reasonable recursive equation for each assumption. Use Q to represent the quantity being modeled and use n to represent the index (term number). Use letters or specific numbers that you make up for any additional quantities you need in your model. Of course, be sure to state what each such letter or number represents!

5. In each situation described below, write an exact recursive equation for the quantity (Q) indicated. Sketch graphs of $Q(n)$ versus n, $Q(n + 1) - Q(n)$ versus n, and $Q(n + 1) - Q(n)$ versus $Q(n)$.

   a) A body builder sets as a goal doing two more repetitions of a particular low-weight exercise each day than the day before. Today ($n = 0$) she did 60 reps. Q = number of reps.

b) After drinking 4 beers in a two-hour period, a typical person can have a peak blood alcohol level around 0.09% about an hour after the last drink. This is well above the level for being declared legally intoxicated in many states. Alcohol is eliminated (linearly) from the body at a rate of approximately 0.015% per hour. Q = blood alcohol level; $n = 0$ when blood alcohol level is at peak.

c) A mutual fund account pays dividends of 4% per quarter. The initial deposit is $5000 ($n = 0$), and no further deposits or withdrawals are made. Q = account balance by quarter.

d) A worker retires with $150,000 in his pension account. The account earns interest at the rate of 0.5% per month and the worker withdraws exactly $1000 at the start of each month for that month's living expenses. Q = balance of pension account; $n = 0$ on day of retirement.

e) A worker retires with $250,000 in her pension account. The account earns interest at the rate of 0.5% per month and she withdraws exactly $1000 at the start of each month for that month's living expenses. Q = balance of pension account; $n = 0$ on day of retirement.

f) The counters on many old cassette players record the number of turns of the take-up reel. That is equivalent to counting the number of layers of tape that have been wound up at any given time. For one particular tape and player, the radius of the reel is about 0.44 inches and the thickness of the tape is 0.0007 inches. Q = total length of tape on the reel after n counts; $n = 0$ when reel is empty.

6. a) Use a recursive equation to set up a spreadsheet model of linear growth. Use the first column for any control numbers you need (and their labels), the second column for n, and the third for Q. Save your spreadsheet for later use. (If you do not have access to a spreadsheet, lay out the appropriate formulas on paper as they would appear on a spreadsheet.)

b) Modify the spreadsheet from (a) so it will model exponential growth. Save it under a different name so it may be used with exponential models you create later. What changes would you need to make in your assumptions about a real-life situation in order that you might need to make these kinds of spreadsheet modifications?

c) Create a spreadsheet to model quadratic behavior. Save it for later use.

ACTIVITY

2

DECISIONS, DECISIONS . . .

Quarter	Cumulative sales
3	265
4	416
5	556
6	699
7	837
8	1031
9	1231
10	1681
11	2056
12	2536
13	3086
14	3706
15	4309
16	4991
17	5548
18	6196
19	6847
20	7270
21	7500
22	7880
23	8068
24	8334
25	8434
26	8519

Figure 6.5.
Cumulative sales for one type of large computer.

In Individual Work 1, you considered a number of situations. It is likely you predicted similar kinds of behavior for several of those situations, even though they had essentially nothing in common. For example, you might have decided that the CD sales and the moose population growth might be similar in that neither can grow forever. The music group would eventually run out of customers; the moose might run out of food. Neither of these situations is like anything you have studied in math before. What kind of model can describe that behavior? This activity marks the beginning of the search for the answer to this question.

Although they're not CD sales, the data in **Figure 6.5** represent the quarterly cumulative sales of a new large computer over a period of several years.

ACTIVITY

2

DECISIONS, DECISIONS . . .

1. Compare the time-series graph of these data with your predicted growth of CD sales in Item 1 of Individual Work 1.

2. Examine these computer sales data to develop a mathematical description of the growth of the sales. If no single model seems appropriate, examine possible piecewise descriptions. Be sure to consider both recursive and closed-form methods in your analysis. Look back at Individual Work 1 for ideas on how to check different kinds of models.

3. How confident would you be in using your model for predicting sales? How does your answer depend on when it is? (That is, if you had worked for the company during these years, how well could you have predicted later data from the early portion of your model? What about predictions for well beyond the end of this table?)

4. Does your model help explain why things went as they did, or does it just describe what happened?

M A T H   A T   W O R K

Feedback loops and innovative behavioral software are at the core of the operations of the robots of IS Robotics. Shown here are several of the company's innovative creations along with Colin Angle (president) and Helen Greiner (vice president). The company was founded in 1990 by individuals from the Massachusetts Institute of Technology and NASA's Jet Propulsion Laboratory with the goal of developing task specific, practical, intelligent, robotic systems. That goal they surely have achieved. Meet a few members of the active robotic group shown: *Fetch 2* (Fieldable Explosive Target Clearer and Hunter), part of a team of semi-autonomous robots designed to clear unexploded munitions under supervisory control; *Hum-De* (Highly Mobile Munition Marking and Mapping Device), a rugged terrain vehicle for mine detection; and *Urban Robot*, a highly maneuverable robot that can climb stairs.

INDIVIDUAL WORK 2

The Cast of Characters

F irst differences are particularly useful in identifying patterns in equally-spaced data. For example, if you suspect quadratic behavior, then graph $Q(n + 1) - Q(n)$ versus n; that graph should be linear. For exponential and mixed growth, the graph of $Q(n + 1) - Q(n)$ versus $Q(n)$ is linear. If the line goes through $(0, 0)$, then the data are exponential, otherwise it's mixed.

Use this information about types of growth, and the data in Figure 6.5 of Activity 2 to respond to Items 1–3 below. Notice, too, that the times considered in these items overlap. Your work in Activity 2 may already contain answers to one or more of these items.

1. a) Plot the time-series graph for cumulative computer sales for quarters 12 through 18. If they appear linear, find an appropriate equation. If they appear non-linear, check for mixed or quadratic growth using the appropriate graph described above.

   b) Write an appropriate recursive equation for cumulative computer sales during that interval, based on your linear graphs.

   c) Put yourself in the position of an employee at the computer firm, and roll the clock back to the 19th quarter. Your boss hands you the data for quarters 12–18 and asks you to predict cumulative sales for the end of the third year. Discuss how you would make your prediction and how accurate you likely would be. (Remember, the later data have not occurred yet.)

2. a) Plot the time-series graph for cumulative computer sales for quarters 6 through 15. It should not appear linear. Verify that a quadratic model is reasonably appropriate by graphing the first differences versus n.

   b) Write an appropriate recursive equation for computer sales during this interval, based on your graph in (a). Remember, $Q(n + 1) - Q(n)$ represents the growth in Q, whether $Q(n)$ represents computer sales or something else. Likewise, $Q(n + 1) = Q(n) + \text{growth}$, no matter what the model.

   c) Again, put yourself in the place of an employee, this time during quarter 16. Discuss how you would make your long-range prediction, and its likely accuracy.

3. a) Plot the time-series graph for cumulative computer sales for quarters 3 through 13. Again, it should not appear linear. Verify that an exponential model is reasonably appropriate by graphing the first differences versus $Q(n)$.

   b) Write an appropriate recursive equation for computer sales during this interval.

   c) Put yourself in the position of an employee during quarter 14. Again, discuss your boss's request for a prediction.

4. Suppose human growth were modeled using a linear or exponential function. A typical height of a newborn baby is 20 inches. In one year, the newborn grows to a height of 26 inches.

   a) If the growth follows a linear pattern, write a recursive model of the person's height.

   b) Use the model to predict the height of the person at age 16. At age 50. Are your predictions realistic?

   c) If the growth follows an exponential pattern, write a recursive model of the person's height.

   d) Predict the height of the person at age 16. At age 50. Are your predictions realistic?

   e) Use your recursive models from (a) and (c) to draw web diagrams for both types of growth. Carry each diagram far enough to show how the nature of the growth can be seen.

5. A closed-form rough approximation based on Olympic records for the discus throw is $d = 1.75t + 175$, where d is distance in feet and t represents years since 1948 (so, $t = 0$ means 1948).

   a) Predict what the winning distance should have been in the 1996 Summer Olympics.

   b) Write a corresponding recursive form, using n as years since 1948.

   c) Interpret your recursive equation into ordinary words.

Year	Total sales ($ in billions)
1977	0.1
1978	0.3
1979	0.65
1980	1.1
1981	2.1
1982	3.0
1983	3.8
1984	4.8
1985	6.7

Figure 6.6.
Sales of Personal Computers.

6. The data in **Figure 6.6** appeared in the form of a graph in an article in *Scientific American*, December 1982, "Personal Computers" by Hoo-min D. Toong and Amar Gupta. The article claimed that the "sales of personal computers would continue its exponential growth." Apply your mathematical skills to determine whether the claim that this represents exponential growth is true or not.

LESSON TWO
Another Model

KEY CONCEPTS

The modeling cycle

Data analysis

Sensitivity

Relative rate of change

Joint proportionality

Logistic growth

The Image Bank

PREPARATION READING
It Can't Do That Forever!

*I*n Lesson 1, you encountered data that were not well described by any of the standard algebraic models you have studied. A number of possible explanations for that fact are possible. One possibility is that no single model *should* describe the data; maybe the data include several changes in the market conditions. However, if your responses in Individual Work 1 included any graphs that had more or less the same form as the graph of the data in Figure 6.5, then it is also possible that the computer sales data really can be described by a single model, just not one of the ones you already know about! This lesson focuses on that possibility.

In Items 1 and 4 of Individual Work 1, you proposed possible recursive descriptions for new-product sales for a CD. Of course, that was without benefit of any data or other information about the actual shape of the corresponding time-series graph. But in Activity 2, you saw the data. How can you pull together your understanding of the context (what *should* happen), as represented by your thinking in Individual Work 1, and your understanding of the data (what *did* happen)?

As is the case in any modeling situation, you should start first with clear statements of the simplest assumptions that seem reasonable from your understanding of the situation. Then examine how the implications of those assumptions differ from reality. The first step is to think about the context to determine which of the possible models is the best one from which to start making adjustments.

CONSIDER:

1. State corresponding contextual assumptions that would allow each of the familiar types of growth (linear, exponential, etc.) to apply to the new-product sales situation.

2. Which assumptions seem (from a contextual point of view) to be closest to reasonable?

3. What is the biggest weakness of the model you identified in Item 2?

ACTIVITY

IMPROVING A FIRST MODEL

3

This activity asks you to revisit the data on computer sales from Lesson 1 and do more mathematical computation to investigate the nature of its growth. Look again at the time-series graph you made in Activity 2 of the data in Figure 6.5. One approach to describing these data is to build a piecewise model, analyzing each of several parts separately. However, if you tried this as an employee of the company while the sales were current, you would never know when to switch pieces. A single model would certainly be better.

Focus your attention on the early portion of the graph. You may have found that a mixed-growth model does a pretty good job of describing the first 3 or 4 years. Perhaps a modification of that model will do the job.

You can develop a model of the growth in two fundamentally different ways. One approach is to use your understanding of the context to *modify the assumptions* describing the growth term. You would then want to find the simplest new formula consistent with your new assumptions, build a model based on the new formula, and compare it to the original data to test for consistency.

Another way to develop a mathematical representation of your new ideas is to look back at the data from Activity 2, focusing on the particular feature that you think needs attention. In this case, that is the growth term. Rather than first assuming something about its behavior, you could *investigate its actual behavior* in the real situation. Then you would need to describe the results of that investigation mathematically and determine their implications on the assumptions. That is the approach requested in this activity.

As was noted in Individual Work 2, checking each of the familiar types of growth—linear, exponential, quadratic, and mixed—involves looking closely at first differences, $Q(n + 1) - Q(n)$. In terms of the computer sales, this is the growth in sales. Both

ACTIVITY

IMPROVING A FIRST MODEL

3

mixed and exponential growth have linear growth-versus-current amount graphs. Since the computer data can't be one of those, its growth-versus-current amount graph should be curved. So, analyze the data and look for a simple model for that curve.

1. From your understanding of sales of products, do you think the growth in cumulative sales of new products should depend most directly on time or on the number of previous customers? Explain.

2. Use one of your spreadsheet models or a calculator to compute a quarterly table of growth amounts for the computer sales data in Figure 6.5. Let $Q(n)$ represent the current cumulative sales total. Then $Q(n + 1) - Q(n)$ is the amount of growth in the cumulative sales during the next period. See the example in **Figure 6.7**.

Quarter	Cumulative sales $Q(n)$	Growth $Q(n + 1) - Q(n)$
3	265	151
4	416	
5		

Figure 6.7.
Sample spreadsheet set-up for computer sales analysis.

3. a) Based on your answer to Item 1, explain why $Q(n)$ is a better choice than n for explanatory variable when studying the growth of the computer sales.

   b) Graph $Q(n + 1) - Q(n)$ versus $Q(n)$; that is, growth versus current cumulative sales. Save your graph for use in Individual Work 3, too.

   c) Carry out an appropriate analysis of the growth data in (b) to determine a descriptive equation for the amount of growth, $Q(n + 1) - Q(n)$.

ACTIVITY

IMPROVING A FIRST MODEL

3

4. Use your results from Item 3 to write a reasonable recursive equation for cumulative computer sales.

5. Test your new model by graphing its time series against that of the original data. That is, use your equation to generate predicted cumulative sales values to compare to the original data. One of your earlier spreadsheets may be helpful here. (Since your model came from the data, it should be a pretty good fit!)

6. Since the graph you examined in Item 3 shows the growth amounts, not the next cumulative sales values, it represents what needs to be added to current sales values to get predicted sales values. That is, adding the growth, $Q(n + 1) - Q(n)$, to the current value, $Q(n)$, gives the next value, $Q(n + 1)$. Thus the graph of $Q(n + 1)$ versus $Q(n)$ is the sum of your graph in (a) and the graph of $Q(n)$ versus $Q(n)$. In the language of Unit 5, *Oscillations*, the graph of $Q(n)$ plays the role of the trend line, and the graph of growth is the seasonal pattern.

   a) Look back at Item 3(b). Describe the main geometric features of the trend of the graph. Interpret what each feature means about computer sales.

   b) Without drawing it, describe the graph of $Q(n)$ versus $Q(n)$.

   c) Use your descriptions in (a) and (b) to sketch a rough graph (the general pattern) of $Q(n + 1)$ versus $Q(n)$ without actually plotting any points or using the data. Then sketch a web diagram for computer sales, based on that graph. Is the information it provides about the sales consistent with that from Item 5?

INDIVIDUAL WORK 3

But What Do You Believe?

Linear, exponential, and mixed growth all exhibit linear growth-versus-quantity graphs. Your work in Activity 3 showed that such is not the case for the computer sales situation.

In fact, your graphs suggest there may be some saturation point—a point at which the growth term becomes 0. The web diagram for cumulative sales also suggests this behavior. What is this limiting value, and does it make sense in terms of the situation?

There are a number of ways to analyze the growth that takes place in the computer sales data. The items below examine several such methods, with the purpose of developing an understanding of what's going on. Remember, a model is more than just an equation that works in a particular situation. A good model should also provide some insight into the structure of the situation itself, so that behavior can be predicted when similar situations are encountered.

1. a) You graphed $Q(n + 1) - Q(n)$ versus $Q(n)$ in Item 3 of Activity 3. Without using any regression methods or equations, sketch by hand a smooth line or curve that reasonably fits that graph. Capture the trend of the graph. Describe the main geometric features of your curve as you would to a friend on the telephone.

   b) It is likely that your curve looks like a parabola. If so, again without using any kind of regression, use the features you described in (a) to help you write an approximate equation for your curve. (Hint: Think about ways to use information such as horizontal-intercepts and the coordinates of the peak. A factored form is fine.)

   c) Compare the equation you wrote in (b) to the equation you obtain using quadratic regression on the same data.

2. One principle in the modeling process is to keep things as simple as possible. The control numbers in the regression equation found in Item 1(c) are all fairly small, at least when compared to the number of sales that appear in the original data. Maybe one (or more) of them is small enough that it can be ignored and treated as though it were 0. Here is how you can use your understanding of sensitivity to help you decide.

a) The smallest of the control numbers in the regression equation is the coefficient of the x^2 term. If that number were 0 instead, what would be the effect on the graph of the curve you sketched in Item 1(a)? Try it. Sketch the graph using 0 instead of the coefficient in your regression equation. Does that change matter? Should you replace this term with 0?

b) The next-smallest control number is the coefficient of the x term. If that number were 0 instead, what would be the effect on the graph of the curve you sketched in Item 1(a)? Again, try it; make the change in the equation and graph it. Does that change matter? Should you replace this term with 0?

c) The only other control number is the constant term. If that number were 0 instead, what would be the effect on the graph of the curve you sketched in Item 1(a)? Once again, check it with an actual graph. Does that change matter? Should you replace this term with 0?

d) Simplify the regression equation according to your observations in 2(a)–(c). Compare the resulting equation to that from Item 1(b).

e) Use your work in (d) to write a reasonable and simple recursive model of the computer sales situation. Then test your equation.

By now you should have a descriptive equation that does a pretty good job on the computer sales data. But all it really is at this point in the modeling process is a summary of some experimenting with numbers. It tells *what* happened, but it does nothing to explain *why* things went as they did. It's time to go back to the context and try to make sense of your equations.

3. Think about products with which you are familiar. Does everyone want the same things you buy? For example, do all students purchase the same CD's as you and your friends? Explain why the assumption you stated in Item 1(a) of Activity 3 can not possibly be correct in the long run. Be as specific as possible.

Figure 6.8 shows a causal-loop diagram for a simple new-product situation based on the idea that happy customers will tell the people they meet about their purchase, and some of the people they tell will want to buy the product. Remember, however, that the product here (computers) is not something that most people think of as consumable—you don't use it up in a few weeks.

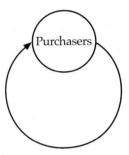

Figure 6.8
Causal-loop diagram for word-of-mouth new-product growth.

4. One factor you may have included in your discussion in Item 3 is the set of all potential customers—everyone who would ever be interested in the product. **Figure 6.9** is a modification of Figure 6.8 that includes this observation. Write a sentence or two explaining what this diagram says about the situation and why you think it is reasonable.

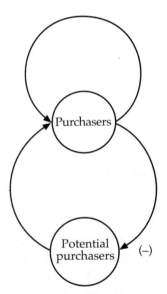

Figure 6.9.
Modified CLD for word-of-mouth new-product growth.

5. The mixed-growth model is one model consistent with the diagram in Figure 6.8. Exponential growth is another form that could arise from the same CLD. Each of these models includes an assumption of direct proportionality: change is directly proportional to the current amount. That assumption shows up explicitly in the recursive representations as a multiplicative constant, k: $Q(n + 1) - Q(n) = k \times Q(n)$.

a) Write in simple language what the multiplicative constant, k, represents in exponential growth. Interpret that explanation in the context of computer sales.

b) How should the modifications shown in Figure 6.9 affect that constant? Be as specific as possible. For example, if it should no longer be constant, how might it vary, and why?

As you know, if a quantity C is directly proportional to another quantity D, then you can write that relationship as $C = k \times D$ for an appropriate constant k. That's the basis of the recursive representation of exponential growth. Sometimes one quantity C varies in such a way that it is proportional to two quantities, say D and E. That is, if either D or E is doubled while the other is held constant, then C also doubles. Such a relationship is called **joint proportionality**; C is said to be jointly proportional to D and E if $C = k \times D \times E$ for some constant k. Both quantities appear in the equation as factors.

6. The area of a rectangle is an example of a quantity that is jointly proportional to two other quantities, length and width. The equation is $A = L \times W$.

a) What is the value of k in this situation?

b) Verify by using specific numbers that doubling either L or W (but not both) does double the area.

c) What happens to the area when both L and W are doubled?

7. Identify several other quantities with which you are familiar and which exhibit joint proportionality. In each case, find the value of k if possible.

8. The CLD in Figure 6.8 suggests that growth in purchasers may be proportional to the number of purchasers thus far. That is the basis of the equation given in Item 5. The modified CLD in Figure 6.9 should suggest a joint proportionality model. Write an equation showing that relationship. You may wish to use words instead of variables to make your equation easier to read, but it must be in the form of an equation.

ACTIVITY

HOW DOES THIS RATE?

4

Your work in Individual Work 3 should give you some rough idea of what might really be going on in the computer sales situation. It should provide a general description of why behavior is as it is. In addition, the joint proportionality idea also suggests another way to look at the equations you developed as a recursive model.

In fact, you really have two separate models of the computer sales situation—one based on analyzing the data to get an equation, the other based on trying to understand the context to get at the mathematical representation. The data lead to specific equations with specific control numbers. The context leads to a possible form for a descriptive equation, but it does not provide any specific values. How can you go about verifying these two models?

As one part of the verification of these models, you should compare them to see if they are consistent. Also ask what each can tell about the other. The CLD in Individual Work 3 suggests modifying an existing, well-understood model (exponential) to describe the sales situation. Therefore, it may be helpful to compare your work on the actual data to what you know about exponentials.

1. Since computers are not consumable, it is reasonable to think of there being some fixed number of potential buyers. Thus, you might suppose that new sales are jointly proportional to previous sales and to the number of potential buyers remaining. Assume that is indeed the case. Explore that situation. Remember that the number of new sales is the growth term, $Q(n + 1) - Q(n)$.

   a) Let $Q(n)$ denote the total number of sales after n months and let $P(n)$ denote the number of remaining potential customers after n months. Write an equation that represents the joint proportionality assumption.

ACTIVITY

4

HOW DOES THIS RATE?

b) Let M represent the number of potential buyers prior to the time the new product was introduced. Write a formula for $P(n)$ in terms of M and $Q(n)$. Remember, $Q(n)$ represents the total sales after n months.

c) Use your answers from (a) and (b) to write an equation for the number of new sales in terms of $Q(n)$ and constants only.

d) Your answer in (c) should be quadratic in $Q(n)$, as was your result in Item 2(e) of Individual Work 3. Are the two equations consistent? The answer in (c) was derived from the context, and the answer from 2(e) from the data. Using the information from 2(e), find values for M and k. What is the meaning of M in this case? The meaning of k?

Recall that the relative growth rate is defined as $r = Q(n + 1) - Q(n))/Q(n)$. Exponential growth is defined as growth in which the relative rate of growth is constant. Thus its recursive representation is just a rearrangement of the definition of r:

$Q(n + 1) - Q(n) = r \times Q(n)$ (multiplying both sides of the growth rate equation by $Q(n)$).

2. a) The joint proportionality model says that a growth model having the form $Q(n + 1) - Q(n) = k \times Q(n) \times (M - Q(n))$ may be appropriate for the computer sales situation. Do the *obvious* arithmetic to this equation so the left side looks like the defining formula for relative growth rate.

b) Based only on your answer to (a), and without actually making a graph, describe what the graph of relative growth rate versus $Q(n)$ should look like.

HOW DOES THIS RATE?

3. a) In Item 2, you predicted what the graph of r versus $Q(n)$ *should* look like. Use a spreadsheet, or list operations on your calculator, and the formula $r = (Q(n + 1) - Q(n))/Q(n)$ to compute the actual relative rates for the computer sales data, month by month. Create a scatterplot of these relative rates versus $Q(n)$ to see what their graph *does* look like.

   b) Use the specific numbers you obtained for k and M in Item 1(d) to overlay the graph of the equation from Item 2(a), and comment.

4. a) Interpret the meaning of the horizontal-intercept of the line in Item 3.

   b) Recall that the original assumptions for exponential growth involve a constant relative rate of growth. The graph in Item 3 represents the relative rate for the computer sales situation, and it clearly is not constant. Interpret the meaning of the vertical-intercept of the line in Item 3.

INDIVIDUAL WORK 4

But What Does It All Mean?

The model you developed in Activity 4 is in many ways the next modification in a sequence of variations of the basic recursive growth model $Q(n + 1) = Q(n) + \text{growth}$. Each model uses a slightly more complex expression for the growth term. Linear growth assumes that growth is constant, just some number that never changes. Exponential growth assumes growth is proportional to $Q(n)$. The latest model assumes that growth is jointly proportional to both $Q(n)$ and some quantity of the form $M - Q(n)$. Thus the growth expression goes from being constant to linear in $Q(n)$, to quadratic in $Q(n)$. Each model is a little more complex than the one before, but each model is still relatively simple.

The most recent model, the one based on joint proportionality with $Q(n)$ and $M - Q(n)$, is called logistic growth. **Logistic growth** is the growth of a quantity Q in which the amount of growth between successive periods is jointly proportional to both $Q(n)$ and $M - Q(n)$, for some constant M. Logistic growth, then, follows the recursive equation $Q(n + 1) = Q(n) + k \times Q(n) \times (M - Q(n))$. This individual work is designed to develop a sense of what the values k and M control.

1. Using a graphing calculator's sequence mode, or a spreadsheet, plot the first 20 points on the time-series graph of the logistic growth relations generated by the recursive descriptions given below. Identify an appropriate window for each graph, then comment on what k seems to control. Create more examples on your own if you wish to investigate the pattern more fully.

   a) $Q(n + 1) = Q(n) + 0.0005 \times Q(n) \times (1000 - Q(n))$, $Q(0) = 10$.

   b) $Q(n + 1) = Q(n) + 0.001 \times Q(n) \times (1000 - Q(n))$, $Q(0) = 10$.

   c) $Q(n + 1) = Q(n) + 0.00025 \times Q(n) \times (1000 - Q(n))$, $Q(0) = 10$.

2. Using a graphing calculator's sequence mode, or a spreadsheet, plot the first 20 points on the time-series graph of the logistic growth relations generated by the recursive descriptions give below. Identify an appropriate window for each graph, then comment on what M seems to control. Create more examples on your own if you wish to investigate the pattern more fully.

a) $Q(n + 1) = Q(n) + 0.0005 \times Q(n) \times (1000 - Q(n))$, $Q(0) = 10$.

b) $Q(n + 1) = Q(n) + 0.0005 \times Q(n) \times (2000 - Q(n))$, $Q(0) = 10$.

c) $Q(n + 1) = Q(n) + 0.0005 \times Q(n) \times (500 - Q(n))$, $Q(0) = 10$.

3. Using a graphing calculator's sequence mode, or a spreadsheet, plot the first 20 points on the time-series graph of the logistic growth relations generated by the recursive descriptions give below. Identify an appropriate window for each graph, then comment on the effect of changing $Q(0)$. Create more examples on your own if you wish to investigate the pattern more fully.

a) $Q(n + 1) = Q(n) + 0.0005 \times Q(n) \times (1000 - Q(n))$, $Q(0) = 10$.

b) $Q(n + 1) = Q(n) + 0.0005 \times Q(n) \times (1000 - Q(n))$, $Q(0) = 250$.

c) $Q(n + 1) = Q(n) + 0.0005 \times Q(n) \times (1000 - Q(n))$, $Q(0) = 1250$.

4. a) If you have not already done so, make a web diagram for the logistic model you developed in Activity 4. Since the numbers are very large, the graph will be difficult to see clearly unless you make it quite large too. If you can use butcher paper or some other large space, do so. Use the same starting value as in the original data. Create more examples on your own if you wish to investigate the pattern more fully.

   b) Repeat using a starting value of 1000. (You can use the same paper as for (a).)

   c) Repeat, starting at 5000.

   d) Repeat starting at 12,000.

   e) Comment on the general behavior of the growth as revealed in these diagrams. In particular, what can you say about the number M for your model? What about the starting value?

   f) Although you can draw the web diagrams in all the cases requested above, they may not all make sense in the context of cumulative computer sales. Explain.

5. Many people think that wildlife populations can't grow indefinitely. For example, although moose growth in a state park may begin quite slowly through migration, births are likely to become a factor at some point. That suggests that exponential growth could occur. But clearly, no exponential model can be a good description for long periods, since that kind of growth would cause the moose eventually to run out of food and space. Thus, the graph of moose population

might be similar in shape to that of the computer sales data. If so, perhaps a logistic model would be appropriate. Suppose the moose population in Adirondack State Park is described by the following recursive expression:

$P(n + 1) = P(n) + 0.00004 \times P(n) \times (12{,}000 - P(n))$, where P is the total moose population in the park.

a) In this model, M is 12,000. Explain what that tells you about this situation.

b) Calculate the next year's population if the current year's population were 27 moose. What is the change in the population?

c) Calculate the next year's population if the current year's population were 12,400 moose. Describe the change in the population. Explain why this might be reasonable.

d) Sketch a diagram of $P(n + 1)$ versus $P(n)$, Overlay the line $P(n + 1) = P(n)$ (Current = Next). Sketch a web diagram beginning at $P(n) = 12{,}400$. Does this agree with your thinking in (b)? Explain.

Logistic growth is defined as growth in which the amount of change during a given period is jointly proportional to the quantity that is growing and to the difference between that quantity and some constant. That is, the amount of growth = $k \times Q(n) \times (M - Q(n))$. The first part indicates exponential growth. The final factor, $M - Q(n)$, may be thought of as a measure of resources available. Since this factor gets smaller as $Q(n)$ gets larger, you might say that $M - Q(n)$ represents negative feedback in the system; it tends to oppose the growth. For populations, resources may be food, space, etc. In the computer sales situation, resources might mean potential customers. The number M itself is usually referred to as the carrying capacity of the system. As you have seen above, the **carrying capacity** is the maximum value that Q can reach and sustain without decrease.

In logistic growth, the introduction of the $M - Q(n)$ term changes the relative rate of growth from being a constant (k) to being a decreasing linear function. The vertical-intercept of the graph of relative growth rate versus $Q(n)$ is sometimes called the intrinsic growth rate. The **intrinsic growth rate** represents the relative rate of growth that would occur per time period if there were no negative feedback from the decrease in available resources as Q grows.

6. Return to the list of situations for which you drew rough graphs back in Individual Work 1, Item 1. For each situation that seems it could be modeled as logistic growth, explain what M would mean in that setting. Also explain why a logistic pattern should be expected in that system; that is, what is the limited resource for the context?

7. a) For each logistic pattern described in Item 1 of Individual Work 4, find the corresponding carrying capacity and intrinsic growth rate, and explain how each number is visible in your graphs.

   b) Repeat for the patterns from Item 2.

   The recursive form for logistic growth is $Q(n + 1) = Q(n) + k \times Q(n) \times (M - Q(n))$. The control numbers are k and M; if you know them, you have a complete description of the growth.

   c) Write a formula to find the intrinsic growth rate in terms of k and M.

   d) Write a formula to find the recursive equation for logistic growth (that is, k and M) from the intrinsic growth rate and the carrying capacity.

8. The data in **Figure 6.10** represent the growth of yeast buds in a laboratory experiment done by Carlson in 1913. These data represent approximately logistic growth. Analyze these data to explain why a logistic model is reasonably appropriate. Then determine the approximate carrying capacity and intrinsic rate for this situation. Based on your analysis, what portion (left, middle, right) seems to depart most from the true logistic model?

Time (hours)	Yeast buds
0	9.6
1	18.3
2	29.0
3	47.2
4	71.1
5	119.1
6	174.6
7	257.3
8	350.7
9	441.0
10	513.3
11	559.7
12	594.8
13	629.4
14	640.8
15	651.1
16	655.9
17	659.6
18	661.8

Figure 6.10.
Carlson's yeast-bud data.
Source: Charles Kreb
Ecology. Harper and
Row. NY: 1992, p.192.

The general assumptions behind the logistic model seem reasonably applicable to a wide range of situations. They surely seem appropriate in describing animal populations, whether living in the wild or managed on farms or ranges, since the available food and space is never infinite.

Species raised as crops are harvested periodically. If the size of the harvest is larger than the amount of growth in the previous period, then the total amount of that crop remaining to grow the next period's harvest is smaller than that for the previous period. If that pattern is continued, the amount will continue to decrease, perhaps hurting future harvests. If the amount harvested is less than the amount of growth for the period, then the total amount remaining increases. Under ideal conditions, the amount of harvest is exactly equal to the amount of growth in the immediately preceding period. That way, growth and harvest balance each other. That is the basic idea behind what are called renewable resources.

9. Suppose you raise a particular species whose population grows according to a logistic model. So $P(n + 1) = P(n) + k \times P(n) \times (M - P(n))$ for some constants k and M. (If you prefer to work with numbers instead of the general case, choose a model from earlier items in this assignment.)

   a) Sketch a graph of the amount of growth versus $P(n)$. (Hint: Look back at your work in Activity 3 and Individual Work 3.) Be sure to label all important features.

   b) How does the graph in (a) provide information about how this population can be harvested?

   c) If the goal is to have the largest possible sustainable harvest, what policy should you follow? That is, with what population should you try to start each growth period? Explain.

10. a) In the computer sales situation that you explored in Activity 3, identify approximately when new computer sales were greatest.

    b) In what way is 10(a) related to the ideas in Item 9?

    c) Explain how someone who knew that the computer sales data would follow a logistic model could have predicted soon after the maximum sales period about when and at what total sales the product would level out.

LESSON THREE
It's Going Around

KEY CONCEPTS

Logistic growth

The modeling cycle

Simulation

Compartment models

Parameter estimation

Parameter interpretation

Equilibrium

Stability

The Image Bank

PREPARATION READING

Give and Take

*I*n the first two lessons, you have carried out the modeling cycle to develop a reasonable model for the growth in sales of a particular computer over the period of several years. You found that a reasonable model is the logistic growth model. Several items throughout the first lessons have also implied that the logistic model may also describe other kinds of situations pretty well. The key assumption upon which the logistic model rests is that the change in the quantity, Q, is jointly proportional to Q itself and to some other quantity that decreases linearly as Q increases.

In the case of computer sales, it is pretty easy to believe that the number of people who still might buy the product decreases as they become actual purchasers. In a sense, the potential customers get "used up" by the process. Another way to look at it is that they move from one category (potential buyer) to another (actual buyer).

The logistic model might also describe population growth. In Activity 4, Item 5, you used a model to describe a moose population. In that case, there are not two categories between which members of the population move. Instead, the second quantity, the one that decreases as Q grows, is a measure of the resources available to the population. If there is plenty of food and water and space and such, then the population can grow rapidly. As the moose population increases, so do the demands on food and other resources, decreasing the rate at which the population can continue growing.

All of this is just fine in principle. The logistic model does describe the computer sales data relatively well. However, do you actually know that there are a fixed number of potential buyers and that sales are generated by word of mouth? Can these assumptions about the mechanics of the growth lead to logistic growth, or is it just an interesting tale that can't be checked? In this lesson, you will build a simulation of a system that really has the characteristics assumed for the computer sales situation. See for yourself. Is it logistic?

THE JOKE'S ON YOU

The assumptions below represent one particular situation (the spread of a joke) that follows the general contextual story that motivated the analysis of the computer sales data and led to the logistic model.

Assumptions:

- One member of your class has heard a new joke.

- Everyone in your class knows everyone else in your class and would tell a joke to each other if they had the chance.

- In each time period, each member of the class who has heard the joke contacts exactly one other member of the class.

- The person who is trying to tell the joke does not know who has already heard it. Thus, the person who is to hear the joke is selected by the teller at random from all members of the class.

- If the person who is selected has already heard the joke, the joke does not spread in that contact. If the person who is selected has not heard the joke, then the joke is told and in the next time period, that new person also tries to spread the joke.

You know how simulation works. Use these assumptions to design a simulation that permits you to role play through the situation and generate data. Then use the methods you developed in Lesson 2 to analyze the data to write a recursive description, complete with control numbers.

Suggestions:

- Analyze the time-series graph of your data and at least one other kind of graph.

- If data do not show clear patterns, average the results of repeated simulations to make the patterns more easily visible (by decreasing random variation).

INDIVIDUAL WORK 5

That's Catchy!

Your simulation of the spread of a joke through members of a class should convince you that reasonable assumptions about the interactions within a group of people can lead to behavior that is reasonably well described by logistic models. In the process, you have seen how to approximate the control numbers for a recursive description of a logistic model for data by plotting observed relative rates or observed growth amounts versus $Q(n)$. The geometric features (slope, intercepts, vertex) of those graphs provide the necessary information for approximating the recursive equation.

For example, logistic models are based on the recursive equation $Q(n + 1) = Q(n) + k \times Q(n) \times (M - Q(n))$. Thus the graph of the relative rate from $Q(n)$ to $Q(n + 1)$ versus $Q(n)$ is linear with slope $-k$ and vertical intercept kM. So k is the opposite of the slope of this graph, the intrinsic rate is the vertical intercept, and the carrying capacity is the intrinsic rate divided by k.

Alternately, the horizontal intercepts of the graph of growth, $Q(n + 1) - Q(n)$, versus $Q(n)$ are 0 and M, so M is easily obtained from such a graph. Since the vertex of the graph occurs at $Q(n + 1) = M/2$, its coordinates may be used to determine k and the intrinsic rate. Also, since k is the opposite of the coefficient of the squared term, k may be read directly from a quadratic regression equation.

In the overall modeling process, you know that certain assumptions lead to logistic behavior. You also have mathematical tools that permit you to estimate the control numbers for the specific equation describing a particular set of data. How can you interpret those control numbers in terms of the starting contextual assumptions? How do facts from the contextual situation relate to the intrinsic rate and the carrying capacity? In order to examine this, you could test the effect on control numbers as you vary the contextual assumptions. You could also start with an equation and try to interpret it back into its contextual meaning. This assignment does both.

The calculator programs JOKES.82P and JOKES.83P can be used to generate data using the same assumptions as those that you used in Activity 5.

Program notes:

- The programs complete several simulations, then plot the averaged data.

- You will need to supply the size of the population, the number of contacts per period, and the number of times to simulate the situation.

- Because of the time it takes for the programs to run, you may wish to carry out only two or three simulations of each situation.

1. Several different scenarios are described below. (The contacts number indicates the number of classmates that each joke-teller speaks to during each time period. In Activity 5, you used contacts = 1.) Simulate each situation using the program JOKES. Then analyze the resulting data to produce an approximate recursive logistic model.

   a) Population = class size you used in your simulation in Activity 5; contacts = 1. (This is a calculator repeat of what you did in your physical simulation.)

   b) Population = 30; contacts = 1.

   c) Population = 100; contacts = 1.

   d) Population = 100; contacts = 2.

   e) Population = 100; contacts = 3.

2. a) Describe the effect of changing the Population number.

   b) Describe the effect of changing the Contacts number.

As you know, the recursive equation for logistic growth is of the form $Q(n + 1) = Q(n) + k \times Q(n) \times (M - Q(n))$. In this form, it is a modification of familiar exponential growth; the relative rate is $k \times (M - Q(n))$ instead of just a constant. Use this equation to complete Item 3.

3. a) What does M represent in a logistic model?

   b) Explain what intrinsic growth rate means in connection with logistic growth, and tell how to find it from the equation given above.

   c) The number of contacts per period determines the intrinsic growth rate of the joke-telling process. Use your understanding of the context itself to explain why this makes sense.

   d) Remember that the intrinsic rate may be estimated as the vertical-intercept of the graph of relative rate versus $Q(n)$. Suppose you are the only person who has heard a particular joke. What is $Q(n)$ at that instant? If you meet one classmate each hour, how many will you get to tell the joke to during the first hour? What does that tell you about the approximate value of the intrinsic rate?

e) If you are the only person who has heard a particular joke, and you randomly meet two classmates each hour, how many will you get to tell it to during the first hour? What does that tell you about the approximate value of the intrinsic rate?

f) In reality, you probably do not always tell a new joke to *everyone* you see when you have heard one. Explain why this is so. What does this have to do with the logistic model?

The intrinsic rate describes the initial, almost exponential, behavior of the system. Your results in Item 3 should convince you that it is closely related to the spreadability of the joke, something that depends on the joke itself and on the people doing the telling. Item 4 considers the behavior later in the spread of the joke.

4. Suppose there are 2000 students in your school and each student normally encounters a random collection of about 20 other students each day outside of class.

a) If a logistic model were used to describe the spread of a joke in such a situation, what would you use as your M?

b) Since there are 20 contacts per day, you should expect to be able to tell your new joke about 20 times during the first day. Thus, that is a reasonable estimate for the intrinsic rate. Use that number and your answer to (a) to write the corresponding recursive equation for this situation. Use the form $Q(n + 1) = Q(n) + k \times Q(n) \times (M - Q(n))$. Remember that the intrinsic rate is $k \times M$.

If 1000 students have already heard a joke, and if contacts within the school are random, then the probability that the next person you see will not yet have heard the joke is 0.5, or 50%.

c) Assume only 100 of the students in your school have already heard a particular joke. What is the probability that the next student you see will *not* already know the joke? What if 300 students have already heard the joke?

d) Repeat (c) if $Q(n)$ students have heard the joke.

e) The growth term of your equation in (b) is of the form $k \times Q(n) \times (M - Q(n))$, with specific values of k and M. Dividing the last factor, $(M - Q(n))$, of this expression by M, and multiplying the first factor, k, by M to compensate gives the equation $kM \times Q(n) \times (1 - Q(n)/M)$. Interpret the newly formed factors, kM and $(1 - Q(n)/M)$. (Hint: Look at your answers to (a)–(d) and at Item 3.)

f) If 100 students, including yourself, have heard the joke, then the probability that the next person you meet has not yet heard it is 95%. Explain why this is correct. You initially assumed that you would meet 20 students during the day. About how many of those 20 students will not yet have heard the joke?

g) Your answer to (f) indicates how many times you should expect to get to tell the joke on the given day. Check that your answer is just kM multiplied by $(1 - Q(n)/M)$. Explain why each of these expressions belongs in the calculation of the number of new tellings you should expect.

h) It would be unusual that every student at your school is a close enough friend that you could tell them every joke you hear. Suppose about 25% of each student's fellow schoolmates are good enough friends that they would tell them jokes. That decreases the intrinsic rate to 0.25 x 20. Repeat part (f) under these new conditions.

i) Write the new equation for the logistic model, reflecting the assumption in (h).

5. Based on your investigations in Items 1–4 of this assignment and Items 1–4 of Individual Work 4, write a short paragraph explaining the relations between the control numbers, time-series graph, and contextual assumptions in a logistic joke-spreading scenario. That is, how can you determine one set of facts from another. For example, how can you sketch a time-series graph from a verbal description of the contextual situation?

6. The spread of diseases is very much like the spread of jokes in many ways. However, there are some important differences, too, and not just in the fact that diseases make you sick and (most) jokes don't.

a) Explain how spreading diseases and jokes are alike. Be as specific as possible.

b) Explain how the spread of disease and of jokes are different. Be as specific as possible.

c) Based on your observations from your simulations in class and in Item 1 above, explain why the differences between jokes and diseases is extremely important.

In Activity 5, you carried out a physical simulation of the spreading of a joke. Your analysis above shows how to relate the facts of a joke-telling situation to logistic growth. Thus, rather than using random-number simulation, now you can use recursive equations for quicker information.

Different people will choose to build simulation models in different ways. **Figure 6.11** shows an example of a spreadsheet model for growth in the computer sales context. It uses the logistic joint-proportionality relation in its defining equation: change in $S = k \times S(n-1) \times P(n-1)$. You could also use the equation: change in $S = r \times S(n-1) \times P(n-1)/M$, where $r = kM$.

In these formulas, S represents the number of cumulative sales to date (what is being modeled), and P represents the remaining number of potential customers (the other quantity in the joint proportionality). The spreadsheet separately calculates the changes in those two quantities. (Remember also that $P = M - S$.)

	A	B	C	D	E	F	G
1	Controls	Time	Total sales	Potential	New sales	Change in	
2				customers		potential cust	
3	k						
4	0.000045	0	20	24980	22	-22	
5		1	42	24958	48	-48	
6	M	2	90	24910	101	-101	
7	25000	3	191	24809	214	-214	
8		4	405	24595	448	-448	
9	S(0)	5	853	24147	927	-927	
10	20	6	1780	23220	1860	-1860	
11		7	3639	21361	3498	-3498	
12		8	7138	17862	5737	-5737	
13		9	12875	12125	7025	-7025	
14		10	19900	5100	4567	-4567	
15		11	24467	533			

Figure 6.11.
A simulation model of logistic growth.

Note: In Figure 6.11, New Sales and Change in Potential Customers represent changes that will take place before the next quarter begins. However, they have not yet occurred. These use the change equations given above. All other columns track current values and are calculated from the change values.

7. Build your own copy of a spreadsheet simulation model for logistic growth, with similar control features.

a) Use the values for the control numbers from Figure 6.11 to be sure your model works properly. Then extend that table to finish time period number 11 and go on to time period 12. Comment on the results.

b) Modify your spreadsheet model so it displays graphs of the time series and of any other relationships you think are important.

c) Relabel the quantities in your simulation model so it applies to the spread of a joke through your school. Use control numbers that make sense for your school. Then run the simulation and explain what it tells you about the situation. Are the results reasonable?

DEAR *S-I-R*

You have examined the contextual assumptions related to the spread of a joke. Such assumptions can lead to approximately logistic behavior. Your explorations related the contextual assumptions to the control constants (carrying capacity and intrinsic rate) for an appropriate model. For example, in a population of M people, the carrying capacity is M. The intrinsic rate is a bit more complicated. It includes information not only about the average number of contacts each joke teller has in a given period but also about the effectiveness of those contacts.

In the case of spreading a joke, you can think of the effectiveness as a measure of the likelihood that a particular contact is a close enough friend that you are willing to tell the joke to that person. Thus the fraction of people who fall into that category represents the probability that any given contact will result in your telling the joke if they have not already heard it. That means you can think of building the intrinsic rate, r, using something like $r =$ (number of contacts per person per period) x (fraction of population that are close friends).

In Item 6 of Individual Work 5, you considered the similarities between spreading a joke and spreading a disease. The new interpretation of intrinsic rate is similar. Not all diseases are equally easy to catch, even given the same contact patterns. Think about how you would modify the joke model to describe the spread of a disease. In this assignment, you will develop a model describing the spread of a disease in a closed population.

In your models for jokes, eventually everyone in the population hears the joke. That is because there are only two kinds of people being considered in your model, those who know the joke and those who don't. The ability to classify each person into one of two distinct groups makes this an example of what is known as a two-compartment model. A **compartment model** is a model in which each quantity is thought of as a container (compartment) with the changes in the quantity represented as flows of the

ACTIVITY

6

DEAR *S-I-R*

material into or out of the compartment. In this case, each category of person represents a compartment, and the action in the system involves moving from one compartment to the other as you hear the joke. **Figure 6.12** illustrates this thinking.

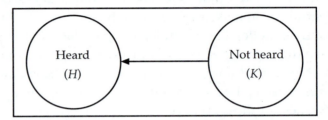

Figure 6.12.
A compartment model for joke-telling.

Together the two groups of persons who know the joke (*H*) and those who don't (*K*), make up the whole population (*P*).

This diagram is different from a causal-loop diagram. In this case, a compartment really consists of a number of objects (students in this model). The arrow says that objects really can move from one compartment to the other.

1. Revisit the causal-loop diagrams you saw in Lesson 1. What exactly do the arrows mean in a causal-loop diagram? Are there any objects moving from one compartment to another?

In Figure 6.12, you see that students from compartment *K* move to compartment *H*.

2. a) What makes a person change from *K* to *H*?

   b) How (and why) are the increases in the number of students who have heard the joke and the decreases in the number of students who have not heard the joke related?

   c) Write two separate recursive equations, one for the number of people who have heard the joke and the other for the number of people who have not heard the joke. Your equations may use some of the same quantities in both.

3. a) What are the types of people in the computer sales model?

   b) The two-type classification of people for the computer

DEAR *S-I-R*

sales model may not be very realistic. What other kind of person should be included? Why does the model do such a good job even though it ignores that other classification?

c) How could you modify the computer sales model to include this third classification?

d) Which one of the two pictures in **Figure 6.13**, model A or model B, do you prefer to describe the movements of persons in the computer sales model? Think about the meaning of the arrows.

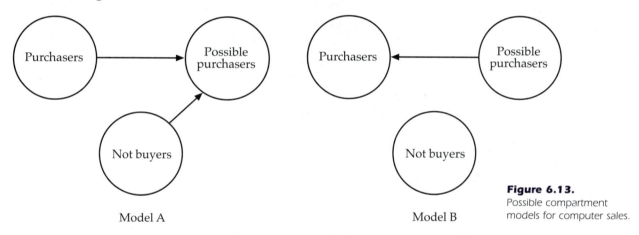

Model A   Model B

Figure 6.13.
Possible compartment models for computer sales.

The joke models have been two-compartment models, assuming that there are only people who know the joke already and those who do not yet know the joke. In the language of diseases, those types would be infectives and susceptibles. Infectives are those who are capable of spreading the disease; susceptibles are those who are capable of getting it. However, diseases differ from jokes in many ways. One practical difference for most diseases is that you get over them. This is usually called the removed category. Since the removed category is separate from the susceptibles, it is usually assumed those people are unable to be re-infected.

4. Identify what might be called the removed category in the joke context. How accurate is that label in this situation?

ACTIVITY

6

DEAR *S-I-R*

5. Draw a diagram showing the three quantities—susceptibles, infectives, and removed—and how people move from one category to another. Your answer will be a diagram of a three-compartment model for disease. Does that seem reasonable to be a reasonable name for this model?

Disease models that include these three categories of people are referred to as *S-I-R* models, based on the initials of the three compartments. Although the behavior may no longer be logistic, the same reasoning you used to describe the joke spread still describes the *S-I* portion of the disease model. The number of new infections is jointly proportional to the number of infectives and the fraction of the population that are susceptibles: new infections = $r \times I \times (S/P)$, where P is the total population, S the susceptibles, I the infectives, and r the proportionality constant. The proportionality constant is now the intrinsic rate and reflects something about the virulence of the disease, too. Much as in the joke case, you can think of r as (contacts) × (probability that a contact will transmit the disease). The first factor depends on the behavior of the population; the second factor depends on the disease.

The *I-R* part of the process can be modeled in several different ways. In general, if you think of removal as recovery from the disease, then the main thing affecting the number of people in that category is time—when they got sick. Suppose your model recomputes the status of everyone on a daily basis and that a typical case of the disease lasts five days. Then you could assume that for everyone who gets the disease it will last *exactly* five days and set up your formulas to remove people from the infectives category five days after they first appear there. Another approach is based on the fact that if the average duration is five days, then on average one-fifth of all the current infectives will be removed each day. This last assumption is more commonly used.

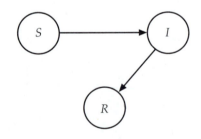

Figure 6.14.
A three-compartment model for disease transmission.

This *S-I-R* model can be described by the three-compartment diagram shown in **Figure 6.14**.

ACTIVITY

DEAR *S-I-R*

6

In the three compartments, you find the number of people at a certain moment in time:

S(*n*) is the number of susceptibles,

I(*n*) is the number of infectives,

R(*n*) the number of removed from the two other compartments, and

P is the total population (*S*(*n*) + *I*(*n*) + *R*(*n*)).

The arrow from *S* to *I* says that, during the time interval from *n* − 1 to *n*, the number of susceptibles changes because people are moving to the compartment of infectives.

The equations that fit the three-compartment model for the spread of the described disease can be written as:

$$S(n+1) = S(n) - r \times I(n) \times \frac{S(n)}{P},$$

$$R(n+1) = R(n) + \frac{I(n)}{5},$$

$$I(n+1) = I(n) + r \times I(n) \times \frac{S(n)}{P} - \frac{I(n)}{5}.$$

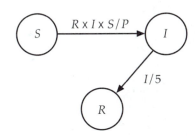

Figure 6.15.
Modified *S-I-R* diagram.

6.a) Explain why these equations fit the description of the spread of this disease. What is the meaning of *r*, *P*, and the number 5 in the formulas? Why are the signs as indicated?

Some parts of the equations can be written along the arrows in the diagram, as shown in **Figure 6.15**. Note that the time, *n*, does not appear.

b) What do the expressions along the two arrows mean for the *S-I-R* model?

ACTIVITY

DEAR *S-I-R*

6

7. Suppose an *S-I-R* model for another disease has the diagram given in **Figure 6.16**.

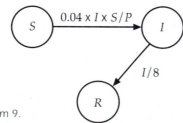

Figure 6.16.
S-I-R diagram for Item 9.

At a certain moment, there are 200 susceptibles, 40 infectives, and 160 removed. The diagram is recalculated on a daily basis.

a) How many persons will be in each of the three compartments next day?

b) Describe this model with an equation for each of the three categories, using $S(n)$, $I(n)$ and $R(n)$ as a start for the equations.

c) What is the average duration of this illness?

8. Modify the ideas behind the simulation model you developed for joke-telling to create an *S-I-R* simulation model. Then simulate the spread of a five-day disease through a school of 2000 students in which each student comes in close contact with 20 other students per day. Start with only one infected student, and use a recursive period of 1 day. Experiment with different proportionality constants, and comment on the behavior of the spread of the disease as that number varies.

What Goes Around Comes Around

1. a) What contextual features make jokes and diseases somewhat similar?

   b) What contextual features make jokes and diseases dissimilar?

2. Suppose that the number of infectives for a particular disease is described by the recursive equation

$$I(n+1) = I(n) + 0.3 \times I(n) \times \frac{S(n)}{1000} - 0.05 \times I(n),$$

with n representing the number of days since the inception of the infection. Based only on this equation, about how long, on average, does the illness last?

3. Equilibrium in a process produces no apparent change. That is, the net change in the quantity under consideration is 0. For example, an equilibrium in the joke-telling process would leave the number of students who have heard the joke and the number of students who have not heard the joke unchanged from one period to the next.

   a) The recursive equation describing the spread of a joke has the form: $P(n + 1) = P(n) + \text{(contacts)} \times \text{(fraction who are friends)} \times P(n) \times (1 - P(n)/M)$, where P denotes the number who have heard it and M represents the size of the school. Use this equation to find all possible conditions under which joke transmission can be in equilibrium.

   b) Use your simulation model from Individual Work 5 to verify your results in (a).

   c) Explain what your analysis tells you about the final state of a joke that starts going around the school.

4. Examine the recursive equations and the *S-I-R* diagram with the expressions written along the arrows in Item 6 of Activity 6.

   a) Under what conditions would the number of infectives be in equilibrium? How can you read this from the diagram? And how from the equations?

   b) In Item 7 of Activity 6, an equilibrium for compartment I is possible only if $P = 3.2 \times S$. Can you explain this from the expressions along the arrows?

  c) Suppose that in the model of Item 7 there are 125 susceptibles, 50 infectives, and 225 removed. Calculate the numbers in each of the three categories for the next day. Explain what you found for compartment I.

The "new infectives" portion of your disease model looks something like: (contacts per infective per period) × (probability of contact resulting in transmission) × (number of infectives) × (probability of contact with susceptible). The last two factors are just I and S/P, and the first two together represent a proportionality constant somewhat like the intrinsic rate for logistic growth.

 5. Pretend you are a public health official. Explain some things you might try to help control a new disease outbreak. Try to think of as many policy changes you could make as you can, and indicate which of the four factors in the above expression each change affects.

Removal can mean different things for different diseases. For many diseases, though, it simply means you have recovered from the illness and have a temporary immunity. In such cases, that immunity gradually diminishes and you return to the susceptibles compartment. In that case, you have what is known as an *S-I-R-S* disease model.

 6. Draw a compartment model showing an *S-I-R-S* structure. That is, identify each compartment and indicate how people flow from compartment to compartment.

 7. As is the case with removal, the transition from removed to susceptible is more dependent on time than on anything else.

  a) Based on your own experience, which do you think takes longer, the *R-S* step or the *I-R* step? A lot or a little?

  b) Using the same idea that you used in modeling the *I-R* process, modify your recursive equations and your change equations for the *S-I-R* model so they describe an *S-I-R-S* situation. Add letters for any constants you do not know.

 8. a) Using the equations you wrote in Item 7, under what conditions would the number of infectives be in equilibrium?

  b) Repeat (a) for the other two compartments in your model.

  c) Suppose a particular community has 1220 residents. A particular disease has a proportionality constant of $r = 0.4$. The illness lasts 5 days and immunity averages 300 days. Use your recursive equations, your change equations, or your simulation model to set up the equilibrium conditions you described in (a) and (b) and carry out two iterations of the simulation. Describe what happens to the equilibrium and explain.

d) Modify your answer to (c) to have one fewer infective and one more susceptible than needed for equilibrium. Describe what happens to the system and explain.

e) Modify your answer to (c) to have one more infective and one fewer susceptible than needed for equilibrium. Describe what happens to the system and explain.

9. An epidemic is an outbreak of a disease characterized by a rapid increase in the number of current cases of the illness.

a) The condition under which an epidemic may begin is known as the threshold condition. Based on your understanding of compartment diagrams, recursive equations, change equations, and simulation models, describe the threshold condition in ordinary language.

b) Use your work in Items 7 and 8 to compute from your answer in (a) the mathematical characterization of the conditions necessary for an epidemic: $rT=P/s$, where T is the average duration of the disease.

Note: Since r represents (number of contacts per period) x (probability that contact between S and I transmits disease), or the expected number of transmissions per period by one infective if all contacts are with susceptibles, the quantity rT may be thought of as the expected number of transmissions during the duration of one infective's illness. The ratio P/S is a rough measure of how many contacts are needed to reach one susceptible. Thus, each infective must be able to contact enough people that the expected number of transmissions is at least one; he must be able to replace himself among the infectives before being removed!

10. Based on your experience with *S-I-R* simulations, sketch a plausible time series graph of the infectives for an *S-I-R-S* situation over a period of time. For example, what would a three-year graph for something like flu, which lasts for a couple of weeks and leaves about a year of immunity, look like?

LESSON FOUR

An Ecological PushMe-PullYou

KEY CONCEPTS

Joint proportionality

Simulation

Equilibrium

Phase plane graphs

The Image Bank

PREPARATION READING

Systems

Throughout this unit, you have examined how quantities change. In the simple case of exponential growth, only one quantity is involved and its change is proportional to its own current level. This is what might be thought of as a direct feedback system. If you have ever heard the effect of placing an input microphone for an amplifier directly in front of the speakers it drives, you know just how quickly such a feedback system can grow!

You also examined how, as in the case of the disease transmission, computer sales, and joke telling, quantities grow not in isolation but as parts of systems, interacting with other varying quantities. These systems involve what might be called indirect feedback. Quantities in such systems frequently exhibit change that is jointly proportional to several system variables. However, each of these models is a compartment model, where the changes in quantities represent movement from one category to another.

As you might expect from what you know about the way the world works, many quantities involve interactions with entirely different quantities. It may be possible to examine the interactions by thinking about how each causes the other to do something. One example of this type of interaction is in the area of biology. If you examine two wildlife species, one of which provides the main source of nourishment for the other, you can see this type of interaction. This particular relationship is known as a predator–prey system.

ACTIVITY

THE OLD RUNAROUND

7

One of the first predator–prey systems studied was the interaction of lynx and hares in nineteenth-century Canada. In that system, the hares (rabbits) were a major food source for lynx. A possible CLD for this system is shown in **Figure 6.17**.

1. a) Write a short sentence indicating why you think your diagram makes sense.

   b) Start with the hares quantity and assume it increases. Go around the CLD diagram at least twice, at each arrow indicating what happens. For example, begin by saying something like, "If the number of hares increases, then . . ."

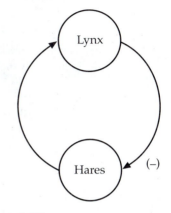

Figure 6.17.
Possible CLD for lynx hare predator–prey system.

   Figure 6.18 shows time-series graphs of hypothetical lynx and hare populations.

   Both graphs are on the same axes to show simultaneous events. The scales are initially not important since you want to get a sense of what is taking place and the relationship between the two populations. Notice that the graphs oscillate.

   c) Describe the relationship between the two oscillating curves. Compare your description of the graphs to your prediction in (b).

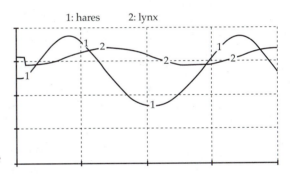

Figure 6.18.
Time-series graphs for hypothetical predator–prey populations.

It may be possible to use trigonometric equations to describe each of these graphs separately. However, equations involving just the time and one population would do nothing to explain the relationship between the two populations. That is, such equations can describe *what* the graphs look like, but they can't say *why* they look that way.

The work that you have done during this unit can help you

explain the relationship. The next few items develop one possible model. As is the case in all modeling problems, we will start with simplifying assumptions and build from them. For simplicity, then, we choose to look at each population separately first.

Remember that populations are described by the general recursive equation: $P(n + 1) = P(n) + \text{growth}$. What matters is what the growth term looks like, so that will need to be the focus once again.

2. Suppose there are no lynx in the system and that there are only a few hares. Under these conditions, it is reasonable to assume that the hares have enough food and other resources to grow.

   a) What kind of growth would you expect in the hare population? Why?

   b) Sketch a time-series graph of this behavior.

   c) Write a general recursive equation that might represent this situation. Use letters for any constants you might need, and indicate what each letter in your equation represents.

   d) One student suggested using an exponential model instead of a logistic model for the first few years. Give reasons for agreeing with this suggestion while developing your first model.

3. Continuing in the spirit of looking at each population separately first, now turn your attention to the lynx. Suppose there are no hares in a system having a number of lynx. Since hares are the main food for the lynx and there are no hares present, the lynx will begin to die out. However, the population decline will not be instantaneous. Births will probably decrease or cease, but those lynx that are alive will do the best they can, finding (maybe not enough) alternative food.

   a) What kind of function (decay curve) do you expect will describe the lynx population? Why?

ACTIVITY

THE OLD RUNAROUND

7

b) Sketch a possible time-series graph of this situation.

c) Write a corresponding recursive equation for the lynx population over the years. Use letters for any constants you might need, and indicate what each letter in your equation represents.

4. a) Based on the CLD in Figure 6.17, explain why the interaction effect of the lynx on the hares could be approximately jointly proportional to the two populations. That is, argue for an equation like:
change in hare population = (_) x H x L.

b) What should be the the sign of (_)?

c) Repeat (a) and (b) for the change in lynx population.

5. Combining Items 2–4 might lead to a model for hares like:

Change in hares = a x $H - c$ x H x L.

a) Explain each of the 2 terms and their signs.

b) Build and explain a corresponding equation for the lynx.

You now have the beginnings of a predator–prey system. You have expressions for each of the populations separately. Each equation tells a detailed story of the underlying assumptions. The model in Item 5 assumes that hares will increase exponentially (with intrinsic rate a) in the absence of lynx, and that the lynx will decrease exponentially without food.

6. a) Use your analysis from Items 1–5 to construct a simulation model for the lynx-hare system. Assume there are initially 70 lynx and 5000 hares, that the intrinsic growth rate for the hares is 0.04, the death rate for the lynx is 0.2, 0.0005 is the constant of joint proportionality for the change in hare population, and 0.00005 is the constant of joint proportionality for the lynx population. Include time series graphs of both hare and lynx populations.

b) Rerun your model with 5000 hares and 0 lynx. Then repeat for 70 lynx and 0 hares. Be sure these extreme cases agree with your predictions in Items 2 and 3.

INDIVIDUAL WORK 7

Balancing Act

1. Consider the system described by the equations:

   change in $P = 0.04P - 0.0005 \times P \times Q$, and

   change in $Q = -0.2 \times Q + 0.00005 \times P \times Q$.

   a) Explain in words what these equations imply about the system they describe. In particular, could they describe a predator–prey system? If so, which letter denotes which species?

   b) One obvious equilibrium of this system is (0, 0)—no prey, no predator. For what non-zero initial values of P and Q would this system be in equilibrium? Explain how you determine your answer.

2. Return to your simulation model from Activity 7.

   a) Draw a coordinate system. Label the horizontal axis Predator and the vertical axis Prey. Plot the initial populations for H and L as a point in this system.

   b) Read the next pair of population values from your spreadsheet and plot them as one more point on your graph. What does the change in location of the point tell you about the contextual situation?

   c) Plot the next five points of this graph and tell their story.

   d) Use your spreadsheet to complete the graph of H versus L. This graph is called a **phase plane graph**—a graph of one varying quantity versus another, other than time. Explain what each point on the graph represents and in which direction to follow the graph.

3. Draw the phase plane graph, P versus Q, of the system in Item 1(b) above. Explain what it shows.

4. Consider the model of quantities Y and X described by the equations

   change in $Y = a \times Y - c \times Y \times X$,

   change in $X = -b \times X + d \times Y \times X$.

   Assume $a > 0$, $b > 0$, $c > 0$, and $d > 0$.

   a) Under what conditions is the quantity X in equilibrium?

b) Under what conditions is the quantity Y in equilibrium?

c) Under what conditions are both X and Y in equilibrium?

d) Graph each of the conditions (other than $X = 0$ or $Y = 0$) from (a)–(c) together in a phase-space graph, Y versus X.

Equilibria (the plural of equilibrium) are sometimes classified as stable or unstable depending on whether or not small changes in the values of the quantities being studied return to equilibrium on their own or not. You are familiar with this idea in physical settings. For example, suppose you place a cylindrical glass on a horizontal tabletop. If the glass does not move when you release it, it is in equilibrium. If it is sitting upright, moving it slightly will not cause it to fall over or roll off the table; it is stable. However, if it were placed on its side, it will not immediately stop rolling if it is pushed slightly; this equilibrium is unstable.

5. a) For the system in Item 4, suppose X is in equilibrium with $X = 0$. Determine whether this equilibrium for X is stable or not. Explain.

   b) Under the conditions described in (a), what happens to Y if it is not also 0?

   c) Repeat (a) and (b) for $Y = 0$ and $X \neq 0$.

   d) Suppose X is in equilibrium, but at a point at which $X \neq 0$. Suppose also that Y is *not* in equilibrium. Describe what happens to the system in the short term.

   e) Discuss the stability of the point (a/c, b/d) for this system.

6. Your analysis in Item 4 shows that two lines in the phase space determine the locations of the (non-zero) equilibria. These two lines divide the plane into 4 regions. Discuss how the system behaves when it is in each of these regions. Use your descriptions to sketch a reasonable graph of the behavior of the system.

FEEDBACK

Wrapping Up Unit Six

1. a) Sketch a diagram of the total amount of money in a savings account where nothing is deposited after the initial amount.

   b. Write a recursive equation that represents this event. Use n to represent the number of compounding periods and $Q(n)$ to represent the amount in the bank at time n.

   c. Sketch a possible graph of $Q(n + 1) - Q(n)$ versus $Q(n)$.

2. **Figure 6.19** represents a population $Q(n)$ of a small animal on an island. What story does it tell?

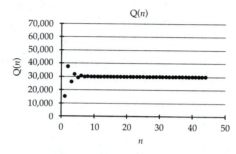

Figure 6.19.
Graph for Item 2.

3. **Figure 6.20** shows the graph of $Q(n + 1)$ versus $Q(n)$ for a particular recursive relation.

   a) Overlay the line representing $Q(n + 1) = Q(n)$, and create a web diagram.

   b. How is the change in Q changing over time? Explain how the web diagram makes that clear.

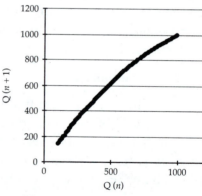

Figure 6.20.
Recursive relation for Item 3.

4. Suppose at a particular moment in the spread of a disease, there are 500 susceptibles, 80 infectives, and 200 removed. Write recursive equations for each group (S, I, and R) described by **Figure 6.21**.

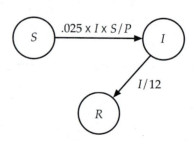

Figure 6.21.
Compartment model for disease transmission for Item 4.

5. Recall that in the past you used an exponential model to approximate growth. For example, if you knew the growth rate was 0.1, you could write

UNIT SUMMARY

the recursive form for this relationship as:

$P(n + 1) = (1 + 0.1) \times P(n); P(0) = $ Initial Population.

Yet another way to describe this relationship is:

$P(n + 1) = P(n) + 0.1 \times P(n); P(0) = $ Initial Population.

a) Which part of this equation describes the change in the population?

b) Modify the change portion of the equation to take into account the fact that there is a limited food supply for the population limiting it to a capacity of 1000.

c) Assume the initial population is 200. Write a complete recursive description of the population as modified in (b) and (c).

d) Sketch a graph of the change in population versus the population, based on your description in 5(c).

6. **Figure 6.22** shows a time-series graph of two populations. Sketch the corresponding phase diagram for the same populations.

7. Consider the following predator–prey system defined by:

Change in $P = 0.1 \times P - 0.0005 \times P \times Q$.

Change in $Q = -0.36 \times Q + 0.0006 \times P \times Q$.

a) Which is the predator population, P or Q? How can you tell from the equations?

b) Determine conditions under which the prey population is in a (non-zero) equilibrium.

c) Repeat (b) for the predators.

d) Use initial populations of $P = 500$ and $Q = 400$. Use appropriate technology to sketch 20 to 100 periods of the time-series graphs for both populations on the same set of axes.

e) Sketch a phase-space graph for these data.

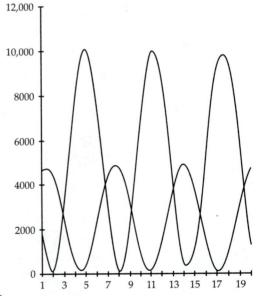

Figure 6.22.
Time-series graph of two populations.

Mathematical Summary

This unit has carried two parallel mathematical themes. Each is a continuation of work begun in other *Mathematics: Modeling Our World* units and courses. They are the modeling process and the use of equations as descriptions.

The main new tool for your use in the modeling process is the Causal-Loop Diagram, or CLD. Such a diagram can help focus thinking in the early stages of model formulation, when it may not even be clear what quantities are important to include in a model. By providing a way to visualize connections among possible components, a CLD can help you decide what to keep and what to ignore, at least temporarily.

Another key idea in your study of modeling is that the mathematics behind the model should match up with your understanding of the contextual facts. There should be good explanations for why your equations look the way they do.

As always, begin models from the simple before moving to the complex. Modify existing models. Test ideas on only one component before adding others. Examine special cases.

As for equations as descriptions, now you can add logistic growth to the old list of linear, quadratic, and exponential. The logistic can be thought of in several seemingly different ways.

It is a modification of exponential growth, replacing the constant relative rate of growth with a decreasing linear function of $Q(n)$:

$$Q(n): \frac{Q(n+1) - Q(n)}{Q(n)} = a \times Q(n) + r.$$

In this formulation, the constant r, the vertical intercept of the relative-rate-versus-$Q(n)$ graph, is the intrinsic rate for the logistic growth. The other quantity of interest in logistic growth, the carrying capacity, is the horizontal intercept, $-r/a$. (Remember, since the relative rate graph is decreasing, a is negative. So $-r/a$ is positive.) Thus the control numbers may be read almost directly off the graph of relative rate versus $Q(n)$.

Logistic growth can also be thought of in terms of its growth per period. The amount of growth per period for logistic growth is jointly proportional to the amount itself, $Q(n)$, and to the percentage of space remaining, $(1 - Q(n)/M)$. The constant of proportionality in this form is again r, the intrinsic rate, and M is the carrying capacity. Of course, the two formulations are really the same. The expression $r \times (1 - Q(n)/M)$ is nothing more than the relative rate of growth, rewritten.

Another way of thinking about logistic growth as a modification of exponential growth is as a move from a linear growth-versus-$Q(n)$ graph to a quadratic one. In this form, $Q(n + 1) - Q(n) = k \times Q(n)$ for exponential growth. One form of logistic looks like: $Q(n + 1) - Q(n) = k \times Q(n) \times (M - Q(n))$. Again, M is the carrying capacity. The new constant, k, is related to the intrinsic rate by $r = kM$. Thus control numbers are easy to determine from the intercepts and vertex of the graph of growth versus $Q(n)$.

The definition of logistic growth as a system in which the change in a quantity varies jointly with several quantities extends to other situations. Particular systems that may be modeled using such relations include the telling of jokes, disease transmission, and predator–prey systems. Most such systems, involving multiple components over long periods of time, are best studied using appropriate simulation tools such as graphing calculators or spreadsheets.

Glossary

CARRYING CAPACITY:
The maximum value that a logistic system can reach and sustain without decrease.

CAUSAL-LOOP DIAGRAM (CLD):
A diagram that shows the main quantities in a situation and indicates the direction of changes that each quantity causes in others if all other factors were held constant.

COMPARTMENT MODEL:
A model in which each quantity is thought of as a container (compartment) with the changes in the quantity represented as flows of the material into or out of the compartment.

FEEDBACK:
The influence of some quantity on itself.

INTRINSIC GROWTH RATE:
The relative rate of growth in a logistic system assuming no negative feedback from limiting resources.

JOINT PROPORTIONALITY:
C is jointly proportional to D and E if $C = k \times D \times E$ for some constant k.

LOGISTIC GROWTH:
Growth of a quantity Q in which the amount of growth between successive periods is jointly proportional to both $Q(n)$ and $M - Q(n)$, for some constant M.

PHASE PLANE GRAPH:
A graph of one varying quantity versus another, other than time.

UNIT

7

Modeling Your World

Throughout your work in the *Mathematics: Modeling Our World* program, and perhaps even in other courses, you have worked with mathematical models in a variety of contexts. You probably have developed your own models using the concepts and modeling principles that you learned. In this unit, you will reexamine the modeling process with a more critical eye. This time you will need to focus on the qualities that distinguish good models from weak models. In order to identify components and characteristics of good models, you will have a chance to examine existing models created by other students with an eye toward evaluating those models. With that background, you will be asked to select a topic of interest to you, define a question within that topic, and develop a mathematical model to answer that question.

CREATING YOUR OWN MODELS

As you know, mathematical modeling is a process used in dealing with problems in the real world. In many ways, the modeling process is a formal version of what we all call thinking. It is a way of looking at situations that helps answer questions. The idea is to simplify a problem enough so you can understand it, but not so much that you lose the essence. In this way a solution may be found, and such solutions will be reasonable. The process of simplification involves sorting the factors defining the problem. You may decide not to use some of the factors, arguing that considering them will not significantly change the problem. You might also explore the effect of one factor by observing what happens as it changes and other factors remain unchanged. Other kinds of explorations are possible. Much as physical models use smaller or fewer parts or different materials (wood, plastic, clay, etc.) to imitate characteristics of an original object, a mathematical model uses mathematical structures (tables, graphs, equations, algorithms, etc.) to capture the features of a situation.

Mathematical models are used in all fields of human endeavor. From planning traffic patterns, to anticipating population changes, to approximating stock market or weather changes, mathematical modeling is used to help us predict what might happen or to explain what has happened. Throughout your modeling experience in the *Mathematics: Modeling Our World* program, you have had quite a bit of guidance. It is now your turn to create mathematical models on your own. Using the tools you have developed over the years, you will be asked to model a situation in which you are interested. Along the way, you will need to refine your understanding of what makes a good mathematical model.

Nobel Prize for Math Model

$$C = SN(d) - Le^{-rt}N\left(d - \sigma\sqrt{t}\right)$$

where the variable d is defined by

$$d = \frac{ln\left(\dfrac{S}{L}\right) + \left(r + \dfrac{\sigma^2}{2}\right)t}{\sigma\sqrt{t}}$$

The equations above may not mean much to most of us, but they essentially earned the 1997 Nobel Prize in Economics for Professor Robert C. Merton of Havard University and Professor Myron S. Scholes of Stanford University. In collaboration with the late Fischer Black, the professors developed this pioneering formula for the valuation of stock derivatives.

As far back as 1900, there have been attempts to value derivatives. These attempts shared a fundamental shortcoming: risk premiums were not dealt with in a correct way. Black, Merton and Scholes showed that it is not necessary to use any risk premium when valuing an option. This does not mean that the risk premium disappears, but rather that it is already included in the stock price.

Source: http://www.nobel.se/announcement–97/economy97.html

LESSON ONE
The Modeling Process

KEY CONCEPTS

Mathematical modeling

Technical reading

Technical writing

Percents

Recursively-defined sequences

Series

Optimization

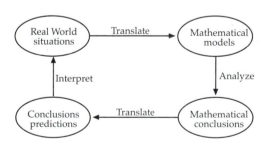

The Image Bank

PREPARATION READING

Picturing Modeling

There are many ways of describing the mathematical modeling process. You, no doubt, have developed your own view of the process through your work in this and earlier years. One model of the modeling process is displayed in **Figure 7.1**. Beginning in the upper left corner, the arrows going from one component of the diagram to the next indicate progress through the modeling process.

Figure 7.1.
A model of mathematical modeling.

As you know, modeling requires thinking about both the contextual situation you are attempting to model and about the mathematics you use in your model. Because of the dual nature of the work, a mathematical model should be checked both for internal accuracy and external accuracy.

Internal accuracy refers to the correctness of the mathematics used within a model. It should be checked internally for mathematical accuracy: Is the mathematics correct? How sensitive is it to the factors involved? Do small changes in the model result in large changes in its predictions? Does the mathematical representation follow directly from—and remain consistent with—the contextual assumptions you made?

External accuracy refers to how well the result fits the problem being modeled. External checks involve comparing the predictions from the model back to the contextual situation it is supposed to represent. Does the model accurately describe the problem it is attempting to model? If it doesn't, check to see if some of the factors omitted during the simplification stage need to be added back into the model. Do other factors need to be removed? Are there characteristics of the problem that have not yet been defined?

INDIVIDUAL WORK 1

Identifying the Steps

*A*nother way to think of mathematical modeling focuses on the component steps in the process. Since modeling is a process, this approach can be more useful. However, there is no one correct list of steps in the modeling process. In this unit, for the sake of consistency, we will use the following description.

Step 1: *Identify the problem to be investigated.*

This step involves becoming familiar with the contextual situation.

Step 2: *Determine the important factors (and assumptions about those factors) in the contextual situation, and represent those factors mathematically.*

This step requires that you simplify by selecting factors about the specific situation that you consider most relevant and ignoring others. List relations among the key factors. Mathematical representations may include symbols, equations, graphs, and simulation programs.

Step 3: *Manipulate (analyze) the mathematical relationship.*

This step is where you do the math. You may want to simulate the situation. You may need to develop appropriate mathematics, solve equations, etc.

Step 4: *Interpret the mathematical conclusions in the context of the real-world phenomenon. Then evaluate how close the conclusions are to the real-world situation. If necessary, reexamine the model's factors and structure and revise the model.*

This step is the external check of the model. Go back to the original situation and see if the resulting model makes sense. If it doesn't, start over.

It is important to keep in mind that these steps are not always followed in a rigid sequence. Although the description above consists of numbered steps, some steps may be revisited and appear out of sequence. This is perfectly fine. It may make sense for the flow to go 1, 2, 3, 2, 3, 2, 4, 2, 4. You may find yourself interpreting the real-world situation and see the need to include other factors while you are doing the math. You may need to refine the model by adding new assumptions. Both the assumptions and mathematics may need to be modified prior to arriving at a solution.

In this assignment, in order to understand the mathematical modeling process better, you will study a model created by another student. Since you will be looking only at the finished product, you may not be able to determine how much work was considered and discarded. However, you should be able to see how the modeling process was used to reach conclusions, or make predictions, to solve a problem of real interest to that student.

Read the modeling problem and solution for "To Buy or Lease." As you read, remember the steps in the modeling process. Identify each part of the problem according to the most appropriate descriptive step in the list above. Note this on a sheet of paper, writing a number (1-4) to represent that component. Of course, some stages may overlap, so not everyone will agree on which is the most appropriate label.

STUDENT MODEL:

TO BUY OR LEASE

Note: This is a student project in the student's own words. It has been edited slightly due to space considerations.

ABSTRACT

The purpose of my project is to decide whether it is cheaper to pay cash up front for a car, take out a loan on a car, or lease a car. To do this I will consider the case of a hypothetical customer who wants to buy a particular car—a 1991 Toyota MR2 Turbo Coupe with T-bar, loaded, with a sticker price of $22,000. I will assume that he has exactly $22,000 in a bank account to spend, and that he deposits $500 a month to this account. I will track his monthly payments over a five-year period and compare end results to see how he should pay for this car.

INTRODUCTION

For many people, driving a car is a necessity. Almost 90% of Americans buy the cars they drive, while the rest lease. I will compare these two options, buying and leasing, to see which is more profitable, or less costly. Many personal factors enter in to the decision of whether to buy or lease; since these factors differ from one individual to the next, I will research strictly the financial aspect of this question. Most leases and loans vary in length between two and five years. I will consider the five-year (more common) time period. I will take into account the down payment, monthly payments, and interest and insurance rates. I will consider an open-end lease, which gives the driver the right to buy the car—at a previously set price—at the end of the five-year lease. I will assume that this price is the same price at which he could sell the car if he had purchased it. I will consider a situation in which the customer has enough money to buy the car up front if he chooses not to lease or finance the car. Since I cannot consider every type of car, I have limited my research to a 1991 Toyota MR2 T-Top, a sports car with a sticker price of approximately $22,000.00. Since interest rates vary from day to day, I will work only with the rates I was given upon my first visit to the bank and car dealership.

DISCUSSION

I will decide the least expensive way of paying for a car by comparing the amount of money in the customer's bank account after 5 years with the total amount of money that he has invested in his car during the five year period. I will assume the customer deposits $500 a month into this specific account and that he has exactly $22,000.00, the sticker price of the MR2, in this account when he decides to get the car. The interest rate on borrowed money was quoted to me at 12%, and the interest rate on a savings account, like this one, was quoted at 8%. I will analyze the following three cases: The customer pays $22,000.00 up front in cash; the customer takes out a loan and finances the car over five years; the customer leases the car with an option to buy after five years. I will assume that a 15% down payment is required on a loan and that the down payment on a lease is the "first and last months' rent." The bank gave me a specific monthly payment for a loan, but many complex computations must be calculated when considering a lease. Banks refuse to perform these calculations unless a car is actually being bought, but the vice president of a First Union bank told me that the monthly payments on a lease are generally $100.00 less than the monthly payments on a loan. Over a 60-month (5-year) period, this is a difference of $6000.00. At the current interest rate of 12%, the monthly payments on a loan for this car are $429.19. The monthly payments on a lease for this car would therefore be $329.19.   If a car is bought with a loan, life insurance must also be bought from the bank at a premium of $596.56. This insurance protects the bank in case of an accident to the purchaser, which would make him unable to pay for the car. In a leasing situation, the title of the car is held by the bank as collateral until the end of the leasing period, so this insurance is unnecessary. The Toyota dealer told me that anyone who leases a car must buy a more expensive insurance policy than anyone who purchases a car. However, both First Union Bank and U.S.A.A. insurance company said that there is no difference in the minimum limits and liability insurance that every driver must have; whether he leases or buys his car, the insurance payments need not factor into my considerations. The warranty is the same on a car whether it is bought or leased, as is the money spent on fuel, so I will consider neither of these factors. I will assume that the (bank) insurance is paid at the same time as the initial payment on the car, and that any withdrawals or deposits are made at the beginning of each month. Interest will be compounded at the end of each month.

RESULTS

Case 1: Cash up front.

Before buying the car, the customer has $22,000.00 in his bank account. Most car dealerships will give some sort of discount if the car is paid for in advance if the customer asks for one. I will assume that this customer does not ask and that he pays the dealership the sticker price of $22,000 from his account.

Let $I = \$$ in bank account the previous month. Then the amount of money in the current month's account is

$(I + \$500) \times (1.08 / 12)$,

$500 represents the monthly deposit,

1.08 represents 8% interest compounded monthly, and

22,000 is the total money that will be paid for the car.

Then a [partial] record of the bank account looks like **Figure 7.2**.

Month	Dollars in bank
Before purchase	$22,000.00
At purchase	$0
1	$503.33
2	$1010.02
3	$1520.09
...	...
...	...
59	$36,077.14
60	$36,820.99

Figure 7.2.
The savings balance under the cash up front plan.
[Note: The dots are used as a space saver and represent months 4-58.]

At the end of five years, the customer will have spent $22,000.00 on his car, and will have $36,820.99 in his bank account. His net gain will be the difference in these two amounts, $14,820.99. As in trying to find out the monthly lease payments from the banker, the car dealer was reluctant in telling me how much the car would be worth in five years. Even though he would have to tell someone who would have an open end lease, he would only tell me that a car is generally worth 40% of its sticker price after five years—if it's in good condition. I looked at car resale value books in the library, and this seemed to be pretty accurate. Using this information, I will assume that the MR-2 will be worth 40% of $22,000, or $8800 in 5 years.

Case 2: Takes a loan.

The customer begins with $22,000 in his bank account, but when he buys the car he must subtract $3300 for the down payment and $595.56 for the life insurance premium. I will keep two running totals for each month: his bank account, which will have a deposit of $70.91 ($500 – $429.19 monthly payment), and the amount of money he spends towards the car, the sum of which will increase by $429.19 each month. Once again, I will assume the interest rate on the [savings] account is constant at 8% and the interest is compounded monthly.

Let I = $ in bank the previous month. Then the amount in bank this month is $(I + \$70.91) \times (1.08/12)$, and a [partial] record of the bank account looks like **Figure 7.3.**

The customer ends up having spent $29,646.96, or $7646.96 above the sticker price, on his car, which is worth $8800 after 5 years. In his bank account, he has $32,981.68 after five years. His net gain is equal to the money in his account minus the money he spent on the car, or $3,334.72. This is $11,486.27 less than his net gain would have been if he had paid cash up front for the car.

Month	Dollars in bank	Dollars toward car
Before purchase	$22,000.00	0
At purchase	$18,104.44	$3,895.56
1	$18,296.52	$4,324.75
2	$18,489.89	$4,753.94
3	$18,684.53	$5,183.13
...	...	...
...	...	...
59	$32,692.35	$29,217.77
60	$32,981.68	$29,646.96

Figure 7.3.
The savings balance under the takes a loan plan.

Case 3: Lease the car.

If the customer leases the car, his monthly payments will be $329.19, and he will add $170.91 ($500 deposit—monthly payment) to his bank account each month. Rather than having a certain percentage required as a down payment, he will have to put down twice his monthly payment, or $658.38. I will assume the [savings] interest rate is still 8% compounded monthly and track these two running totals over the course of the 60-month period. Every lease has certain requirements about the condition the car must be in upon its return, and additional money must be paid to the dealer if the car is not in good enough shape, or if too many miles have been driven. I will assume the driver will meet all of these specifications, and buy the car from the dealership at $8800 after the five years. This is the same price that he would be able to sell the five-year old car at if he owned it. Once he owns the car, his situation can be accurately compared to the first two situations.

Month	Dollars in bank	Dollars toward car
Before purchase	$22,000.00	0
At purchase	$21,341.62	$658.38
1	$21,655.95	$987.57
2	$21,972.37	$1,316.76
3	$22,290.90	$1,645.95
...	...	...
...	...	...
59	$43,972.18	$20,080.59
60	$44,437.37	$20,409.78

Figure 7.4.
The savings balance under the lease a car plan.

Let I = $ in bank the previous month. Then the amount in bank this month is $(I + 170.91) \times (1.08/12)$, and a [partial] record of the bank account looks like **Figure 7.4.**

At the end of this five-year period, if the customer decides not to buy the car, he will have put $20,409.78 towards it and will have $44,437.37 in his bank account. This will give him a net gain of 24,027.67. However, if I am to compare his situation to that of buying the car, then I will assume that he buys the car from the dealership at the set price of $8800 at the end of the five years. Now, his net gain would be $15,227.59.

After 5 years:

After 5 years	Dollars in bank	Dollars in car	Net gain
Cash up front	$36,820.99	$22,000.00	$14,820.99
Buy with loan	$32,981.68	$29,646.96	$3,334.72
Lease the car	$44,437.37	$29,209.78	$15,227.59

CONCLUSIONS AND RECOMMENDATIONS

Obviously, paying off a loan over a five-year period is the most expensive way to pay for a car. My calculations have shown that the best way to pay for a car is cash up front. My hypothetical buyer would have over three times as much money after five years if he paid up front rather than took out a loan for the MR2; he would have twice as much money than if he had leased the car. These numbers depend directly on the accuracy of my monthly payment estimates and on the interest rate remaining 8% throughout the five years. If the interest rate were less than 8%, then paying cash up front would be even more profitable; his money in the bank is not as heavily relied on for profits from interest as are the other two options. It appears that leasing a car is the better alternative to taking out a loan, but if the difference in monthly payments of the two is substantially less than $100 a month, then the two options would be more equivalent if the dealer had offered the customer a discount for paying up front then it would be even more profitable. The exact amount of money that the MR-2 will be worth in five years could change the outcome of the problem, possibly making buying the car a better choice than leasing it. If the car is expected to be worth $11,000 or more in five years, then leasing would become the least profitable option. Also, if you own a car you are not penalized for putting too many miles on it or for having it not meet certain standards of cleanliness. If these expectations are not met, there is a surcharge on the lease (between 8 and 12 cents for every extra mile + $ for poor condition) that must be paid at the end of the five-year period. Other than finance, the most important question here is: Does the customer want to continue driving the same car after the five years are over? If the answer is no, then he should definitely lease the car to save the hassle and cost of trying to sell a used car. Realistically, most people are unable to pay up front and in full at the time of purchase. My calculations considered the same car in three different situations. Many of the people who lease are actually driving more expensive cars than they could afford to buy. The results of my study were shocking since the overwhelming majority of car drivers take out loans to buy their car. I was especially surprised to see that leasing saved money over taking out a loan to pay for the car since only about 10% of the drivers lease their automobiles. This might stem from the fact that not all leases are open ended and the drivers might have a strong desire to own the cars they drive. Or they might be positive that they could not meet the mileage restrictions on a leased car. The car dealerships do not seem to promote leasing, although they do offer it as an alternative to buying.

EXTENSIONS

This model had to involve very specific, unchanging values in order for me to make my calculations. I considered only a savings account rather than a money market account, stock investment, or government bond. I did not shop around for a savings account with greater than 8% interest simply because the banker told me that interest rates often depend on a customer's individual relationship with the bank, and I used the relationship that my family had with First Union. I was surprised to find out that leasing was more profitable than taking out a loan. I know I shortchanged the customer in the cash-up-front situation, because I started his account at $0 after he paid for the car. I did this for the sake of keeping my numbers small, but I realize that he really lost out when it came to the interest his money was earning. The instability in my project lies in the estimates that I had simply to take on faith from the bank and car dealership; this car's value will probably not be exactly 40% of $20,000 in five years, and the monthly payments on a lease of this car are probably slightly more or less than $329.19 I had hoped to discover that paying cash up front was the most economical solution because that is how my family has always bought its cars. I wish I had had the opportunity (time) to experiment with the price of the car, amount of money in the bank, and interest rate of the account. The only question that I am left with is: Why aren't more people leasing their cars rather than taking out loans?

ELEMENTS OF A GOOD MODEL

The two most important tests of a mathematical model are:

1. Does the resulting solution make sense in the particular context?

2. Is the solution mathematically correct?

There are many other things that go into a modeling problem and its solution. Assumptions are made when the problem is formulated. Are they clearly stated, and do they make sense? Are they reasonable? What factors are ignored? Is it reasonable to assume that these will have no major effect when the results are compared back to the contextual reality?

How clear is the presentation? Are visual representations including diagrams, tables, graphs used where appropriate? Is the paper readable and presentable? Is language used well? Is the oral presentation (if any) understandable and easy to follow?

These questions outline some of the considerations that go into making a good model. In order to create a good model, it is necessary to define what good means. As is the case with an English essay, some of the assessment will be subjective, but even subjective decisions should be based on agreed-upon principles.

This activity is designed to help you define characteristics of good models. Then you will have a chance to use your definition to assess the sample student model "To Buy or Lease" from Individual Work 1.

Follow these guidelines to assist you in creating a set of rules that you can agree will provide a fair assessment of a mathematical model.

1. List the characteristics (accuracy, clarity, etc.) that you think are critical to a mathematical model. Keep in mind that this may include presentation as well as the process and content.

2. Create a **rubric,** or assessment tool, by assigning a score for each of the characteristics you identify. The value that you suggest should be based on the relative importance of each of these characteristics.

ACTIVITY

1

ELEMENTS OF A GOOD MODEL

3. Compare your guidelines to those of at least two other students, modifying the characteristics and scores as you deem necessary.

4. Apply your guidelines to the model "To Buy or Lease," coming up with individual scores for each of the characteristics you included in your assessment. Then give a total score for the model.

5. Compare your ratings with those of at least two other students. Are your scores lower or higher than most? What factors led to the differences in your scores?

6. In a class discussion, be prepared to justify the characteristics you selected as important and the scores you assigned to "To Buy or Lease."

LESSON TWO
Analyzing Mathematical Models

KEY CONCEPTS

Mathematical modeling

Technical reading

Assessment

Optimization

Ratio

Game theory

The Image Bank

PREPARATION READING

What's In a Rubric?

E very day you are faced with information you must analyze to make informed decisions. Newspaper articles suggest the choice of one idea over another. Politicians make statements about the strength of one plan versus another. City planners make decisions about where to place shopping centers, fire stations, and other facilities that might be needed. How can you assess which decision is best for a given situation? It is ineffective to say that you either agree or disagree with a decision and not be able to explain the reasons for your position. As you did in Lesson 1, you can use a rubric or a set of guidelines to help you to evaluate the information, make a decision, and justify it.

In Lesson 1, the rubric you developed helps you to assess whether or not a model is good. In this lesson, you will use this rubric to evaluate several models developed by other students. This activity will allow you to follow the development of other mathematical models and to evaluate the strengths and weaknesses of the models' methods and solutions.

As you read the three student models and, later, listen to the presentations of other models and assessments, note the wide variety of problems that may be addressed using mathematical modeling. With that in mind, start thinking about a problem in some area of particular interest to you because you will be creating a mathematical model based on your own topic in Lesson 4.

ACTIVITY

2

RUBRIC CUBED

Select one of the following three student modeling solutions. For the selected model,

1. Read the model.

2. Using the rubric you developed in the previous lesson, evaluate the model. Be able to justify to others how you evaluated the model.

3. Get together with others who worked on the same model. Compare your results. Arrive at a consensus of a score and justification for that score.

4. Be prepared to present your conclusions and justifications to the entire class.

STUDENT MODEL #1

TESTING VARIOUS VOTING METHODS

MATH MODELING AND APPLICATIONS

Different voting methods used to elect the President have been debated for many years. Not everyone can come up with one fair method, and no one will compromise. Because the electoral college has been mostly untouched since it was founded, some people claim we need to modernize it because it isn't fair anymore. Also, different methods actually produce different winners in certain circumstances (although very rarely). I wanted to see which system of finding our president would be the fairest.

I designed this model which tests two voting systems in three actual presidential elections; 1976, 1980, and 1984. The first method is the proportional plan. For each state, a candidate receives the number of electoral votes proportional to the percentage of popular votes he/she receives. The current method, the second method I looked at, gives all the electoral votes in a state to the candidate who has a greater percentage of popular

RUBRIC CUBED

votes in that state. I compared these two methods to a third which is called the direct method. This declares as the winner the candidate who gets the popular majority (at least 40%) in the whole United States.

To compare these methods, I looked at the percentage of votes the top two candidates received in the first two methods and compared the error [(expected – initial)/expected], assuming the third method, direct, was the expected results. I also assumed that the assignment of electoral votes per state is a fair method, and that changes in them from election to election was ambiguous. When I rounded the electoral votes, I rounded up 0.5 and above. Also, if I was one vote short, I compared the decimals under 0.5 and whichever was higher, got the extra vote.

After comparing the methods, I found that method one was a lot fairer than method two. The error differed in one circumstance from 0.37% to 94.03%. In the 1976 election, the values are a lot closer because the election was a lot closer, but method one was still significantly better. If the race is a blow out, like in 1984, method two gets extremely unfair for the second candidate, and helps out the candidate that is winning. This increases his lead, making it a landslide, when in reality the voting was split 58.77% to 40.56%. If you use method two, the percentages are 97.58 to 2.42. In the first method, the percentages are less than one percent away from the control.

Overall, I believe my model is fair because the three elections were all different and so it included all circumstances. One was close, one was really close, and one wasn't close at all. My method of rounding was very fair, although those methods have also been debated, but that's another story. The one problem is that I assumed the third method was fair, and not everyone would agree with me. Also, other methods are also under debate that could be even fairer than method one, but because of limited resources and time, I couldn't look at them. Because my model included all factors and fairly compared them, it was very stable.

ACTIVITY

2

RUBRIC CUBED

The following is the summary data for the three methods.

Summary results–1976				
	Carter votes	**Percentage**	**Ford votes**	**Percentage**
Method 1	274	50.93	263	48.89
Method 2	297	55.20	240	44.61
Method 3	40,830,763	50.10	39,147,793	48.00
Comparison				
One v. three		2		2.08
Two v. three		10		6.25

Summary results–1980				
	Reagan votes	**Percentage**	**Carter votes**	**Percentage**
Method 1	278	51.67	277	51.49
Method 2	489	90.89	49	9.11
Method 3	43,904,153	50.70	35,483,883	41.00
Comparison				
One v. three		2.51		25.59
Two v. three		79.27		77.78

RUBRIC CUBED

Summary results–1984				
	Reagan votes	**Percentage**	**Mondale votes**	**Percentage**
Method 1	319	59.29	219	40.71
Method 2	525	97.58	13	2.42
Method 3	54,455,074	58.77	37,577,137	40.56
Comparison				
One v. three		0.89		0.37
Two v. three		66.04		94.03

STUDENT MODEL #2

THE WAR OF THE SPANISH SUCCESSION

The year 1713 was highlighted by the signing of the Peace of Utrecht. This document marked not only the end of the War of the Spanish Succession, but also the end of the Age of Kings. A century of absolute monarchies and protracted conflicts had ended in a huge European war. At stake was not merely the Spanish Hapsburg empire, but also the whole balance of power in Europe. The closing of the Age of Kings was followed by a period of enlightenment and revolution. The world had changed.

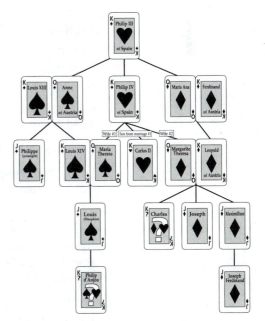

ACTIVITY

2

RUBRIC CUBED

TWO TITANS COLLIDE

The Spanish Hapsburg line was dying. The Spanish king, Carlos (Charles) II was deformed, lame, epileptic, and bald. All these defects could have been forgiven, but one could not. The last male Spanish Hapsburg was impotent. Since no women were allowed to inherit the crown, all Europe wondered who would succeed Carlos as King of Spain.

Two men made claim to the Spanish crown. One represented the Bourbon line: Louis XIV, the King of France. The other represented the Austrian Hapsburg line: Leopold I, the Holy Roman Emperor. If either ruler gained the Spanish holdings, it would cause a huge shift in the balance of power, something the rest of Europe would not tolerate. Therefore, both men made their claims through someone else. Leopold I claimed the crown through his son Archduke Charles. Leopold argued that Louis's wife, Marie Theresa, had renounced any claims to the Spanish throne when she became Queen of France. Plus, Hapsburg lands should, after all, remain in Hapsburg hands. Louis XIV claimed the crown through his grandson, Philippe d'Anjou. Louis's mother had been the older sister of Leopold's mother, and Louis's wife was the older sister of Leopold's wife. On the basis of seniority, Louis XIV's grandson had a stronger claim to the Spanish throne. Also, the renunciation made by Marie was based on the condition that France was to receive a dowry of 500,000 gold crowns which had not yet been paid.

When a possible third claimant, Joseph Ferdinand, died, only the two previously mentioned options remained. Negotiations were held to find a middle ground. One treaty (called Treaty I in the project) gave Archduke Charles the Spanish crown and the Spanish holdings except those in Italy which would go to France. Leopold I greedily refused. Throughout the summer of 1700, poor Carlos II was being tugged from all sides. Finally, on October 2, 1700, based on France's superior military strength and at the insistence of the Spanish nobility, Carlos II named Philippe his heir (Treaty II). Carlos died a month later. In February of the following year Philippe d'Anjou was crowned Philip V of Spain. Conflict immediately followed.

ACTIVITY

RUBRIC CUBED

2

THE GAME THEORY BEHIND THE WAR OF THE SPANISH SUCCESSION

The game of world dominance has no real beginning nor end. Therefore initial power and final power is not a good indicator of prowess. The change in power, measured in this project by prestige points, is of paramount importance. When modeling the War of the Spanish Succession, first we assigned each state with an initial power status as follows:

French Empire	80
Austrian Empire	55
Spanish Empire (sans Italy and New World)	30
Italy	10
New World	3
England	45
Netherlands	25
All German states except for Bavaria	30
Bavaria	15
Portugal	20

We also had a number of assumptions:

1) When two groups fight, the group with the higher combined prestige point total will prevail.

2) If lands are gained through fighting, you gain 1/2 of the points. The reason why you do not gain all the points is due to transition of power difficulties and the drain that war has on both the treasury as well as the army.

3) If lands are gained through negotiations, you gain 2/3 of the points. The reason why you gain more than 1/2, is because you did not have to spend money and you did not lose troops.

4) If lands gained border your territories, you gain another 1/5 of the points.

RUBRIC CUBED

5) If you are claiming through another person, you gain 2/3 of the points he would receive.

At stake in this game is a very important forty-three points. To simplify the game, there are only two main players : Louis XIV and Leopold I, but other countries can get involved by forming coalitions with either France or Austria. There are two options, negotiating and fighting. Therefore, the game matrix for each move looks like this:

		Leopold I	
		Negotiate	**Fight**
Louis IV	**Negotiate**	(0,0)	(−8,8)
	Fight	(8,−8)	(5,−5)

The game of war is a zero sum game because if one side wins, the other side loses the corresponding amount. Only after a peace treaty is signed can negotiating sides receive lands so if both sides negotiate, for the time being no one gains anything, and each side gets zero. If one side negotiates while the other fights, the aggressor will gain eight prestige points, and the negotiator will receive the sucker's payoff of negative eight. If both sides fight, the stronger side will receive five prestige points, and the weaker side will lose five prestige points.

ANALYSIS OF THE CONFLICT

After the crowning of his grandson, Louis XIV made an immediate blunder by agitating England and the Netherlands. While he did have a military advantage (France and Spain = 110 prestige points vs. England and Netherlands = 70 prestige points), Louis should have looked to the bigger picture. He gained five quick points, but forced England and the Netherlands into an alliance with Leopold. France along with her allies: Spain, Portugal, and Bavaria (145 pts) was weaker than the Grand Alliance: Austria, England, the Netherlands, and Germany (155 pts). In a series of great military defeats, Blenheim, Ramilles, and Oudenarde, France lost a total of fifteen prestige points.

RUBRIC CUBED

Portugal deserted Louis and joined the Grand Alliance in 1703. By 1708, Louis was willing to negotiate. The conditions for peace were harsh. Archduke Charles would become King of Spain, Louis would recognize Queen Anne as the legitimate ruler of England, France would surrender its claims to the Spanish colonies and relinquish captured Hapsburg possessions. Unfortunately, there was one condition Louis could not accept. He would not help the Grand Alliance drive his grandson out of Spain. War would resume.

The power balance was now more in favor of the Grand Alliance ($175 > 125$). After the French defeat in September of 1709, in the bloody battle of Malaplaquet where 40,000 men were killed, negotiations resumed. This time, Louis had to lead the campaign to drive Philippe from Spain. Again the Sun King refused, and again the war resumed.

Good news was in store for the French after weathering a rather nasty Grand Alliance storm. In 1710, the Whig government in England was overthrown by the Tories who were opposed to the conflict. In 1711, Leopold I died, and Archduke Charles became Holy Roman Emperor. The rest of the Grand Alliance was put on the spot. They did not want Archduke Charles to have control of both Austria and Spain. The power shift resulted in England, Portugal, Germany, and Netherlands only offering half the support they had previously given. With the upper hand in power: ($125 > 55 + (1/2)(45 + 25 + 30 + 20) = 115$), the French came away with a victory at Denain in 1712. Everyone was now willing to negotiate. The result was the Peace of Utrecht which gave Philippe d'Anjou the Spanish throne. England received Gibraltar and the Mediterranean island of Minorca, as well as the French territories in Newfoundland and Nova Scotia. Even more importantly, England got the shipping rights of the slave trade between Africa and Latin America. Austria procured the Spanish Netherlands, Milan, Sardinia, and Naples. Louis had to recognize the Protestant succession to the English throne, and Frederick I was recognized as the King of the Sovereign States of Prussia.

ACTIVITY

2

RUBRIC CUBED

Louis left the war with a final prestige score of eighty-three, a gain of three points. Leopold I (or rather his son Archduke Charles) left the war with a final prestige score of seventy-seven, a gain of twenty-two! The Austrians had played the game more skillfully. Where did Louis go wrong? He should not have invaded the Netherlands in 1703. Then his prestige points would have outnumbered his opponent's 145 to 80. Leopold should have been more open to earlier negotiations before the Grand Alliance fell apart. He would have ended with slightly higher scores of eighty and eighty-five. Various nonviolent options are also explored on the following pages. The prestige points were calculated according to the assumptions.

CONCLUDING REMARKS AND CRITICISMS

Due to the inclement weather, this project was not as robust as Christel and I [student authors] had initially hoped. While the model closely paralleled the actual results of the War of the Spanish Succession, the model was simple at best. It was difficult to produce more than a rudimentary project, but we did try to compensate by doing a lot of research, and among others a fair division solution to the question, Who should inherit the Spanish throne? If we had had more time, we would have experimented with more objective ways of determining initial prestige score (e.g. area of land holdings, amount of money in treasury, number of troops, etc.), as well as a more objective group of assumptions. We had hoped to include more rounds of fighting and negotiating in our project rather than only ten, but a natural disaster and a slow start prevented us. I do, however, believe Christel and I came up with an interesting problem and an interesting solution. We also had an interesting time doing the project.

Finis

ACTIVITY

RUBRIC CUBED

2

List of Calculations

Events	Louis	Leopold
Louis attacks England & Netherlands on behalf of Spain	80 +5 (since 110 > 70) 85	55 55
Blenheim	–5 (since 145 < 155)	+5
Ramilles	–5	+5
Oudenarde (loss Sp.Ne.)	–5	+5
Negotiations (break down)	70	70 (80)
Malaplaquet	–5 (since 125 < 175)	+5
Negotiations (break down)	65	75 (85)
Denain	+5 (since 125 > 115)	–5
Negotiations	70	70
Peace of Utrecht	+13 (Spanish Poss)	+7 (Italy)
Final totals	83 (+3)	77 (+22)

ACTIVITY

RUBRIC CUBED

2

Long run: France should not have agitated England and the Netherlands.

Alternatives to War		
Events	Louis	Leopold
Peace of Utrecht without fighting	93 (+3)	62 (+7)
Treaty 1	87 (+7)	69 (+14)
Treaty 2	105 (+25)	55 (+0)
"Fair" division	88 (+8)	63 (+8)
"Actual" division since Louis & Leopold would get a portion of everything on their branches	98 (+18)	68 (+8)

Example of calculations using assumptions:

Treaty 1:

Since Louis would get Italy through negotiations, he would receive $(2/3)(10) = 7$ points. Since, Archduke Charles would get all the Spanish possessions also through negotiations which would be $(2/3)(30 + 10 + 3) = 29$ points, Leopold would then get 2/3 of those points by claiming them through his son. So Leopold would gain $(2/3)(29) = 19$ points. Therefore, Louis would end up with 87 points and Leopold would end up with 74 points.

A "FAIR" DIVISION SCHEME FOR CARLOS II'S ESTATE:

Inheritances come in the form of prestige points. The division procedure is that each living relative will receive a portion. Those a level above will receive twice as much as those a level below. With those assumptions, the resulting division is as follows: parentheses denote the relative is unable to inherit any of the estate because they have either predeceased Carlos II, or they are female.

RUBRIC CUBED

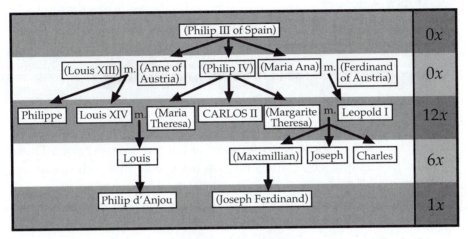

x = one portion of Carlos's estate

$1x$ = portions on lowest level of family tree

$3(2x)$ = portions on next lowest level of family tree

$3(4x)$ = portions on highest level of family tree with living issue

$x + 6x + 12x = 30$ (Spain) + 10 (Italy) + 3 (New World)

$19x = 43$ (Carlos's estate)

x = approx. 2

Louis and Leopold would each get eight prestige points. Louis would have a prestige rating of $80 + 8 = 88$, and Leopold would have a prestige rating of $55 + 8 = 63$.

In actuality, however, Louis would also get 2/3 of all the points on his half of the tree and Leopold would get 2/3 of all the points on his half of the tree, since they are the only rulers with the military strength to defend the estate. Therefore, Louis's "actual" rating would be $80 + 2/3(14) + 8 = 98$, and Leopold's "actual" rating would be $55 + 2/3(8) + 8 = 68$.

ACTIVITY

2

STUDENT MODEL #3

A MATHEMATICAL MODEL FOR NEWSPAPER LAYOUT

MATHEMATICAL MODELING AND APPLICATIONS

INTRODUCTION

As far as is known by the staff of the *Washington Post* and the *Fairfax Journal*, there is no set way to lay out a newspaper. These two newspaper companies rely on the eye of their editors and layout staff to create a visually pleasing and convenient newspaper. (A convenient newspaper is one that minimizes page turning). In the layout of the *Washington Post*, they first set aside room for advertisements then lay out the article in the remaining free space (this free space is called a news hole).

A mathematical approach to laying out a newspaper might help with the production of a newspaper. With a mathematical model, we could automate the entire process. We'd be able to feed into a computer all the advertisements and their desired space, and all the news articles and pictures. The computer then would use the model to produce the entire newspaper error-free!

Through my research, I found that the most difficult thing about modeling a newspaper's layout is that the layout can vary greatly day to day. The layout depends on many things that would change with every day's news. For the sake of simplicity, I changed most of these variables into assumptions. These could however be changed day to day.

ASSUMPTIONS

I assumed that the model would be the first major section of the *Washington Post* from the front page to the "Federal Page" section. I assumed that the page was 22 inches top to bottom, and 6 columns wide. Measurements for a newspaper area are usually in column inches: that is 1 col. wide and 1 inch high. Thus there are 132 column inches available per page. Another thing that is assumed is that there are no ads on the front page, only ads on

RUBRIC CUBED

the bottom half of the next two pages, and after that the ads can be as long as wanted and placed wherever. Another assumption is that the five most important articles have a spot of 22 column inches allotted on the front page, to be continued later in the paper.

Let us assume for this model that there is a given amount of advertising and its placement is predetermined (the better position costs more). We can then determine, given the total amount of news on that day, the number of pages required, and how much of a news hole there is on each page. A chart listing all the pages, their news hole size, and the size and importance of each article follows. Another assumption made is that articles have importance over each other, and that the most important articles on a page are placed to the left and top of the page.

DISCUSSION OF MODEL

The placement of articles in a newspaper can, after some assumptions are made, be simplified into a scheduling problem. If the advertisements have a predetermined placement and size, and there is a given amount of news in a day, the 'news holes' are simply filled using a variant of the bin-packing algorithm. If there is extra room left on a page it can be filled with a 'filler ad', an advertisement that the newspaper writes for itself describing future articles or feature stories or sections. They tend to be about 1-3 col-inches, but can be even larger.

On the data pages, you can see that I have assumed the number of articles to be 26. They are ordered by importance in alphabetical order, and I have assigned a length to each one. I also had 25 pages with different news hole sizes. I used two different algorithms to fill the pages. At first, I used the "first-fit" algorithm, which is pretty standard in scheduling and bin packing problems The second algorithm I used was one I created, the Split-Fit algorithm. This works by placing as much of every article in order on each page, and then splitting the article to fit on the page. For example, if there's a hole of 22 col-inches, but my article is 50 col-inches I put the 22 on the page that it fits and the rest goes on the next page.

ACTIVITY

2

RUBRIC CUBED

Data – first fit algorithm			Article	Size	Data – split fit algorithm		
Page	News hole	Articles	Article	Size	Page	News hole	Articles
1	110	A,B,C,D,E	A	60	1	110	A,B,C,D,E
2	66	A,D	B	70	2	66	A,D
3	66	B,E	C	80	3	66	B,E
4	0		D	50	4	0	
5	99	C,H,V	E	40	5	99	C,F
6	99	F,X	F	70	6	99	F,J
7	110	G,V	G	90	7	110	G,H
8	99	I,V	H	50	8	99	H,I, filler
9	85	J,X	I	60	9	85	K,L
10	24	X	J	70	10	24	L
11	0		K	70	11	0	
12	66	M	L	90	12	66	L,N
13	66	N,Y	M	66	13	66	M
14	80	K,Y	N	60	14	80	N,O
15	90	L	O	40	15	90	O,P,Q
16	76	P,Y	P	50	16	76	Q,R, filler
17	80	O,R	Q	80	17	80	S
18	24	Y	R	40	18	24	T
19	66	T,filler	S	80	19	66	T,U
20	66	U,filler	T	60	20	66	U,V
21	90	Q,Z	U	60	21	90	V,W
22	90	S,Z	V	70	22	90	W,X
23	99	W,Z	W	80	23	99	X,Y,Z
24	22	Z	X	68	24	22	Z
25	33	Z	Y	66	25	33	Z
26	0		Z	94	26	0	

ACTIVITY

2

RUBRIC CUBED

SUMMARY

The data received from this preliminary model actually lends itself to not being used. The two algorithms I used for placing the articles and the pages did not work as well as was hoped. The first-fit algorithm was by far the worse of the two. It had unimportant articles on early pages and the last few were split onto as many as five different pages. This makes the newspaper hard to read, in the fact that there is so much page-turning and the importance of the articles does not show itself in the positioning of the articles. In the split-fit algorithm, the importance is most definitely preserved, but there is a bit of page turning added, for many articles are on two different pages.

The algorithms that I chose to test the model were not very good. The model would become much more applicable if another algorithm were developed or used. This model could actually create a more efficient newspaper if the right algorithm were developed. In the future, it is very possible that news companies will be virtually completely automated to allow for quicker and easier access to the news. In effect, this model could be the beginning of research into automated newspaper development.

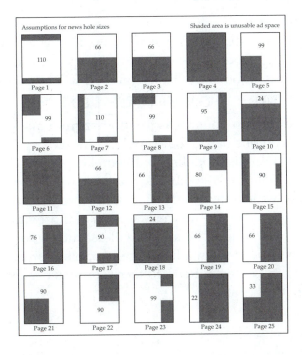

LESSON THREE
Modeling Our World

KEY CONCEPTS

Mathematical modeling

Technical writing

Technical reading

Rate of change

Optimization

Area

Perimeter

Linear functions

Step functions

Ratio

Exponential functions

The Image Bank

PREPARATION READING

Mathematical Modeling

*I*n the past two lessons, you have used mathematical models written by other students to help clarify the modeling process and define the components of a good mathematical model. In this lesson, you will be given a problem to answer using mathematical modeling.

With feedback on your ideas from other students, your group will work on one of the four problems in Activity 3. As you work through this modeling problem, keep in mind the strong and weak points of the models you have worked on in the previous two lessons. The goal should be to keep the strengths and to improve upon the weak aspects of those models. The mathematical concepts that you will use are up to you. Keep in mind the steps of the mathematical modeling process as described in Lesson 1. Refer to these steps as needed as you work on your problem.

STEPS OF THE MODELING PROCESS

1) Identify the problem to be investigated.

2) Determine the important factors (and assumptions about those factors) in the contextual situation, and represent those factors mathematically.

3) Manipulate (analyze) the mathematical relationship.

4) Interpret the mathematical conclusions in the context of the real-world phenomenon. Then evaluate how close the conclusions are to the real-world situation. If necessary, reexamine the model's factors and structure and revise the model.

A Master Modeler

Jeff Griffiths, head of Mathematics at the University of Cardiff, Wales, has spent much of his career modeling a myriad of situations worldwide. He has worked on many traffic and queuing models to solve situations ranging from selecting appropriate blocks of time for pedestrians and cars at crossings to organizing the traffic in the Suez Canal. He has also turned his modeling skills to medical issues such as trying to distinguish effective from ineffective measures of fighting the AIDS virus.

MODELING A PROBLEM

Four situations requiring modeling solutions are described below. Discuss each of the situations with your group, and select one of them for your group to solve. Then begin the modeling process—be sure you agree on what the problem really is, then begin step 2 (and step 3, if possible). Include written records of, and justifications for, each decision your group makes.

As you begin to develop the model, discuss among your group the context, the development, and the anticipated mathematics needed. Once you have agreement, each person in your group will be asked to present your initial discussion to another group. Take notes on the other group's reaction to your presentation. You will then discuss this feedback and related suggestions with your original group members. As the development of your model progresses, all members of your group should work together. The feedback that you provide each other will assist you in turning in the best possible report. Your group is finished when all members of your group are satisfied with the model and you have turned in the report as your teacher directs.

1. Elevator problem—Suppose a building has 5 floors (1-5) that are occupied by offices. The ground floor (0) is not used for business purposes. Each floor has 80 people working on it and there are 4 elevators available. Each elevator can hold 10 people at one time. The elevators take 3 seconds to travel between floors and average 22 seconds on each floor when someone enters or exits. If all of the people arrive at work at about the same time and enter the elevator on the ground floor, what is the most efficient use of the elevators?

2. Pasture land problem—A rancher has a prize bull and some cows on his ranch. He has a large area for pasture that includes a stream running along one edge. He must divide the pasture into two regions, one region large enough for the cows and a smaller region to hold the bull. The cows' grazing pasture must be at least 10,000 sq. feet, and the bull's grazing

MODELING A PROBLEM

pasture must be at least 1000 sq. feet. The shape of the pasture is basically a rectangle measuring 120 feet by 150 feet. The river runs all the way along the 120-foot side. Fencing costs $5/foot and each fence post costs $10. Any straight edge of fence requires a post every 20 feet, and any curved length of fence requires a post every 10 feet. Help this rancher minimize the total cost of fencing.

3. Faculty problem—When confronted with a rise of 142 students in a school of 480, and a capacity for 7 new teachers, in what departments should the new teachers be placed? Placing the new teachers should maintain the ideal student-to-teacher ratio. The current makeup of the (student: teacher) enrollment in each department is: Art (99: 1); Biology (319: 4); Chemistry (294: 3); English (480: 5); French (122: 1); German (51: 1); Spanish (110: 1); Mathematics (613: 6); Music (95: 1); Physics (291: 3); and Social Studies (363: 4).

4. Flu epidemic problem—A certain population of 20,000 people is hit by a strain of flu. One percent of the susceptible population is stricken each day. The flu effects last 5 days, after which the person is then immune to this virus. Ten percent of the population is naturally immune to the virus.

   (a) If the epidemic were allowed to run its course, how long would it take for the entire population to become immune?

   (b) The Health Service would like to institute an immunization program in an attempt to knock out the epidemic quickly—within a month, if possible. However, they would also like to inoculate as few people as possible because the serum does occasionally make people feel sick. Devise an immunization procedure that will meet these guidelines.

M A T H   A T   W O R K

At the National Institute of Standards and Technology, Fern Hunt applies her mathematical modeling skills to some of the problems being worked on by about 2000 scientists and engineers. Most of these problems relate to measuring the physical and chemical properties of materials of commercial importance to U.S. industry. As Fern describes some of these experiences: "I have worked on problems involving the structure of magnetic materials, modeling fluid flow through a pipe with a constant but very irregular cross section, and modeling of weathering of paint film." All of these problems involve probability theory—a branch of mathematics that she also uses in her theoretical research. (You may want to visit http://math.nist.gov/mcsd/Gallery/montecarlo to view three figures related to the project on fluid flow.)

LESSON FOUR
Creating Your Model

KEY CONCEPTS

Mathematical modeling

Technical writing

The Image Bank

PREPARATION READING

It's Your Turn

T hroughout the *Mathematics: Modeling Our World* program, the modeling process has guided your study of a variety of mathematical models. These have included models for analyzing voting, analyzing ways to measure the cost of pooling blood samples, finding the optimal location for a fire station, analyzing motion, and measuring fairness. Until now, most, if not all, of the models have come from suggestions from the text or from your teacher. Now, it's your turn to take charge.

ACTIVITY

FROM YOUR PROBLEM TO YOUR MODEL

4

In this lesson, you will decide on a topic that is of interest to you. You will then complete the modeling process in its entirety. You will research, ask questions about your topic, make assumptions, decide on important factors, develop a model, and report your answer to the questions that you posed. In other words, you will experience the mathematical modeling process from start to finish.

Keep in mind the discussions of this unit. The ideas of mathematical accuracy and presentation are important in your final result. Keep a record of what you do as you work so you can report on all aspects of your activity, not just your final result.

Don't be content with your first result. Ask questions such as: What would the result be if I were to make different assumptions? Did I eliminate something in my original model that I should now add? In other words, continue the cyclic nature of the modeling process until you are satisfied you have the best representation of the situation that you are capable of producing.

If you are unable to come up with a problem that interests you and is feasible to model, look at the topics listed below to get an idea of some of the kinds of questions that may be done.

Keep in mind the stages of modeling that were identified in Lesson 1.

1) Identify the problem to be investigated.

2) Determine the important factors (and assumptions about those factors) that exist in a real-world phenomenon and represent those factors as mathematical symbols.

3) Manipulate (analyze) the mathematical relationship.

4) Interpret the mathematical conclusions in the context of the real-world phenomenon. Then evaluate how applicable the conclusions are to the real-world situation. If necessary, re-examine the model's factors and structure and revise the model.

FROM YOUR PROBLEM TO YOUR MODEL

Also, keep in mind that you do not have to follow these steps in numerical order. In many cases, you may need to cycle through steps 2, 3, and 4 many times prior to arriving at a final model and solution. In addition to checking your model against reality, it is also important to check your results against your assumptions. If your model violates your assumptions, something needs to be changed.

Share your work with the people in your group, and use their feedback as you develop your model. If you need further consultation, find someone else to discuss your modeling project with as well. The goal is to develop the best model and most complete solution given the time and background that you have.

POSSIBLE MODELING TOPICS

1. Select a voting process in your school. Analyze the fairness of the structure and make a recommendation for making it more fair.

2. Develop a coding process to use over the Internet.

3. Develop a computer/calculator model to morph a figure.

4. Develop a mathematical model to predict the wolf population in the Yellowstone Park area (or some other population or region).

5. Select a land-use decision that is being made in your area. Develop a model that will argue the pros/cons of the decision.

6. Select an event, or series of events, in history and use game theory to analyze the decision(s).

7. Find a business that uses route deliveries and analyze their algorithms for delivery. Suggest an alternative process.

8. Select a product and develop a model that will optimize the cost of packaging.

9. Select a company and analyze its stock.

10. Compare two or more works of art/architecture in terms of the incorporated mathematics.

11. Predict grade point averages in the junior year based on some other school data.

ACTIVITY

FROM YOUR PROBLEM TO YOUR MODEL

4

12. Develop and implement a research questionnaire.

13. What is the optimal reordering policy for a company that maintains some inventory?

14. Do a product comparison.

15. How are streaks related to probability of success? Develop a method of predicting a team's final win/loss percentage based on its streaks in the first two months of play.

16. Is strength (velocity of release) or form (angle of release) more important for success in the shot put event?

17. Given a map showing the locations of all gas stations and the prices each one charges, how should you determine the best station at which to buy gas?

18. What is the most efficient use of parking space at your school? Should lines be redrawn?

19. What are the best points from which a soccer player should shoot? Where should the goalkeeper be positioned?

20. Tall tennis players tend to serve more hard serves and fewer spin serves than do short players. Examine the geometry of such serves and servers. What effect does position along the baseline have?

21. At what time should the air conditioning (or heating) system for the auditorium (gym) be turned on for an assembly? What about for nights when the auditorium (gym) is used for special events?

22. Investigate the interaction of two dependent species in an ecosystem.

23. How large and how often should drug doses be in order to maintain both safe and effective results?

24. What was wrong with the proposed First Amendment to the U.S. Constitution?

25. When is the hottest part of the day?

Wrapping Up Unit Seven

Mathematical Summary

Mathematical modeling may be used to answer many questions from a range of disciplines—including the projected price of a stock, fairness of voting schemes, predicting the weather, and analyzing history.

This process is made up of components that may be used to assist you in dealing with some of your own problems and questions. There are many examples of people using mathematical models in the world. From economics to weather prediction to computer graphics, mathematical modeling is used. The modeling process is essential in all fields to solve problems and answer questions.

The modeling process is, in its basic design, a way of learning — simplifying something you want to learn about, then adding complexity as the concepts and results become clear. This is not only the power of mathematics, but the power of the modeling process. Using mathematical modeling to solve interesting problems about how our world works is an enjoyable and rewarding experience that you can continue to apply throughout your life.

Glossary

INTERNAL ACCURACY:
the correctness of the mathematics used within a model, and the agreement of the mathematics with the underlying assumptions.

EXTERNAL ACCURACY:
the correctness of the model's result in terms of the real-world situation being modeled.

RUBRIC:
an assessment tool used to evaluate mathematical models.